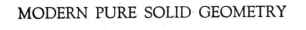
MODERN PURE SOLID GEOMETRY

THE MACMILLAN COMPANY
NEW YORK · BOSTON · CHICAGO · DALLAS
ATLANTA · SAN FRANCISCO

MACMILLAN & CO., LIMITED
LONDON · BOMBAY · CALCUTTA
MELBOURNE

THE MACMILLAN COMPANY
OF CANADA, LIMITED
TORONTO

MODERN PURE SOLID GEOMETRY

BY

NATHAN ALTSHILLER-COURT, D.Sc.

PROFESSOR OF MATHEMATICS
UNIVERSITY OF OKLAHOMA

Author of *College Geometry*

NEW YORK

THE MACMILLAN COMPANY

1935

PREFACE

The development of Modern Solid Geometry has not kept pace with the development of Plane Geometry. This has been pointed out by many writers, and various reasons, more or less plausible and always apologetic, have been adduced to explain this regrettable and "unavoidable" anomaly. But when all is said, it remains quite evident that the main trouble with Modern Solid Geometry is sheer neglect.

Contributors to Modern Solid Geometry implicitly admit this neglect when they preface, as they often do, their writings with a list of established propositions: they dare not assume that their readers are familiar with this preliminary material and they cannot offer a readily accessible reference to it. A considerable part of Modern Solid Geometry has never appeared in book form anywhere, least of all in English. It remains scattered in the various and numerous mathematical periodicals, old and new, in the form of articles and isolated propositions.

In this book an attempt has been made to present Modern Solid Geometry in a connected form that would enable the interested reader to become acquainted with the subject. Many a "missing link" had to be provided here and there, and quite a few terms, altogether new or new to the English language, had to be introduced without previous authority. The author offers all due apologies for their barbarity.

It is convenient to identify a proposition by a distinctive name, preferably by the name of its originator. But it is not always certain whose name should be attached to a given proposition, nor which of the propositions of a given author should bear his name. It is hoped that this book is guilty of no greater blunders, in this connection, than those that have been committed ever since the time a certain theorem was named after Pythagoras.

The subject matter has been limited to the point, line, plane, circle, and sphere. Conic sections are not dealt with, nor are their properties invoked in the proofs. The treatment is exclusively synthetic, adhering closely to the methods of classical Solid Geometry.

112

The only serious encroachment upon the methods of synthetic Projective Geometry is the free use of the harmonic ratio. Notions like the anharmonic ratio, involution, and even the complete quadrilateral have not been used, although the temptation was great. The force to resist it was found in the consciousness that for the limited application that could be made of these notions it would not be fair to steal the thunder of Projective Geometry.

However, the elements at infinity would have been very useful. Their omission compelled repetitions and, what is worse, made it necessary, in order to avoid undue lengths, to pass over in silence the cases of parallelism. But the elements at infinity must be treated adequately, as is done in Projective Geometry, or not at all. For an inadequate treatment is likely to confuse the reader and arouse in his mind wrong notions, both geometrical and philosophical. Of the two evils the lesser was chosen.

But the author yielded to the temptation to introduce the imaginary sphere. It is easy to show that the imaginary sphere is an abbreviation for geometric relations which are real and expressible in terms of real elements. The reader is thus led to acquire confidence in the geometric validity of this "imaginary" geometrical entity. This experience with the imaginary sphere may give him the confidence that the imaginary elements he may meet in other connections may also be susceptible of a similar interpretation, after adequate study.

The subject matter of this book and the method of treatment assume on the part of the reader a knowledge of the elements of Solid Geometry and some acquaintance with Modern Plane Geometry,* and very little else. However, in many places considerably more mathematical maturity may be required on the part of the reader than this limited appeal to erudition may indicate.

Figures have been supplied rather sparingly. The text is written so that the reader is able to draw the figures for himself, an ability worthy of cultivation. The reader should also realize that in Solid Geometry a rough sketch is often as serviceable as a painstaking figure. Furthermore, many of the figures in the

---

* The places where reference is made to a proposition in Modern Plane Geometry are designated by the letters C. G. The readers acquainted with the author's *College Geometry* may find the respective proposition in the place indicated by the number.

text are drawn so as to convey the idea to the reader that a fragmentary figure is often as useful as a complete figure, and often much more so.

An effort has been made to include a considerable number of exercises, in the belief that the only conclusive test of one's mastery of a branch of Mathematics is his ability to handle and to apply its principles independently. Some of the exercises are almost obvious, while others rival in importance many a proposition given in the text and may call for the best efforts of almost any reader. However, it is by no means intended that all these exercises should be taken in a row. The reader may select as few or as many as may suit his convenience, for the text is practically independent of the exercises.

For that matter, neither is it necessary to follow the book paragraph after paragraph. The reader may make his own choice. In particular, readers with a limited amount of time at their disposal may wish to reach the chapter on spheres. For their benefit the following omissions may be suggested, as a rough and tentative guide: Chapter I, §§ 11–13, 21–24, 56, 57, 59–63. Chapter II, §§ 81–129. Chapter III, §§ 136–142, 147–149. Chapter IV, §§ 167, 168, 223–227, 234, 243–273, 277–328. All of Chapters V and VI may also be skipped.

Most of the subject matter in this book has been used, at one time or another, in a course I have offered at the University of Oklahoma during the last several years. With little to guide me in the choice and organization of the material, save my own preferences and prejudices, I am painfully aware of the book's inevitable shortcomings and would appreciate any suggestions from my kind readers, for possible future use.

It is with sincere pleasure that I acknowledge my indebtedness to my many friends among my former students who read different portions of this book in its various stages of preparation and made many valuable suggestions and corrections.

Prof. C. A. Barnhart, University of New Mexico, has read all the proofs of the entire book. Many improvements in the text are due to him. Prof. A. D. Campbell, University of Syracuse, has rendered a similar service. I owe both of them a debt of gratitude.   N. A.-C.

Norman, Oklahoma,
August, 1935.

TABLE OF CONTENTS

MODERN PURE SOLID GEOMETRY

MODERN PURE SOLID GEOMETRY

CHAPTER I

PRELIMINARY

1. Introductory Propositions and Problems

1. Definitions. (a) Lines parallel to each other will sometimes be referred to as having a given *direction.*

(b) Planes parallel to each other will be said to have the same *orientation.*

(c) Two lines which do not lie in the same plane will be referred to as "skew lines." The angle between two skew lines is, by definition, the angle formed by the parallels to these lines through an arbitrary point.

(d) A plane parallel to two (or more) skew lines will be called a "directing plane," or a "director plane," or, more briefly, a *director* of the given lines.

A director of skew lines is fixed in orientation, but not in position. To determine the position of the director plane a further condition must be imposed upon it, say, that it pass through a given point.

(e) The plane through the mid-point of a given segment and perpendicular to that segment will be referred to as the "mediating plane," or, more briefly, the *mediator* of the segment or the mediator of the end-points of the segment.

2. Theorem. *A director of two skew lines is perpendicular to the line of shortest distance of these two lines.*

The proof is left to the reader.

3. Geometric Constructions in Space. When speaking of constructions in space we assume that we are able (a) to construct a plane given three of its points not lying in a straight line; (b) to construct the line of intersection of two planes; (c) to construct the point of intersection of a line and a plane; (d) to carry out all plane constructions in any plane in space.

2 MODERN PURE SOLID GEOMETRY

These constructions are purely theoretical, for we have no practical method to actually carry them out. However, in Descriptive Geometry all these constructions are executed by ruler and compasses.

4. Problem. *Through a given point to draw a line meeting two given skew lines.*

The two planes Pa, Pb determined by the given point P and the two given lines a, b intersect along the required line s. For s passes through P and is coplanar with each of the lines a, b.

REMARK. The construction shows that the line s will be parallel to one of the given lines, say a, if a is parallel to the plane Pb. In order to free the problem from exceptions it should be modified to read "coplanar with each of two given skew lines," instead of "meeting two given skew lines."

5. Problem. *Given three mutually skew lines to draw a line parallel to one of them and meeting the other two.*

The line of intersection s of the two planes as, bs drawn through each of the two given lines a, b and parallel to the third given line c constitutes the solution of the problem.

6. Theorem. *Through two given skew straight lines one and only one pair of parallel planes may be drawn.*

Let α, β be two parallel planes passing through the two given lines a, b, and let P, Q be the feet of the common perpendicular to these two lines. The parallel a' to a through Q lies in β, hence β is perpendicular to PQ at Q. Similarly α is perpendicular to PQ at P. This is therefore a condition that the required planes must fulfill. On the other hand the two planes perpendicular to PQ at P and Q respectively will contain the given lines and will be parallel to each other, hence the proposition.

7. Theorem. *If two skew lines are cut by three (or more) parallel planes, the pairs of corresponding segments are in proportion.*

This proposition is known from Elementary Solid Geometry.

8. Converse Theorem. *If on two skew lines two series of three (or more) points are marked so that the corresponding pairs of segments are in proportion, the lines joining pairs of corresponding points on the given skew lines have a director.*

Suppose that on the given skew lines ABC, $A'B'C'$ we have

$$AB : BC = A'B' : B'C'.$$

Through the lines AA', BB' draw the pair of parallel planes passing through them (§ 6). A plane of the same orientation as these planes and passing through C will meet the line $A'B'C'$ in a point, say, C'', and according to the direct theorem, we will have

$$AB : BC = A'B' : B'C''.$$

From a comparison of the two proportions it follows that C'' coincides with C', and the proposition is proved.

9. Corollary I. *The locus of the mid-point of the segment which two fixed parallel planes intercept on a variable line is the plane parallel to the given planes and equidistant from them.*

10. Corollary II. *If a variable line meets two fixed skew lines, the locus of the mid-point of the segment comprised between the skew lines is a plane.*

The proposition is proved by drawing through the given lines the pair of parallel planes passing through them (§ 6).

Notice that every point in the plane belongs to the locus, for through any such point a line may be drawn meeting the given lines (§ 4).

11. Oblique Projections. The foot A' of the perpendicular AA' dropped from the point A upon the plane (P) is called the "orthogonal projection" of the point A upon the plane (P). If A describes a straight line s in space, A' describes a straight line s' in (P), and s' is called the "orthogonal projection" of s upon (P). Orthogonal projections are of current use in Elementary Geometry. They will be frequently employed in what follows.

It is sometimes convenient to project A upon (P) by a line AA' having a given direction d, not perpendicular to (P). The point A' is then the "oblique projection of direction d" of A upon (P).

THEOREM. *If A describes a straight line s, its oblique projection of direction d upon the given plane (P) describes a straight line.*

Indeed this projection s' is the intersection of the plane (P) with the plane through s parallel to d.

The line s' is the "oblique projection of direction d" of the line s upon (P).

12. Problem. *Place the ends of a segment of given length on two skew lines so that the segment shall be parallel to a given plane.*

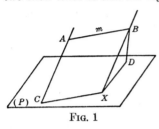

FIG. 1

Let C, D be the traces in the given plane (P) (Fig. 1) of the two given skew lines AC, BD, and AB the required position of the segment m. Project the figure $ABCD$ upon the plane (P) obliquely in the direction of AC. The line BD will project into a line DX, and the segment AB into a segment $CX = AB = m$. Hence the point X lies on a known line DX at a known distance m from the known fixed point C, therefore X may be determined. The parallel to AC through X will meet BD in B. There may be two, one, or no solutions.

13. Theorem. *If three given mutually skew lines have a director, any three (or more) lines meeting the given lines also have a director.*

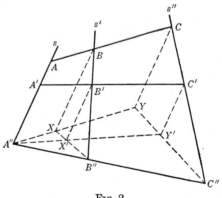

FIG. 2

Let the given lines s, s', s'' (Fig. 2) having a director (P) be met by the lines ABC, $A'B'C'$, $A''B''C''$ (§ 4). Through $A''B''C''$ draw a plane parallel to ABC and upon this plane project the lines s', s'', obliquely in the direction s (§ 11). Let X, X'; Y, Y' be the projections of B, B'; C, C' respectively. We have

$$BB' : B'B'' = XX' : X'B'', \qquad CC' : C'C'' = YY' : Y'C''.$$

Now the planes XBB'', YCC'' are parallel to (P), hence the lines $XX'B''$, $YY'C''$ are parallel, and we have

$$XX' : X'B'' = YY' : Y'C'',$$

hence

$$BB' : B'B'' = CC' : C'C'',$$

and therefore the lines BC, $B'C'$, $B''C''$ have a director plane (§ 8).

14. Theorem. *A plane perpendicular to one face of a right dihedral angle cuts this angle along a right angle.*

Let p, q be the lines of intersection of the faces α, β of the given right dihedral angle with the secant plane pq. If pq is perpendicular to one of these planes, say, α, then the line q common to the two planes pq, β, both perpendicular to α, is perpendicular to α and therefore to the line p, hence the proposition.

15. Converse Theorem. *If a plane cuts a right dihedral angle along a right angle the secant plane is perpendicular to at least one of the faces of the dihedral angle.*

Suppose that the plane pq cuts the faces α, β of a right dihedral angle along two perpendicular lines p, q. If p is perpendicular to β (and therefore to the line $\alpha\beta$), the proposition is proved. Assume therefore that p is not perpendicular to β. The line q perpendicular to p, by assumption, lies in the plane γ perpendicular to p at the point pq, and since p lies in α, the plane γ is perpendicular to α. But β is also perpendicular to α, hence $q \equiv \beta\gamma$ is perpendicular to α, which proves the proposition.

16. Remark. The last two propositions (§§ 14, 15) may be expressed as follows: *The necessary and sufficient condition for two given orthogonal planes to determine a right angle in a (third) secant plane is that the secant plane shall be perpendicular to one of the given planes.*

17. Theorem. *The locus of a point the sum of the squares of whose distances from two fixed points is constant is a sphere having for center the mid-point of the given segment.*

18. Theorem. *The locus of a point the difference of the squares of whose distances from two given points is constant is a plane perpendicular to the line joining the given points.*

19. Theorem. *The locus of a point the ratio of whose distances from two given points is constant is a sphere.*

The proofs of these propositions are readily obtained by analogy with the proofs of the corresponding propositions in plane geometry (*College Geometry*, pp. 13–15).

20. Definition. The above sphere (§ 19) may be called, by analogy with the corresponding circle in the plane, the *sphere of Apollonius*.

21. Problem. *Find the locus of the mid-point of a segment of fixed length the ends of which move on two fixed rectangular (i. e., perpendicular) skew lines.*

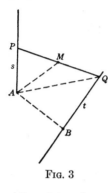

Let A, B (Fig. 3) be the feet of the common perpendicular of the two given lines s, t, and PQ one position of the moving segment. The line $s \equiv AP$ is perpendicular to $t \equiv BQ$ and to AB, hence s is also perpendicular to AQ, and in the right triangle APQ the segment AM joining A to the mid-point M of PQ is equal to one half of PQ, which length is constant. Similarly $BM = PQ/2$. Consequently M lies on the circle (M) common to the two spheres having for centers the points A, B and for radius $PQ/2$, i.e., (M) lies in the mediator of AB and has for center the mid-point of AB.

Fig. 3

22. Theorem. *If a segment of constant length moves so that its ends remain on two fixed skew lines, the variable sphere determined by the ends of the segment and the ends of the common perpendicular of the two skew lines is of constant size.*

Let AB (Fig. 4) be one position of the given segment and CD the common perpendicular of the two given skew lines AC, BD. Let P, Q denote the orthogonal projections of A, B upon the mediator of CD, which plane will pass through the mid-point N of AB. Let M be the mid-point of CD and O the circumcenter of the triangle MPQ.

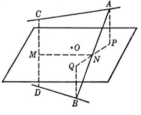

Fig. 4

We have

$$CM = DM = AP = BQ, \quad \text{and} \quad OM = OP = OQ.$$

Hence from the congruent right triangles OAP, OBQ, OCM, ODM we have: $OA = OB = OC = OD$. Thus O is also the center of the sphere determined by the points A, B, C, D.

As the segment AB moves, the points P, Q describe the lines MP, MQ. On the other hand the segment NP is constant in length as the leg of the right triangle ANP, the other two sides of which are constant in length. Similarly for NQ. Hence the segment PQ is constant in length, and therefore the circumradius OM of the triangle MPQ, where the angle M is fixed, is constant in length, and from the right triangle OCM we conclude that the circumradius OC of the sphere $ABCD$ is fixed in length, hence the proposition.

REMARK. The angle PMQ is equal to the angle between the given skew lines AC, BD. The center of the sphere $ABCD$ describes a circle with M as center.

23. Problem. *Construct a triangle having its vertices on three given skew lines and its sides parallel to three given planes, respectively.*

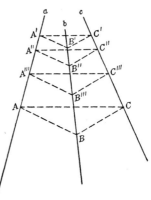

Let a, b, c (Fig. 5) be the lines on which the vertices A, B, C of the required triangle ABC are to lie and let α, β, γ be the planes to which BC, CA, AB are to be parallel.

Draw a series of planes parallel to γ meeting a, b in the points A', A'', A''', $\cdots$; B', B'', B''', $\cdots$. Through the points B', B'', B''', $\cdots$ draw planes parallel to α meeting the line c in C', C'', C''', $\cdots$. The three given lines are thus divided in proportional parts (§ 7), hence the lines $A'C'$,

FIG. 5

$A''C''$, $A'''C'''$, $\cdots$ are parallel to a certain fixed plane β_1 (§ 8). Now if β_1 has the same orientation as β, the triangles $A'B'C'$, $A''B''C''$, $A'''B'''C'''$, $\cdots$ satisfy the conditions of the problem, and we have an infinite number of solutions.

If the planes β, β_1 are not parallel, let b' be their line of intersection. Draw the line parallel to b' and meeting a, c (§ 5) in A and C, respectively. The planes through A and C parallel, respectively, to γ and α will cut b in the same point B, and ABC is the required triangle.

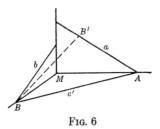

FIG. 6

24. Problem. *Through three given skew lines to draw three mutually orthogonal planes.*

Let c' (Fig. 6) be the parallel to the given line c which meets the other two given lines a, b (§ 5), in the points A, B, respectively. If M be a point such that the planes Ma,

Mb, *Mc′* be mutually orthogonal, the planes *Ma*, *Mb*, and the plane through *c* parallel to *Mc′* would constitute a solution of the proposed problem.

Now suppose *M* is known. The line *BM* is thus perpendicular to the plane *Ma*. Drop the perpendicular *BB′* from *B* upon the line *a*. The line *a* is perpendicular to the plane *BMB′*, hence this plane is known, and in this plane the point *M* lies on the circle having the known segment *BB′* for diameter.

Similarly, *AA′* being the perpendicular from *A* to *b*, the point *M* lies in the known plane *AMA′* through *A* perpendicular to *b* and on the circle having the known segment *AA′* for diameter.

The point *M* is thus determined as the intersection of two circles, or as the intersection of one circle with the line common to the two planes considered.

EXERCISES

1. If each of two planes contains a line parallel to the other plane, the two planes are parallel. What is the exceptional case?

2. Through a given line to draw a plane equidistant from two given points. Discuss special cases.

3. In a given plane through a given point to draw a line making a right angle with a given line not lying in the given plane.

4. Find the locus of the variable line which passes through a given point and makes equal angles with two fixed lines passing through the given point.

5. If a line is parallel to a plane, the shortest distance between this line and any line of the given plane not parallel to it is constant.

6. Through a given line to draw a plane cutting a given right dihedral angle along a right angle.

7. If a line and a plane are parallel to each other, a plane perpendicular to the line is also perpendicular to the plane.

8. If a line and a plane are both perpendicular to the same plane (or line), they are parallel to each other.

9. If two planes are respectively parallel to two given intersecting planes, the line of intersection of the first pair of planes is parallel to the line of intersection of the other two planes.

10. Within a given sphere to find a point through which three noncoplanar chords may be drawn which are bisected by this point. How many solutions may the problem have?

11. Construct a line perpendicular to a given plane and meeting two given skew lines.

12. A variable line meets the two fixed skew lines *u*, *v* in the points *P*, *Q*. Show that the point *M* determined by the relation $PM : MQ = k$, where *k* is a given ratio, describes a plane.

13. A variable plane of fixed orientation meets two given skew lines in the points *P*, *Q*. (a) Show that the mid-point of *PQ* describes a straight line.

(b) Show that the point M which divides PQ in a given ratio describes a straight line.

14. Through a given point in space to draw a line meeting a given circle and a given line not in the plane of the circle.

15. Through a given line to draw a plane making equal angles with two given planes. Discussion.

16. Determine a plane which will cut a convex polyhedral angle of four faces along a parallelogram.

17. Find a plane in which the edges of a given trirectangular trihedral angle determine a triangle congruent to a given triangle.

18. A trihedral angle having one right dihedral angle is cut along a right triangle by any plane perpendicular to one of its edges. HINT. Use § 14.

19. The face ABC of the tetrahedron $ABCD$ is perpendicular to the faces ABD, ACD. If the edge BC is perpendicular to the edge DC, the faces ADC, BDC are mutually perpendicular.

20. Construct a parallelepiped so that three of its edges shall lie on three given mutually skew lines. HINT. Use § 5 or § 6.

21. Given the two skew segments AB, $A'B'$, find the locus of the point M such that the two triangles MAB, $MA'B'$ are similar.

22. If at the ends C, D of a chord CD of a sphere two variable chords AC, BD are drawn perpendicular to CD and making a constant angle with each other, the distance between the other two ends A, B of these two chords is constant. HINT. Use § 22.

23. The points U, V, W lie on the edges DA, DB, DC of the tetrahedron $DABC$. Find a point M such that the three lines MU, MV, MW shall meet, respectively, the edges BC, CA, AB of $DABC$.

24. L, N, P, Q are the feet of the perpendiculars dropped from a point M in space upon the sides AB, BC, CD, DA of the skew quadrilateral $ABCD$. Prove that

$$AL^2 + BN^2 + CP^2 + DQ^2 = LB^2 + NC^2 + PD^2 + QA^2,$$

and conversely.

25. From the given point M the perpendiculars MP, MQ are dropped upon the two lines a, b. Let $M'P'$, $M'Q'$ be the perpendiculars dropped upon a, b from another point M' in space. Could the point M' be so chosen that the lines PQ, $P'Q'$ shall be parallel?

26. A variable triangle has a fixed vertex, the opposite side being a variable diameter of a fixed sphere. Prove that: (a) The sum of the squares of the other two sides is constant. (b) The foot of the altitude from the fixed vertex describes a sphere. (c) The mid-points of the variable sides lie on a sphere. (d) State and prove other analogous properties of the figure.

2. The Hyperbolic Group of Lines

25. Given three mutually skew lines a, b, c (Fig. 7) an infinite number of lines l, m, n, $\cdots$ may be drawn meeting the lines a, b, c, for, through any point, say of c, a line may be drawn meeting a and b (§ 4).

DEFINITION. All the lines meeting three given mutually skew lines form, by definition, a "ruled system of the second degree."

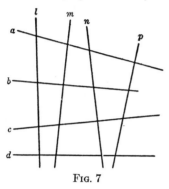

FIG. 7

Any two lines of a ruled system of the second degree are mutually skew, for if any two of them were coplanar, the lines a, b, c would lie in their plane, and would not be mutually skew, which is contrary to our assumption.

We shall state, without proof, that *all the lines l, m, n, $\cdots$ of the ruled system of the second degree are met not only by the lines a, b, c, but by an infinite number of other lines* which form, by definition, the "*supplementary ruled system*" of the system l, m, n, $\cdots$.

The two systems a, b, c, $\cdots$ and l, m, n, $\cdots$ form, by definition, a "*ruled surface of the second degree.*" The study of this surface is beyond the scope of this book. No use of its properties will be made in what follows.

26. Three mutually skew lines a, b, c are always met by an infinite number of straight lines (§ 25). Four mutually skew straight lines a, b, c, d may also be met by an infinite number of straight lines, if the four given lines belong to the same ruled system of the second degree. However, four mutually skew lines do not necessarily belong to such a ruled system. We shall state, without proof, the following

THEOREM. (a) *Four mutually skew lines are always met by two lines, real or conjugate imaginary.*

(b) *If four mutually skew straight lines are met by three lines, they are met by an infinite number of such lines,* i.e., they belong to the same system of the second degree.

27. Definition. Four mutually skew lines which are met by three (and therefore by an infinite number of) straight lines shall be referred to as "*four hyperbolic lines,*" or "*a hyperbolic group of lines.*"

Hyperbolic groups of lines are of frequent occurrence in the study of Solid Geometry. Such a group is often the space analogue of three concurrent lines in the plane.

28. Four hyperbolic lines have the following properties:

(a) *Through any point of any one of four hyperbolic lines a line may be drawn meeting the remaining three lines.*

(b) *A line meeting any three of four given hyperbolic lines also meets the fourth line.*

(c) *A plane passing through one of four hyperbolic lines meets the remaining three lines in three collinear points.*

These are immediate consequences of the above definition (§ 27).

29. Theorem. *If four lines passing through the four vertices of a tetrahedron form a hyperbolic group, through each vertex a line may be drawn meeting the three lines which pass through the remaining three vertices of the tetrahedron* [§ 28 (a)].

30. Converse Theorem. *If four given mutually skew lines passing through the four vertices of a tetrahedron are such that through each vertex but one it is possible to draw a line meeting the three lines passing through the remaining three vertices, the fourth vertex also has this property, and the four given lines are hyperbolic* [§ 26 (b)].

31. Theorem. *If four lines drawn in the four faces of a given tetrahedron form a hyperbolic group, each face is met by the lines situated in the remaining three faces in three collinear points.*

The four given lines p, q, r, s being hyperbolic, the plane ABC of the tetrahedron $ABCD$ containing the line p meets the remaining three lines in three collinear points [§ 28 (c)]. Now the points common to ABC and the lines q, r, s are the traces of these lines in ABC, hence the proposition.

32. Converse Theorem. *If four mutually skew lines drawn in the four faces of a tetrahedron are such that each face but one is met by the lines situated in the remaining faces in three collinear points, the same is true about the fourth face, and the four lines are hyperbolic.*

The conditions of the problem imply that the four given lines are met by three lines, hence the proposition [§ 26 (b)].

EXERCISES

1. If a variable line meets constantly three given lines parallel to the same plane, the variable line is divided by the given lines in a constant ratio and, furthermore, this line is parallel to a fixed plane.

2. Draw a line so that it shall meet three given skew lines and be divided by them in a given ratio.

3. A line moves so that it constantly meets two given skew lines d, d' and is parallel to a fixed plane (P). Find the locus of the point which divides the variable line in a given ratio.

3. Harmonic Forms

33. Definition. All the planes passing through a given line in space form a "pencil of planes," of which the given line is the "axis." The planes of a pencil are said to be "coaxal."

34. Theorem. *If four coaxal planes determine a harmonic range on one line, they determine a harmonic range on any other line, which meets the four planes.*

Suppose the traces A, B, C, D of the four given planes on the secant s are harmonic, and let A', B', C', D' be the points of intersection of these planes with any other line t. (Fig. 8.)

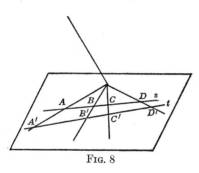

FIG. 8

(a) The line t is coplanar with s. The lines AA', BB', CC', DD' form a pencil of rays having for its vertex the trace, in the plane (st), of the axis of the given pencil of planes. Now the pencil of rays is cut by s in four harmonic points, hence the same is true about the points of intersection A', B', C', D' of t with this pencil.

(b) The lines s, t are not coplanar. Draw any line m so that it intersects both s and t and cuts the four given planes, in the points A'', B'', C'', D''. The lines s and m are coplanar, hence, according to case (a), the points A'', B'', C'', D'' are harmonic; again the lines m and t are coplanar, hence the points A', B', C', D' are harmonic, for the same reason. The proposition is thus proved for any position of t.

35. Definition. Four coaxal planes which determine a harmonic range on one line (and therefore on every line) form a "harmonic axal pencil," or a "harmonic pencil of planes," or "four harmonic planes."

One pair of planes is said to be "harmonically separated" by the other pair.

To construct a harmonic pencil of planes take a harmonic range of points and through these four points and any line not coplanar with the base of the range pass four planes.

A harmonic pencil of planes is cut by a plane not passing through its axis in four harmonic lines.

36. Theorem. *If four coaxal planes are respectively parallel to four other coaxal planes, and one of these pencils is harmonic, then the other is also harmonic.*

The proposition is readily proved by translation and superposition.

37. Theorem. *If a line is parallel to one of the planes of a harmonic pencil, the harmonic conjugate of this plane meets the line in the mid-point of the segment determined on this line by the other pair of planes of the pencil.*

CONVERSE THEOREM. *Given a harmonic pencil of planes, if the segment determined on a line by one pair of conjugate planes has its mid-point in a (third) plane of the pencil, the line is parallel to the fourth plane of the pencil.*

The two propositions are readily proved by passing a plane through the given line (C. G., p. 139).

38. Theorem. *The perpendiculars dropped from a point upon four harmonic planes form a harmonic pencil.*

The feet P, Q, R, S of the perpendiculars AP, AQ, AR, AS dropped from the given point A upon the four given planes lie on a circle. The plane (U) of this circle passes through A and is perpendicular to the axis s of the pencil, and the points A and $B \equiv s\text{-}(U)^*$ are diametrically opposite on this circle. Thus the angles between the lines AP, AQ, AR, AS of the pencil (A) are respectively equal to the angles between the lines BP, BQ, BR, BS of the pencil (B). Hence the pencils (A) and (B) are superposable. Now the pencil (B) is harmonic (§ 35), hence the same is true about the pencil (A).

39. Theorem. *If through a point in space planes are drawn perpendicular to the rays of a harmonic pencil, the planes will form a harmonic axal pencil.*

Indeed the four planes will pass through the perpendicular from the given point to the plane of the given pencil of rays (A). The

---

* A symbol of this kind indicates that the point B is the intersection of the line s with the plane (U).

proof is completed in the same way as the proof of the preceding proposition (§ 38).

40. Theorem. *The internal and external bisecting planes of a dihedral angle are separated harmonically by the faces of the dihedral angle.*

41. Converse Theorem. *If one of two pairs of harmonic planes are rectangular, the latter planes are the bisecting planes of the angles formed by the first pair.*

The two theorems are readily reduced to the corresponding propositions in the plane by cutting the given pencil by a plane perpendicular to its axis.

42. Theorem. *A plane perpendicular to one of the two bisecting planes of a dihedral angle cuts these bisecting planes along the bisectors of the angle along which it cuts the dihedral angle.*

Let u be the edge of the dihedral angle and let a, b, s, t be the lines of intersection of the secant plane ab with the faces and with the bisecting planes of the dihedral angle. The pencil $abst$ is harmonic (§ 40). Now the plane ab is perpendicular to one of the two bisecting planes us, ut, hence the angle st is a right angle (§ 14), consequently the lines s, t bisect the angle ab (C. G., p. 140).

43. Converse Theorem. *If a plane cuts the bisecting planes of a given dihedral angle along the bisectors of the angle along which it cuts the dihedral angle, the secant plane is perpendicular to at least one of these two bisecting planes.*

With the same notations as in the direct theorem, if the lines s, t are the bisectors of the angle ab, the angle st is a right angle, hence the plane ab is perpendicular to one of the two planes us, ut (§ 15).

44. Theorem. *The locus of the harmonic conjugate of a given point with respect to the two points of intersection of a variable line through the given point with the two faces of a dihedral angle is a plane.*

Let a variable line ALM through the given point A meet the faces λ, μ of the given dihedral angle in the points L, M. The harmonic conjugate B of A with respect to L, M lies in the plane $\lambda\mu-B$ which is harmonically separated from the plane $\lambda\mu-A$ by the planes λ, μ. Now the three planes λ, μ, $\lambda\mu-A$ are fixed, therefore the fourth plane $\lambda\mu-B$ is fixed, hence the proposition.

45. Definition. Given two skew lines a, b and a point P, the line is drawn through P meeting the lines a, b (§ 4), in the points A, B. The harmonic conjugate Q of P with respect to A, B is said to be "the harmonic conjugate of P with respect to the lines a, b."

46. Theorem. *If a point describes a plane, the harmonic conjugate of this point with respect to two skew straight lines describes a plane.*

Let C, D (Fig. 9) be the traces of the given two lines a, b in the given plane PCD, and P any point in this plane. Through P draw the line meeting a, b, say, in X, Y. The harmonic conjugate Q of P with respect to a, b lies in the plane CDQ which is harmonically separated from the given plane CDP by the two planes $CD-a$, $CD-b$. Now the three planes CDP,

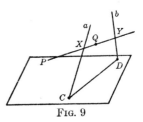

Fig. 9

$CD-a$, $CD-b$ of the harmonic pencil having CD for axis are fixed, hence the fourth plane CDQ is also fixed, which proves the proposition.

47. Theorem. *If a point describes a straight line its harmonic conjugate with respect to two skew lines describes a straight line.*

Let a, b be the two given skew lines and let the point P describe the line u. Let Q, Q', Q'', $\cdots$ be the harmonic conjugates of the points P, P', P'', $\cdots$ of u with respect to a, b. That the locus of Q, Q', Q'', $\cdots$ is a straight line u' is evident from the fact that these points must lie in the harmonic conjugate plane, with respect to a, b, of any plane passing through u (§ 46).

48. Definition. The line u' may be called the "harmonic conjugate" of u with respect to a, b.

The lines a, b are obviously harmonically conjugate with respect to u, u'.

The two pairs of lines a, b; u, u' form a hyperbolic group, which may be referred to as a "harmonic hyperbolic group."

49. Theorem. *If the points C, D divide the segment AB harmonically, and O is the mid-point of CD, we have*

$$OA : OB = (AC : CB)^2.$$

Let $AC : CB = r$. Hence

$$AO + OC = (CO + OB)r,$$

or

$$AO - OB \cdot r = (1 + r)CO.$$

Eliminating CO between this equality and the relation (C. G., p. 135)

$$OA \cdot OB = OC^2,$$

we obtain

$$(AO - r \cdot OB)^2 = OA \cdot OB \cdot (1 + r)^2.$$

Squaring and collecting terms we obtain

$$OA(OA - OB) = OB(OA - OB) \cdot r^2,$$

which leads directly to the announced relation.

EXERCISES

1. Through a given line to draw a plane cutting the faces of a given dihedral angle along the lines a, b, and the bisecting planes of this dihedral angle along the lines c, d, so that c, d shall be the bisectors of the angles formed by the lines a, b.

2. (a) Given a trihedral angle $S\text{-}ABC$ and a line p passing through S, let u, v, w be the lines of intersection of the pairs of planes $SA\text{-}p$, SBC; $SB\text{-}p$, SCA; $SC\text{-}p$, SAB. Show that the harmonic conjugates u', v', w' of u, v w with respect to the pairs of edges SB, SC; SC, SA; SA, SB lie in the same plane π. (b) Conversely, if a plane π cuts the faces of $S\text{-}ABC$ along u', v', w', then the planes $SA\text{-}u$, $SB\text{-}v$, $SC\text{-}w$ are coaxal.

3. If four mutually skew lines determine harmonic ranges on two transversals, the four lines form a harmonic hyperbolic group.

4. (a) If the points C, D divide the segment $AB = d$ harmonically in the ratio $p : q$, the radius of the corresponding sphere of Apollonius is equal to $pqd : (p^2 - q^2)$. (b) The distance between the mid-points of the segments AB, CD is equal to $d(p^2 + q^2) : 2(p^2 - q^2)$.

4. Homothetic Figures

50. Definition. Given a group of points A, B, C, $\cdots$ distributed in any way whatever in space, on the rays SA, SB, SC, $\cdots$ joining these points to a given point S the points A', B', C', $\cdots$ are constructed so that

$$\frac{SA'}{SA} = \frac{SB'}{SB} = \frac{SC'}{SC} \cdots = k,$$

where k is a given ratio. The group of points A', B', C', $\cdots$ thus obtained is said to be *homothetic* to the group A, B, C, $\cdots$. The point S is called the *homothetic center* of the two groups, and k their *homothetic ratio*.

If k is a positive number, the points A, A'; $\cdots$ lie on the same side of S, and the two systems are said to be *directly homothetic;* if k is negative the points A, A'; $\cdots$ are on opposite sides of S, and the two systems are then said to be *inversely homothetic.*

When $k = -1$, the two groups are symmetrical with respect to S.

REMARK. The above definition of homothetic figures in space is the same as the definition of such figures in the plane. There is this difference, however. For two values of k equal in magnitude and opposite in sign we obtain two groups which are symmetrical with respect to S, but unlike the case in the plane, these two figures are not superposable.

51. Theorem. *The homothetic of a straight line is a straight line.*

The proof is identical with the proof of the corresponding proposition in the plane.

COROLLARY. *The angle between two straight lines is equal to the angle between their homothetic lines, or, in other words, two homothetic plane angles are equal.*

52. Theorem. *The homothetic of a plane is a plane, and the two planes are parallel.*

Let A be any point of the given plane α and a any line of α through A. The homothetic of a is a line a' parallel to a through the homothetic A' of A, hence a' is parallel to the plane α. As a revolves about A in the plane α, its homothetic a' will revolve about A' and will describe a plane α', parallel to α.

COROLLARY. *The angle between two planes is equal to the angle between their homothetic planes, or, in other words, homothetic dihedral angles are equal.*

53. Theorem. *The homothetic of a circle the plane of which does not contain the homothetic center is a circle.*

Let S be the homothetic center, α', O', A', the homothetics of the plane α of the given circle, of its center O, and of any point A of this circle, respectively. We have then

$$\frac{O'A'}{OA} = \frac{SO'}{SO} = \frac{SA'}{SA} = k.$$

Thus in the plane α' the point A' lies at a fixed distance $O'A'$ from the fixed point O', hence A' describes a circle in the plane α'.

REMARK. This theorem is more general than the corresponding theorem in the plane, for in the latter case the center of similitude lies in the plane of the given circle.

54. Theorem. *The homothetic of a sphere is a sphere.*

Let S be the homothetic center, O' the homothetic point of the center O of the given sphere, and A' the homothetic of any point A of this sphere. We have

(1)
$$\frac{SO'}{SO} = \frac{SA'}{SA} = \frac{O'A'}{OA} = k.$$

Hence the point A' is at a fixed distance from the fixed point O' and therefore its locus is a sphere having O' for center.

55. Remark. The above proportion (1) shows that the homothetic center S divides the line of centers OO' of the two homothetic spheres in the ratio of the radii $O'A'$, OA, which ratio, in turn, is equal to the given homothetic ratio.

This division is external, if the spheres are directly homothetic, and internal, if the spheres are inversely homothetic.

56. Theorem. *Two figures homothetic to the same third figure are homothetic to each other. Their homothetic center is collinear with the first two homothetic centers, and their homothetic ratio is equal to the quotient of the two given homothetic ratios.*

FIG. 10

Let A (Fig. 10) be any point of the given figure and A', A'' its homothetic points with respect to the two homothetic centers S', S'', the homothetic ratios being k', k'' respectively.

Consider the triangle $AS'S''$ and the transversal $A'A''$ which meets $S'S''$ in S. By Menelaus' theorem (C. G., p. 122) we have

$$\frac{AA''}{A''S''} \cdot \frac{S''S}{SS'} \cdot \frac{S'A'}{A'A} = -1.$$

But we have, by assumption,

$$S'A' : S'A = k',$$

hence

$$S'A' : A'A = k' : (1 - k')$$

and

$$S''A'' : S''A = k'',$$

hence

$$AA'' : A''S'' = (1 - k'') : k''$$

and therefore

$$\frac{S'S}{SS''} = - \frac{k'}{k''} : \frac{1 - k'}{1 - k''}.$$

Thus the two points A', A'' are collinear with the point S of the line $S'S''$, and the point S does not depend upon the particular point A taken in the first figure.

Again considering the triangle $AA'A''$ and the transversal $SS'S''$ we have, by Menelaus' theorem,

$$\frac{AS'}{S'A'} \cdot \frac{A'S}{SA''} \cdot \frac{A''S''}{S''A} = - 1,$$

hence

$$SA'' : SA' = k'' : k'.$$

The proposition is thus proved.

REMARK. The two figures A', $\cdots$, A'', $\cdots$ will be directly homothetic, if the figures A, $\cdots$, A', $\cdots$; A, $\cdots$, A'', $\cdots$ are both directly or both inversely homothetic. Otherwise they will be inversely homothetic.

57. Corollary. *If three figures are homothetic in pairs, their homothetic centers are collinear.*

This follows immediately from the preceding proposition (§ 56). It may be proved directly as follows.

Let A be a point of the first figure and A', A'' its homothetic points in the two other figures. Now let B be any other point of the first figure, not situated in the plane $AA'A''$, and B', B'' its homothetic points.

The lines AA', BB' meet in the homothetic center S' of the figures A, B, $\cdots$, A', B', $\cdots$. The lines AA'', BB'' meet in the homothetic center S'' of the figures A, B, $\cdots$, A'', B'', $\cdots$, and the lines $A'A''$, $B'B''$ meet in the homothetic center S of the figures A', B', $\cdots$, A'', B'', $\cdots$. Thus the points S, S', S'' lie on the line of intersection of the planes $AA'A''$, $BB'B''$.

58. Theorem. (a) *Two triangles, in different planes, whose sides are parallel are homothetic.*

(b) *Two tetrahedrons whose faces are parallel are homothetic.*
The proof is left to the reader.

59. Problem. *Construct a tetrahedron having its vertices in the four faces of a given tetrahedron and its faces parallel to the faces of a second given tetrahedron.*

Let a plane (T) parallel to the face $A'B'C'$ of the second given tetrahedron $A'B'C'D'$ meet the edges DA, DB, DC of the first given tetrahedron $ABCD$ in the points P, Q, R. In the triangle PQR inscribe a triangle $A''B''C''$ with sides parallel to the sides of the triangle $A'B'C'$ (C. G., p. 43). Through A'', B'', C'' draw parallels to $A'D'$, $B'D'$, $C'D'$. These parallels will meet in a point D''.

Now if (T) is made to vary, the vertices of $A''B''C''$ will describe straight lines passing through D, hence D'' will also describe a line passing through D, and the trace U of DD'' in the plane ABC is a vertex of the required tetrahedron $UXYZ$.

Otherwise. Through the vertices of $A'B'C'D'$ draw planes parallel to the faces of $ABCD$ thus forming a tetrahedron $MNPQ$. The two tetrahedrons $A'B'C'D'$, $MNPQ$ form a system similar to the system formed by $ABCD$ and the required tetrahedron $UXYZ$. Hence the parallels through A, B, C to the lines MD', ND', PD' will meet in the required point U.

EXERCISES

1. A plane cuts the edges of a given trihedral angle in the points A, B, C. Find the locus of the centroid of the triangle ABC (a) if the plane varies while one of the vertices remains fixed; (b) if the plane varies while one side remains fixed.

2. Find the locus of the lines passing through a given point and divided in a given ratio (a) by two fixed planes and the given point; (b) by three coaxal planes.

3. Given the homothetic ratio of two figures determine their homothetic center so that the homothetic of a given line shall meet another fixed line in space.

4. Determine the homothetic center of two given figures so that the homothetic points, in the second figure, of three given points of the first figure shall lie in three given planes. What is the locus of the homothetic center?

5. Given three non-collinear points A, B, C and a plane (P) not passing through any of these points, find a point such that the lines joining it to A, B, C shall determine in (P) a triangle homothetic to ABC.

6. $ABC \cdots$, $A'B'C' \cdots$ are two homothetic figures, and $AA'' : A''A' = BB'' : B''B' = \cdots = m$. Show that $A''B''C'' \cdots$ is homothetic to $ABC \cdots$.

7. Find the locus of the point M from which a given fixed segment AB is projected upon a given plane parallel to AB into a segment $A'B'$ of given length.

8. Construct a triangle having its vertices on three given skew lines so that the centroid of the triangle shall coincide with a given point.

9. If the faces of two trihedral angles are respectively parallel, the three pairs of corresponding edges determine three planes which pass through the line joining the vertices of the dihedral angles.

10. If the edges of two trihedrons are respectively parallel, the two trihedrons determine in a transversal plane two homothetic triangles, the homothetic center of which is collinear with the vertices of the two trihedrons.

11. If two tetrahedrons are homothetic, a face of one cuts the three non-corresponding faces of the other along a triangle homothetic to the triangle of this face, and the homothetic center of these two triangles lies on the line joining the homothetic center of the two tetrahedrons to the vertex of the tetrahedron opposite the face considered.

5. Perspective Tetrahedrons

60. Definition. Two tetrahedrons are said to be *perspective* or *homological,* if the four lines joining pairs of corresponding vertices in the two tetrahedrons meet in a point.

This point is called the *center of perspectivity* or the *center of homology.*

61. Theorem. *The four lines of intersection of the pairs of corresponding faces of two perspective tetrahedrons are coplanar.*

Let S (Fig. 11, p. 22) be the center of homology of the two tetrahedrons $ABCD$, $A'B'C'D'$. Any two corresponding edges of these two tetrahedrons lie in a plane containing S, hence the two lines meet in a point. Let X, Y, Z, U, V, W be the points of intersection of the edges BC, CA, AB, DA, DB, DC of $ABCD$ with the corresponding edges of $A'B'C'D'$.

The line of intersection of the two planes ABC, $A'B'C'$ contains the points X, Y, Z; and the line of intersection of the planes DAB, $D'A'B'$ contains the points U, V, Z, hence the two lines considered have the point Z in common.

In the same way it may be shown that any two of the four lines considered in the proposition have a point in common, hence the four lines are coplanar.

DEFINITION. The plane $XYZUVW$ is called the *plane of homology* or the *plane of perspectivity* of the two tetrahedrons.

62. Converse Theorem. *If the four lines of intersection of the four pairs of corresponding faces of two tetrahedrons are coplanar, the tetrahedrons are in perspective.*

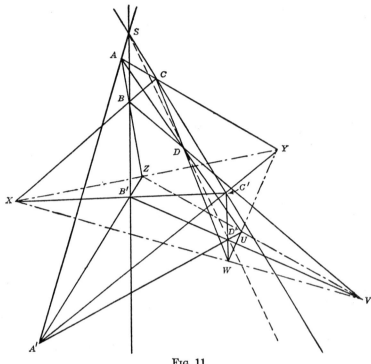

FIG. 11

If the line of intersection of the planes ABC, $A'B'C'$ has a point Z in common with the line of intersection of the planes DAB, $D'A'B'$, the lines AB, $A'B'$ pass through Z, hence the lines AA', BB' are coplanar. It may thus be shown that any two of the four lines AA', BB', CC', DD' are coplanar, hence the four lines are concurrent.

63. Definition. If the plane of homology meets the line AA' (§ 61) in the harmonic conjugate of S with respect to A, A', the same will obviously take place for the lines BB', CC', DD'. In such a case the homology is said to be *harmonic.*

MISCELLANEOUS EXERCISES

1. A triangle having its vertices on three fixed mutually skew lines varies so that its centroid describes a fixed straight line. Find the loci of the mid-points of the sides of this triangle.

2. If one line makes equal angles with three coplanar and concurrent lines, the first line is perpendicular to the plane of the latter lines.

3. Through two given skew lines a, b a variable pair of perpendicular planes is drawn meeting along the line u. Find the locus determined by u in a plane perpendicular to a.

4. A segment is revolved about an axis x not coplanar with the segment. If AB, $A'B'$ are two given positions of the segment, determine the position of the axis x.

5. Given the angle AOB, find the locus of the point M in space such that the sum of the projections of OM upon OA and OB shall have a constant value.

6. A line PM is drawn within the dihedral angle (MOA, MOB), meeting the edge MO in M. A plane perpendicular to MP at P cuts the dihedral angle along the angle AOB. Show that if P lies on the bisector of AOB, the line MP lies in the bisecting plane of the dihedral angle.

7. Through a given line s a variable plane is drawn cutting two given planes α, β along two lines a, b. Through a and b planes are drawn perpendicular to α and β, respectively. Show that the line of intersection of these two planes meets three fixed lines.

8. If Q is the center of the sphere determined by the four symmetrics of the point P with respect to the four faces of a tetrahedron, then P is the center of the sphere determined by the four symmetrics of Q with respect to the faces of the same tetrahedron.

9. A variable sphere is tangent to two given skew lines and has its center in the mediator of the common perpendicular of the given lines. Find the locus of the center of the sphere.

10. Find the locus of the third vertex of a variable triangle two of whose vertices describe two given planes and whose sides are parallel to three given lines having a director plane.

11. In a parallelepiped the sum of the squares of the diagonals is equal to the sum of the squares of the edges.

12. Find two skew lines u, v such that the symmetric of u with respect to v and the symmetric of v with respect to u shall be coplanar.

13. (a) If the sum of the distances of a point on a given line from two given planes is equal to the sum of the distances of a second point on the same line to the same two planes, this sum is the same for every point on the line. (b) If the sum of the distances of each of three given points from two fixed planes is the same for the three points, this sum is the same for every point of the plane determined by the three points considered.

14. If two triangles (tetrahedrons) have their vertices on three (four) parallel lines, the segments intercepted on a transversal parallel to these lines by the angles (dihedral angles) of the first triangle (tetrahedron) are proportional to the segments intercepted on this transversal by the corresponding angles (dihedral angles) of the second triangle (tetrahedron).

15. If in a skew hexagon each side is equal and parallel to its opposite side, the six mid-points of the sides are coplanar.

16. If in a skew polygon $ABCD \cdots A'B'C'D' \cdots$ having an even number of sides, each side AB, BC, $\cdots$ is equal and parallel to its opposite side $A'B'$, $B'C'$, $\cdots$, the lines AA', BB', $\cdots$ joining the pairs of opposite vertices, and the lines LL', MM', $\cdots$ joining the mid-points L, M, N, $\cdots$, L', M', N', $\cdots$ of pairs of opposite sides all have a point in common.

17. In the mediator of the common perpendicular CD of two skew lines AC, BD, a circle is drawn having the mid-point M of CD for center. A sphere having for center any point of this circle and passing through C, D will meet the lines AC, BD in two points A, B such that the segment AB will be of constant length.

18. The points B, B' lie on the perpendiculars erected to the plane (P) at the points A, A'. Find the locus of the point, in the plane (P), at which the segments AB, $A'B'$ subtend equal angles.

19. Let D, E, F be any three points on the edges SA, SB, SC of the tetrahedron $SABC$, and let $U \equiv (BF, CE)$, $V \equiv (CD, AF)$, $W \equiv (AE, BD)$. Show that (a) the three lines AU, BV, CW have a point, say, P in common; (b) the lines DU, EV, FW have a point, say, Q in common; (c) the three points P, Q, S are collinear.

20. In a frustum of a triangular pyramid, the three lines joining the mid-points of the edges to the points of intersection of the diagonals of the respectively opposite faces have a point in common.

21. A point P is taken in the same plane as two straight lines $ABC \cdots$, $A'B'C' \cdots$; any number of straight lines AA', BB', CC', $\cdots$ are drawn through P, and terminate on the given lines. Upon these, as diameters, circles are drawn, with their planes at right angles to the plane $AA'BB' \cdots$; if tangents are drawn to these circles at the points where they are met by a perpendicular line from P to the plane $AA'BB'$, these tangents meet the plane $AA'BB'$ in a straight line.

22. Given two similar triangles ABC, $A'B'C'$, in space, find a point M such that the two tetrahedrons $MABC$, $MA'B'C'$ shall be similar.

23. The three segments AA', BB', CC' lie on three mutually perpendicular lines which meet in the point S. Show that the centers of the eight spheres $SABC$, $SA'B'C'$, $SA'BC'$, $\cdots$ are cospherical.

24. Any plane parallel to a face of a regular octahedron cuts the solid along a hexagon the length of whose perimeter is thrice the length of an edge of the octahedron.

25. ABC, $A'B'C'$ are two parallel sections of the same trihedral angle, and D is a point in the plane ABC. The parallels to the lines DA', DB', DC', through the points A, B, C, meet the plane $A'B'C'$ in the points P, Q, R. The planes parallel to the planes $DB'C'$, $DC'A'$, $DA'B'$, through the points A, B, C, meet the plane $A'B'C'$ along three lines forming a triangle $P'Q'R'$. Show that the size of the triangles PQR, $P'Q'R'$ is independent of the position of the point D in the plane ABC.

26. If P, Q, R, S are the traces of a plane on the edges MA, MB, MC, MD of the pyramid $MABCD$ whose base $ABCD$ is a parallelogram, we have

$$\frac{MA}{MP} + \frac{MC}{MR} = \frac{MB}{MQ} + \frac{MD}{MS}.$$

27. The eight points which divide in a given ratio the eight lines joining, in any way, the vertices of a parallelepiped to the vertices of a second parallelepiped are the vertices of a third parallelepiped.

28. AA', BB', CC' are three parallel non-coplanar segments. The planes $A'BC$, $B'CA$, $C'AB$ meet in S, and the planes $AB'C'$, $BC'A'$, $CA'B'$ meet in S'. Show that (a) SS' is parallel to AA'; (b) SS' meets the planes ABC, $A'B'C'$ in two points T, T' such that $TS = SS' = S'T'$; (c) TT' is the harmonic mean of AA', BB', CC'.

29. The points A', B', C' are marked on the edges AD, BD, CD of the tetrahedron $DABC$ so that $AA' = BB' = CC' = k$. When k varies the point of intersection of the three planes BCA', CAB', ABC' describes a straight line.

30. X, Z are the areas of the circumsphere and the inscribed sphere of a regular tetrahedron, and Y is the area of the sphere touching the edges of the tetrahedron. Show that $X + 3Z = 4Y$. Show also that this formula is valid for a regular octahedron and a regular icosahedron.

31. In a plane are given three concurrent lines making angles of 120 degrees with each other. A variable point in space moves so that its projections upon these three lines form a triangle of given area. Find the locus of the variable point.

32. (a) A sphere passing through the vertex A of the parallelepiped $ABCDA'B'C'D'$ cuts the edges AB, AD, AA' and the diagonal AC' in the points Q, S, P', R'. Show that $AB \cdot AQ + AD \cdot AS + AA' \cdot AP' = AC' \cdot AR'$. (b) Show that the locus of the center of the variable sphere passing through the vertex O of a given trihedral angle and cutting the edges in the points A, B, C so that $OA + OB + OC$ is constant, is a plane.

33. $ABCD$ is a quadrilateral, O the intersection of its diagonals, V the vertex of the pyramid which has $ABCD$ as its base. Every section of the pyramid perpendicular to VO is found to be a parallelogram. Find the locus of V.

34. A variable pyramid has a fixed square base, while its vertex describes the perpendicular to this square through its center. Show that the orthocenter of a lateral face of the pyramid describes a circle.

35. The base of a variable triangle is fixed, the opposite vertex describing a straight line perpendicular to the base but not coplanar with it. Show that the orthocenter of the triangle describes a circle.

36. A variable quadrangular pyramid $SABCD$ has a fixed base $ABCD$, the opposite vertex S varying so that the *angle* $ASB = CSD$, and the *angle* $BSC = DSA$. Find the locus of S.

37. If A', B', C', D' are the feet of the perpendiculars dropped from any point upon the faces of the tetrahedron $ABCD$, show that

$$AC'^2 - BC'^2 = AD'^2 - BD'^2, \text{ etc.}$$

38. The areas of the faces of a given polyhedron are inversely as the perpendiculars from a point O, and OO' meets these planes in P_1, P_2, P_3, $\cdots$, P_n, respectively; prove that

$$\frac{O'P_1}{OP_1} + \frac{O'P_2}{OP_2} + \cdots + \frac{O'P_n}{OP_n} = n.$$

39. If in a tetrahedron $OABC$ the angles at the triangular faces are denoted by a, b, or c; all the angles opposite to OA or BC being a, those opposite to OB

or CA are b, and those opposite to OC or AB are c; the angles at O have the suffix 1, those at A, B, C, the suffixes 2, 3, 4, respectively; prove that if

$$a_1 + b_1 + c_1 = a_2 + b_2 + c_2 = \pi,$$

then

$$c_1 + a_1 - b_1 = c_4 + a_4 - b_4,$$
$$a_1 + b_1 - c_1 = a_3 + b_3 - c_3,$$
$$c_2 + a_2 - b_2 = c_3 + a_3 - b_3,$$
$$a_2 + b_2 - c_2 = a_4 + b_4 - c_4.$$

CHAPTER II

THE TRIHEDRAL ANGLE

1. The Orthocentric Line

64. Definition. For the sake of brevity we shall sometimes use the term *trihedron* to designate a trihedral angle.

65. Notation. The vertex of the trihedral angle will be denoted by S and the edges by a, b, c. Produced beyond the vertex S these lines will be denoted by a', b', c'.

The three lines considered determine four pairs of trihedrons: (1) $S\text{-}abc$, $S\text{-}a'b'c'$; (2) $S\text{-}a'bc$, $S\text{-}ab'c'$; (3) $S\text{-}ab'c$, $S\text{-}a'bc'$; (4) $S\text{-}abc'$, $S\text{-}a'b'c$.

The trihedral angle $S\text{-}abc$ will be referred to as the "principal trihedral angle" or the "principal trihedron," or, more briefly, the "trihedron." The three trihedrons $S\text{-}a'bc$, $S\text{-}ab'c$, $S\text{-}abc'$ will be referred to as the "external trihedrons" of the trihedral angle $S\text{-}abc$. The trihedron $S\text{-}a'bc$ will be said to "correspond" to the edge a or to the face bc of $S\text{-}abc$. Similarly for the other two external trihedrons.

66. Definition. The plane through an edge of a trihedral angle drawn perpendicularly to the opposite face is called an *altitude plane* of the trihedron.

67. Theorem. *The three altitude planes of a trihedron are coaxal.*

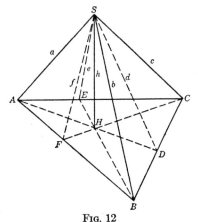

Fig. 12

Let e, f (Fig. 12) be the traces of the two altitude planes be, cf in the faces ca, ab of the trihedron $S\text{-}abc$, and let h be the common line of the two planes be, cf. Consider a plane perpendicular to h at any point H of this line and cutting a, b, c, e, f in the points A, B, C, E, F.

27

The plane *SBHE* is perpendicular to the line *AC*, i.e., the line *BHE* is the altitude of *ABC* through *B*. Similarly the line *CHF* is the altitude of *ABC* through *C*, hence *H* is the orthocenter of *ABC*, and *AHD* is perpendicular to *BC* at *D*. Thus the line *BC* is perpendicular to the plane *SAHD*, hence this latter plane is the altitude plane to the face *bc*, which proves the proposition.

68. Definition. The common axis of the three altitude planes of a trihedron may be called the **orthocentric line** of the trihedral angle.

69. Remark I. We have incidentally proved, in the above proposition (§ 67), the

THEOREM. *The triangle determined by the edges of a trihedron in a plane perpendicular to its orthocentric line has for its orthocenter the trace of the orthocentric line in this plane.*

70. Remark II. *The orthocentric line of a trihedral angle is also the orthocentric line of each of the three external trihedrons of the principal trihedral angle.*

71. Definition. Let *a*, *b*, *c* be the edges and *h* the orthocentric line of the trihedron (*S*). Let *d*, *e*, *f* be the traces of the altitude planes *ah*, *bh*, *ch* in the faces *bc*, *ca*, *ab* of (*S*). The trihedron *S–def* may be called the **orthic trihedron** of the given trihedron.

72. Theorem. *The orthic triangle of the triangle determined by the edges of a given trihedron in a secant plane perpendicular to the orthocentric line of this trihedron is determined in the secant plane by the orthic trihedron of the given trihedron.*

The proof is left to the reader.

73. Definition. The three edges of a trihedron and its orthocentric line form a group of four lines such that the plane determined by any two of these lines is perpendicular to the plane determined by the remaining two lines. Such a group of lines may be referred to as an **orthocentric group of lines.**

74. Theorem. *Each of the four lines of an orthocentric group is the orthocentric line of the trihedral angle determined by the remaining three lines of the group.*

The proof is left to the reader.

75. Remark. *A group of orthocentric lines determines an orthocentric group of points in any plane perpendicular to one of these lines (§ 69).*

76. Definition.   The edges of a trihedral angle and its ortho-centric line determine four trihedral angles which may be referred to as an **orthocentric group** of trihedral angles.

77. Theorem.   *The four trihedrons of an orthocentric group have the same orthic trihedron.*

Let d, e, f (Fig. 12) be the edges of the orthic trihedron $S-def$ of the given trihedron $S-abc$, and let h be the orthocentric line of $S-abc$.   We have, by assumption, $d \equiv (bc, \ ah)$, $e \equiv (ca, \ bh)$, $f \equiv (ab, \ ch)$.

Now consider, say, the trihedron $S-bch$.   Its orthocentric line is a (§ 74) and the altitude planes perpendicular to the faces bc, $ch, \ hb$ are respectively $ah, \ ab, \ ac$.   The three pairs of perpendicular planes determine the lines $d, \ e, \ f$.   Similarly for the trihedrons $S-chb$, $S-hbc$.   Hence the proposition.

78. Problem.   *Construct four lines such that the plane deter-mined by any two of them shall be perpendicular to the plane of the remaining two lines.*

The four lines cannot be coplanar, and, on the other hand, each of them must be coplanar with each of the remaining three, hence the four required lines must be concurrent, and therefore form an orthocentric group (§ 73).

Three of the lines may be taken arbitrarily, and the orthocentric line of the trihedral angle formed by these three lines will be the fourth line of the required group.

An expedite way to form such a group is to erect a perpendicular to the plane of a triangle at the orthocenter of the triangle and join any point of this perpendicular to the vertices of the triangle.

79. Theorem.   *The faces and the altitude planes of a trihedron are the three pairs of bisecting planes of the dihedral angles of the orthic trihedral angle of the given trihedron.*

Let A, B, C, H (Fig. 12) be the traces of the edges a, b, c and of the orthocentric line h of the trihedron $S-abc$ in a plane perpen-dicular to h.   The point H is the orthocenter of ABC (§ 69), and the orthic triangle DEF of ABC is determined in the plane ABC by the orthic trihedron $S-def$ of $S-abc$ (§ 72).

The lines AD, BC are the bisectors of the angle EDF of the triangle DEF (C. G., pp. 85–86), hence the pencil $D(BFHE)$ is harmonic (§ 35).   But the planes SDB, SDH are perpendicular to each other, hence they are the bisecting planes of the angles formed by the planes SDE, SDF (§ 41). Similarly for the other dihedral angles of the trihedron S–def.

80. Remark. The orthic trihedron S–def of S–abc is also the orthic trihedron of S–bch, S–cha, S–hab (§ 77), hence S–def may be said to be the orthic trihedron of the orthocentric group of lines $abch$, and the above proposition may be stated as follows: *The three pairs of perpendicular planes determined by four orthocentric lines are the three pairs of bisecting planes of the dihedral angles of the orthic trihedron of the given group of lines.*

EXERCISES

1. If a plane cuts four orthocentric lines in four orthocentric points, the plane is perpendicular to one of these four lines.

2. Given a triangle ABC and the perpendicular erected to its plane at the incenter I of ABC, a point S of this perpendicular is joined to the excenters I', I'', I''' of ABC. Show that the three pairs of bisecting planes of the three dihedral angles of the trihedron S–ABC coincide with the three pairs of planes SII', $SI''I'''$; SII'', $SI'''I'$; SII''', $SI'I''$.

3. Where is the orthocentric line of a trirectangular trihedron (i.e., a trihedron whose face angles are right angles)?

2. The Supplementary Trihedral Angle

81. Preliminary Remark. If through a point of a plane two lines are drawn, one perpendicular and the other oblique to the plane, the angle between these lines is acute, if the two lines are situated on the same side of the plane, and obtuse, if the lines are drawn on opposite sides of the plane. Thus the angle between the two lines enables us to tell whether these two lines are, or are not, on the same side of the plane.

82. Definition. Given the trihedral angle S–abc, let p, q, r be the perpendiculars at S to the faces bc, ca, ab of S–abc, respectively, on the same sides of these planes as the edges a, b, c (§ 81). The trihedral angle S–pqr is called the *supplementary*, or *reciprocal* of the given trihedron S–abc.

It follows from this definition that if p', q', r' denote the lines p, q, r produced beyond the point S, the angle S–$p'q'r'$ is the supplementary angle of S–$a'b'c'$ (§ 65) and that the trihedrons S–$p'qr$, S–$pq'r$, S–pqr' are the supplementary angles of the trihedrons S–$a'bc$, S–$ab'c$, S–abc', respectively.

83. Theorem. *If a trihedron is supplementary to another trihedron the second trihedron is supplementary to the first.*

Let $S-pqr$ be the trihedron supplementary to the trihedron $S-abc$. We have, by assumption,

$$p \perp b, c, \qquad q \perp c, a, \qquad r \perp a, b,$$

hence

$$a \perp q, r, \qquad b \perp r, p, \qquad c \perp p, q,$$

which proves the proposition.

84. Definition. We shall say that p, a; q, b; r, c are pairs of "corresponding edges" of the two supplementary trihedral angles $S-abc$, $S-pqr$, and that the faces ab, pq; bc, qr; ca, rp are pairs of "corresponding" faces of these two trihedrons.

85. Theorem. *The three planes determined by the three pairs of corresponding edges of two supplementary trihedral angles are coaxal.*

The altitude plane ah of the trihedron $S-abc$ contains the edge p of the trihedral angle $S-pqr$ supplementary to $S-abc$. Similarly for the altitude planes bh, ch of $S-abc$. Hence the three planes ap, bq, cr have the orthocentric line h of $S-abc$ in common.

86. Theorem. *Two supplementary trihedral angles have the same orthocentric line.*

Indeed, the planes ahp, bhq, chr, where the notations are the same as in the preceding proposition (§ 85), are the altitude planes of the trihedral angle $S-pqr$.

87. Theorem. *The three lines of intersection of the three pairs of corresponding faces of two supplementary trihedral angles are coplanar.*

The two faces ab, pq of the two supplementary trihedrons $S-abc$, $S-pqr$ are perpendicular to their common altitude plane chr (§ 85), hence the line of intersection of ab and pq is perpendicular to the common orthocentric line h of the two trihedrons. Similarly for the lines of intersection of the pairs of planes bc, qr; ca, rp, hence the proposition.

88. Corollary. *A plane perpendicular to the common orthocentric line of two supplementary trihedrons cuts the faces of these trihedrons along two triangles the sides of which are respectively parallel to each other and which have a common orthocenter* (§ 69), i.e., two triangles which are homothetic, the homothetic center being their common orthocenter.

EXERCISES

1. In each face of a trihedral angle a line is drawn through the vertex perpendicular to the corresponding opposite edge. Show that the three lines thus obtained are coplanar.

2. Given three mutually skew lines, the three planes obtained by passing a plane through each line parallel to the common perpendicular of the remaining two given lines are parallel to a line.

3. Let x, y, z be the orthogonal projections of the edges a, b, c of the trihedral angle $S-abc$ upon the opposite faces bc, ca, ab of $S-abc$. (a) The three lines determined by the pairs of planes ab, xy; bc, yz; ca, zy are coplanar. (b) The harmonic conjugate plane of the plane bc with respect to the planes xy, xz and the two analogous planes are coaxal.

4. The three planes through a vertex of a tetrahedron and perpendicular to the three edges of the tetrahedron passing through this vertex meet the respectively opposite edges of the tetrahedron in three points which are collinear. HINT. Use § 87.

3. Isoclinal Lines and Planes

89. Definition. A plane making equal angles with the three edges of a trihedron will be referred to as an "isoclinal plane" of the trihedron. It is clear that an isoclinal plane is determined in orientation only.

90. Theorem. *An isoclinal plane of a trihedron cuts off equal segments on the three edges of the trihedron.*

Let A, B, C be the points of intersection of the edges a, b, c of the trihedron $S-abc$ with an isoclinal plane ABC of this trihedron. Let O be the foot of the perpendicular SO from S upon the plane ABC. The angles SAO, SBO, SCO are equal, by assumption, hence the right triangles SAO, SBO, SCO are congruent, and $SA = SB = SC$.

91. Converse Theorem. *If a plane cuts off equal segments on the three edges of a trihedron, the secant plane is an isoclinal plane of the trihedron.*

Using the same notations, if $SA = SB = SC$, the triangles SAO, SBO, SCO are congruent, and therefore the angles SAO, SBO, SCO are equal.

92. Let A', B', C' be the symmetric points of A, B, C (§ 90) with respect to S. The plane $A'BC$ cuts off equal segments on the edges of the external trihedral angle $S-a'bc$ (§ 65) of the trihedron $S-abc$. We shall refer to such a plane as an "external isoclinal plane" of $S-abc$ relative to the edge a or to the face bc. Similarly for $S-ab'c$, $S-abc'$. Thus: *A trihedral angle has isoclinal planes of four different orientations.*

93. Definition. A line making equal angles with the edges of a trihedral angle will be called an "isoclinal line" of the trihedral angle.

94. Theorem. *A line passing through the vertex of a trihedral angle and perpendicular to an isoclinal plane of this trihedron is an isoclinal line of the trihedron.*

Indeed, from the congruent right triangles SOA, SOB, SOC (§ 90) it follows that the angles OSA, OSB, OSC are equal.

95. Converse Theorem. *A plane perpendicular to an isoclinal line of a trihedral angle is an isoclinal plane of this trihedron.*

Indeed, if the angles OSA, OSB, OSC (§ 91) are equal, the right triangles are congruent, and we have $SA = SB = SC$, hence the proposition.

96. To the four sets of isoclinal planes (§ 92) correspond thus four isoclinal lines (§ 94). One of these lines will lie inside the principal trihedral angle and may be referred to as the "internal isoclinal line," or, more briefly, the "in-isocline." The remaining three may be referred to as the "ex-isoclines." One of these will lie inside the trihedron $S-a'bc$ and may be said to be the ex-isocline of $S-abc$ relative to the edge a, or to the face bc. Similarly for the ex-isoclines relative to the faces ca, ab.

97. Theorem. *The locus of a point equidistant from three concurrent non-coplanar lines consists of the four isoclinal lines of the trihedron determined by the given three lines.*

If O is a point on an isoclinal line of the trihedral angle $S-abc$ formed by the given lines a, b, c, and D, E, F are the feet of the perpendiculars from O upon a, b, c, it follows from the congruence of the right triangles SOD, SOE, SOF that $OD = OE = OF$, hence O is equidistant from a, b, c. Conversely, if $OD = OE = OF$, the triangles SOD, SOE, SOF are congruent, and angle $OSD = OSE = OSF$. The proposition is thus proved.

98. Notation. The in-isocline will be denoted by i, and the ex-isoclines relative to the edges a, b, c by i_a, i_b, i_c respectively.

99. Theorem.   *Through three concurrent lines in space pass four cones of revolution.*

Indeed, each of the four isoclinal lines of the trihedron formed by the three given lines (§ 96) may be taken for an axis of such a cone.   There can be no other such axis, for any point of such an axis must be equidistant from the three given lines and therefore must lie on one of the isoclinal lines considered (§ 97).

100. Theorem.   *The external bisectors of the face angles of a trihedron are coplanar.*

Let A, B, C be the traces of the edges a, b, c of the trihedron S–abc in an isoclinal plane of this trihedron.   The triangle SBC being isosceles, the line joining S to the mid-point A' of BC is the internal bisector of the angle BSC, hence the external bisector of this angle is parallel to BC and therefore to the plane ABC. Similarly the bisectors of the other two face angles of S–abc are parallel to ABC, hence the proposition.

101. Remark.   We have proved incidentally (§ 100) that *the plane of the three external bisectors of the three face angles of a trihedron has the orientation of an isoclinal plane.*

102. Theorem.   *The internal bisectors of two face angles of a trihedron and the external bisector of the third face angle are coplanar.*

Using the same notations as in the preceding theorem (§ 100) let B' be the mid-point of AC.   The plane ABC and the plane ϵ of the external bisectors of the face angles of S–abc being parallel (§ 100), the trace of the plane $SA'B'$ in the plane ϵ is parallel to $A'B'$, and therefore to AB, i.e., the plane ϵ is cut by $SA'B'$ along the external bisector of the angle ASB.

OTHERWISE.   Consider the external trihedron S–abc'.   The internal bisectors SA', SB' of the two face angles of S–abc are the external bisectors of two face angles of S–abc', hence they are coplanar with the external bisector of the third face angle of S–abc'.   But this third external bisector of a face angle of S–abc' is also an external bisector of the face angle of S–abc, hence the proposition.

103. Remark.   From the second proof of this proposition (§ 102) it follows that *the plane determined by the internal bisectors of two face angles of a trihedral angle and the external bisector of the third face angle has an isoclinal orientation.*

We have thus a direct geometric interpretation of the isoclinal orientation of a trihedron and we observe that these orientations are respectively perpendicular to the four isoclinal lines.

104. Theorem. *The isoclinal line perpendicular to the plane containing three of the six bisectors of the faces of a trihedron is the orthocentric line of the trihedron determined by the remaining three bisectors.*

The in-isocline i of the trihedral angle $S\text{-}abc$ is perpendicular to the plane ϵ (§ 102), and a corresponding isoclinal plane ABC is met by the three internal bisectors in the mid-points A', B', C' of BC, CA, AB. Now i meets ABC in the circumcenter O of the triangle ABC, the point O is therefore the orthocenter of the medial triangle $A'B'C'$, and the plane of $A'B'C'$ is perpendicular to i, hence i is the orthocentric line of $S\text{-}A'B'C'$ (§ 69). Similarly for the other isoclinal lines. Hence the proposition.

105. Theorem. *The four isoclinal lines of a trihedron form an orthocentric group having for orthic trihedron the supplementary trihedron of the given trihedron.*

Let t_a, t_b, t_c be the internal bisectors of the faces bc, ca, ab of the trihedron $S\text{-}abc$, and t_a', t_b', t_c' the corresponding external bisectors. We have (§ 104)

$$i \perp t_a't_b't_c', \qquad i_a \perp t_a't_bt_c, \qquad i_b \perp t_at_b't_c, \qquad i_c \perp t_at_bt_c'.$$

If $S\text{-}pqr$ is the supplementary angle of $S\text{-}abc$, we have

$$p \perp t_at_a', \qquad q \perp t_bt_b', \qquad r \perp t_ct_c'.$$

Consequently

$$t_a \perp p i_b i_c, \qquad t_b \perp q i_c i_a, \qquad t_c \perp r i_a i_b,$$
$$t_a' \perp p i i_a, \qquad t_b' \perp q i i_b, \qquad t_c' \perp r i i_c.$$

But $t_a \perp t_a'$, hence

$$p i i_a \perp p i_b i_c$$

and similarly

$$q i i_b \perp q i_c i_a, \qquad r i i_c \perp r i_a i_b,$$

which proves the proposition.

106. Theorem. *The two planes passing through the two bisectors of any face angle of a trihedron and perpendicular to the face considered contain the four isoclinal lines of the trihedron.*

The two planes passing through the two bisectors t_a, t_a' of the face angle bc of the trihedron $S\text{-}abc$ and perpendicular to bc constitute the locus of the points equidistant from the two lines b, c, hence these two planes contain the isoclinal lines of $S\text{-}abc$ (§ 97).

107. Consequence I. *The three planes perpendicular to the faces of a trihedral angle and passing through the internal bisectors of the respective face angles are coaxal.*

This common axis is the in-isocline of the trihedron.

108. Consequence II. *The two planes perpendicular to two faces of a trihedron and passing through the external bisectors of the respective face angles are coaxal with the plane perpendicular to the third face and passing through the internal bisector of the face angle of this face.*

109. Consequence III. *The three pairs of planes perpendicular to the three faces of a trihedron and passing through the pairs of bisectors of the respective face angles intersect by threes in four lines, the isoclines of the trihedral angle considered.*

110. Theorem. *The two bisecting planes of a dihedral angle of a trihedron cut the corresponding face of the supplementary trihedron along the bisectors of the angle of this face.*

The supplementary trihedron $S\text{-}pqr$ of the given trihedron $S\text{-}abc$ is the orthic trihedron of the orthocentric group formed by the isoclinal lines i, i_a, i_b, i_c of $S\text{-}abc$ (§ 105). The planes ii_a, $i_b i_c$ pass through the edge p of $S\text{-}pqr$, hence these two planes are the bisecting planes of the dihedral angle of $S\text{-}pqr$ having p for edge (§ 80). Now these two planes pass through the bisectors of the face angle bc of $S\text{-}abc$ (§ 106), and $S\text{-}abc$ is the supplementary trihedron of $S\text{-}pqr$ (§ 83), hence the proposition.

111. Theorem. *The angle determined in the face of a trihedron by the two non-corresponding faces of the supplementary trihedron has the same bisectors as the face angle of the face considered.*

The face bc of $S\text{-}abc$ is perpendicular to the edge p of the supplementary trihedron $S\text{-}pqr$, hence the angle determined in bc by the faces pq, pr of $S\text{-}pqr$ has for its bisectors the traces in bc of the bisecting planes of the dihedral angle of $S\text{-}pqr$ having p for edge. Now these bisecting planes meet bc along the bisectors of the angle bc (§ 110), hence the proposition.

EXERCISES

1. Through a given point in space to draw a line making equal angles with three given skew lines.

2. Find the locus of the point such that the plane determined by the feet of the perpendiculars from the point upon three concurrent lines shall be perpendicular to the line joining the point to the common point of the three given lines.

3. (a) The tangent planes to the circumcone of a trihedron along the edges of this trihedron meet the respectively opposite faces of the trihedron in three coplanar lines.

(b) The three planes determined by the pairs of corresponding edges of a trihedron and its tangential trihedron are coaxal.

4. The two planes perpendicular to a face of a trihedron and passing through the bisectors of its face angle are the bisecting planes of the corresponding dihedral angle of the supplementary trihedron of the given trihedron.

4. Axes

112. Theorem. *The internal bisecting planes of the three dihedral angles of a trihedron are coaxal.*

The two internal bisecting planes of the dihedral angles having for edges the edges a, b of the trihedron $S–abc$ have the point S in common, hence they intersect along a line j, inside the trihedron. Any point M of j is equidistant from the three faces of $S–abc$, hence M lies on the internal bisecting plane having for edge c, which proves the proposition.

113. Definition. The common axis of the three internal bisecting planes of the three dihedral angles of a trihedron may be referred to as the **axis** of the trihedron. It will be denoted by j.

114. Theorem. *The internal bisecting plane of a dihedral angle of a trihedron and the external bisecting planes of the remaining two dihedral angles are coaxal.*

The proof is analogous to the one of the preceding proposition (§ 112) and is left to the reader.

115. Definition. The common axis of the internal bisecting plane of the dihedral angle a and the two external bisecting planes of the two dihedral angles b, c of the trihedron $S–abc$ may be referred to as the "external axis relative to the edge a." It will be denoted by j_a. Likewise for j_b, j_c.

116. Theorem. *The four axes of a trihedron form an orthocentric group, the orthic trihedron of which coincides with the given trihedron.*

117. Remark. *The three pairs of bisecting planes of the dihedral angles of a trihedron intersect along four straight lines. Each plane contains two of these lines, and through each line pass three of the six planes.*

118. Theorem. *The four axes of a trihedron are the locus of the points equidistant from the faces of the trihedron.*

The bisecting planes of the dihedral angle a constitute the locus of points equidistant from the faces ab, ac of the trihedron. Similarly for the other two pairs of bisecting planes. Now the three pairs of bisecting planes determine the lines j, j_a, j_b, j_c (§ 117), hence the proposition.

119. Theorem. *An axis of a trihedron makes equal angles with the faces of the trihedron.*

Let X, Y, Z be the feet of the perpendiculars dropped from a point M of the axis j of the trihedron $S–abc$ upon the faces bc, ca, ab. The line SX being the projection of j upon the plane bc, the angle XSM is the angle between j and bc. Similarly for the lines SY, SZ.

Now M being equidistant from the faces bc, ca, ab (§ 112), we have $MX = MY = MZ$, hence the right triangles MSX, MSY, MSZ are congruent, and the angles MSX, MSY, MSZ are equal.

A similar proof may be given for the three external axes of the trihedron.

120. Theorem. *A plane perpendicular to an axis of a trihedron makes equal angles with the faces of the trihedron.*

The proof is left to the reader.

121. Theorem. *There are four cones of revolution touching three given intersecting (non-coaxal) planes.*

Indeed, each of the four axes of the trihedron determined by the three given planes may be taken as the axis of such a cone (§ 119). There can be no other such cones, for each point on the axis of such a cone is equidistant from the three given planes, hence the axis of the cone must be an axis of the trihedron.

The lines of contact of the given planes with the inscribed cones are the projections of the axes of the cones, or, what is the same thing, of the axes of the trihedron upon the faces of the trihedron.

122. Definition. The cone (j) having the axis j for axis of revolution may be called the "inscribed cone" of the trihedron;

the other three cones may be called the "escribed cones" of the trihedron, the cone (j_a) having j_a for axis of revolution being relative to the face bc, or to the edge a, and similarly for the remaining two cones.

123. Theorem. *The isoclinal lines of a trihedron are the axes of the supplementary trihedron.*

The isoclinal lines i, i_a, i_b, i_c of the given trihedron S–abc form an orthocentric group of which the orthic trihedron is the supplementary trihedron S–pqr of S–abc (§ 105). Now the planes determined by an orthocentric group of lines are the bisecting planes of the dihedral angles of the orthic trihedron of the orthocentric group (§ 79). But the axes of the trihedron S–pqr are determined by the bisecting planes of its dihedral angles (§ 115), hence these axes coincide with the lines i, i_a, i_b, i_c.

124. Theorem. *The axes of a trihedron are the isoclinal lines of its supplementary trihedron.*

This proposition follows immediately from the preceding one (§ 123), if we consider S–pqr as the basic trihedron and S–abc as the supplementary trihedron (§ 83).

125. The isoclinals i, i_a, i_b, i_c and the axes j, j_a, j_b, j_c of S–abc being the axes and the isoclinals of the supplementary angle S–pqr, some of the propositions which hold for these lines with respect to S–abc may be readily restated with respect to S–pqr. Thus the proposition of § 100 gives rise to the following:

The plane through the vertex of the trihedron and perpendicular to the axis of the trihedron cuts the faces of the supplementary trihedron along the external bisectors of the face angles of this trihedron.

The reader may formulate other propositions in a similar way.

EXERCISES

1. If through an axis of a trihedron planes are drawn perpendicular to the faces of the trihedron, the traces of these planes in the faces and the respectively opposite edges determine three planes having a line in common.

2. Find the locus of the point such that the plane of the feet of the perpendiculars from the point to three given non-parallel planes shall be perpendicular to the line joining this point to the common point of the given planes.

3. The three planes determined by the edges of a trihedron and the lines of contact of the opposite faces with the inscribed cone are coaxal.

4. Through each edge of a trihedron two planes are drawn symmetric with respect to the internal bisecting plane of the corresponding dihedral angle. If three of these six planes, passing through three different edges, (a) are coaxal, the remaining three planes are also coaxal; (b) determine in the respectively opposite faces three coplanar lines, the same is true about the remaining three planes.

5. (a) The external bisecting planes of the three dihedral angles of a trihedron meet the respectively opposite faces in three coplanar lines. (b) State a similar proposition involving internal bisecting planes.

5. Centroidal Lines

126. Theorem. *The three planes determined by the edges of a trihedral angle and the internal bisectors of the respectively opposite faces are coaxal.*

If A, B, C are the traces of the edges a, b, c of the trihedron S–abc in an isoclinal plane, the internal bisectors t_a, t_b, t_c of the face angles bc, ca, ab pass through mid-points A', B', C' of BC, CA, AB. Now the medians AA', BB', CC' of ABC meet in the centroid G of ABC, hence the planes at_a, bt_b, ct_c have the line SG in common.

127. Definition. The common line of the three planes considered (§ 126) may be referred to as the "centroidal line" of the trihedron. It will be denoted by g.

REMARK. We have proved incidentally (§ 126) that *the centroidal line meets an isoclinal plane in the centroid of the triangle determined in this plane by the edges of the trihedron.*

128. Theorem. *The plane determined by an edge of a trihedral angle and the internal bisector of the opposite face angle is coaxal with the two planes determined by the remaining two edges and the external bisectors of the face angles respectively opposite them.*

The external bisectors of the face angles of S–abc being parallel to the plane ABC (§ 100), the planes at_a', bt_b', ct_c' will cut the plane ABC along three lines $B''C''$, $C''A''$, $A''B''$ parallel to the sides of the triangle ABC and passing through its vertices, i.e., they form the anti-complementary triangle $A''B''C''$. Now the triangles ABC and $A''B''C''$ have the same medians, hence the trace AGA'' of the plane at_a in ABC passes through the point of intersection A'' of the traces $A''C''$, $A''B''$ of the planes bt_b', ct_c', and the three planes have the line SA'' in common.

OTHERWISE. The external bisectors of the face angles ab, ac of the principal trihedron S–abc are the internal bisectors of the angles in the face ab', ac' of the trihedral angle S–$ab'c'$, and the proposition follows immediately from the preceding one (§ 126).

129. Definition. The lines $g_a \equiv SA''$, $g_b \equiv SB''$, $g_c \equiv SC''$ may be referred to as the "excentroidal lines" of $S\text{-}abc$, the line g_a being the excentroidal line relative to the edge a or to the face bc, etc.

EXERCISE

Find the locus of the centroid of the triangle determined by the edges of a trihedron in a variable isoclinal plane of this trihedron.

MISCELLANEOUS EXERCISES

1. Through a given point to draw a plane so that the triangle determined in this plane by a given trihedron shall have the given point for its centroid.

2. The foot of the perpendicular dropped from the vertex of a trirectangular trihedral angle upon any plane cutting the edges of the trihedron is the orthocenter of the triangle determined by the edges in the plane considered.

3. Show that it is impossible to find a plane which would cut a trirectangular trihedral angle along a right triangle.

CHAPTER III

THE SKEW QUADRILATERAL

130. Definition. A quadrilateral whose opposite sides are skew to each other will be referred to as a *skew quadrilateral*.

A skew quadrilateral may be conceived as obtained from a plane quadrilateral by raising one vertex, and the two sides passing through it, of a plane quadrilateral from the plane of the three remaining vertices of the plane quadrilateral.

A skew quadrilateral is referred to by some writers as a "gauche," or as a "spatial" quadrilateral.

131. Theorem. *The mid-points of the four sides of a skew quadrilateral are the vertices of a parallelogram.*

If E, F, G, H are the mid-points of the sides AB, BC, CD, DA of the skew quadrilateral $ABCD$, each of the segments EH, FG is equal to one half of the diagonal BD of $ABCD$, and is parallel to this line, hence the proposition.

132. Definition. The line joining the mid-points of two opposite sides of a skew quadrilateral will be referred to as a *bimedian* of the quadrilateral relative to the pair of sides considered.

A skew quadrilateral has two bimedians.

133. Theorem. *The two bimedians of a skew quadrilateral bisect each other.*

Indeed, these two segments are the diagonals of the parallelogram determined by the mid-points of the sides of the quadrilateral (§ 131).

134. Theorem. *The segment joining the mid-points of the diagonals of a skew quadrilateral is bisected by the point common to the bimedians of the quadrilateral.*

Let X, Y be the mid-points of the diagonals AC, BD of $ABCD$. From the triangles BAD, CAD it follows that the segments EY, GX are equal to one half of AD and are parallel to AD (§ 131), hence $EYGX$ is a parallelogram, and the bimedian EG bisects XY, which proves the proposition.

42

REMARK. The three lines EG, HF, XY have a point in common, but they cannot be coplanar, unless $ABCD$ becomes a plane quadrilateral.

135. Definition. A plane parallel to two opposite sides of a skew quadrilateral is called a *directing plane*, or, more briefly, a *director* of the quadrilateral relative to the sides considered.

A skew quadrilateral has directing planes of two different orientations.

136. Theorem. *A director plane relative to one pair of opposite sides of a skew quadrilateral divides the other pair of opposite sides in direct proportion.*

Let E, F be the traces on the sides AB, CD of the skew quadrilateral $ABCD$ of a director plane relative to AD, BC. Imagine the two director planes through AD and BC which are relative to these two opposite sides of $ABCD$. We have thus three parallel planes, hence (§ 7)

$$AE : EB = DF : FC.$$

137. Converse Theorem. *If a line divides two opposite sides of a skew quadrilateral in direct proportion it is parallel to the director of the other pair of opposite sides of the quadrilateral.*

The proof is left to the reader.

138. Theorem. *If a line divides two opposite sides of a skew quadrilateral in direct proportion, and a second line divides the other two opposite sides in direct proportion, the two lines are coplanar.*

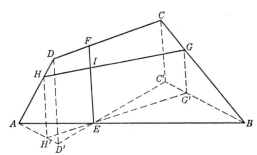

FIG. 13

Let EF (Fig. 13) divide proportionally the sides AB, CD, and GH divide proportionally the sides BC, AD of the skew quadrilateral $ABCD$.

Through EF a plane may be drawn parallel to AD, BC (§ 137), hence if through C and D we draw parallels CC' and DD' to EF, the two planes ADD', BCC' will be parallel to the plane through EF and therefore to each other. If C', D' are the traces of CC', DD' in a plane (P) passing through AB, the lines AD', BC' will be parallel, for they are the traces, in (P), of the two parallel planes ADD', BCC'; the point E will lie on the line $C'D'$, for $C'D'$ is the trace, in (P), of the plane $CC'DD'$, and this plane contains EF. Thus the triangles $EAD,'$ EBC' are similar.

Let G', H' be the points of intersection of BC', AD' with the parallels GG', HH' through G, H to EF, respectively. We have

$$AH' : AD' = AH : AD,$$

and

$$BG' : BC' = BG : BC.$$

Now we have, by hypothesis,

$$AH : AD = BG : BC,$$

hence

$$AH' : AD' = BG' : BC',$$

or

$$AH' : BG' = AD' : BC'.$$

But the triangles EAD', EBC' are similar, therefore

$$AD' : BC' = AE : BE,$$

hence

$$AH' : BG' = AE : BE,$$

i.e., the points H', E, G' are collinear.

We thus obtain the plane quadrilateral $HGH'G'$, and the parallel EF to HH' through E will meet the side GH opposite to $G'H'$, which proves the proposition.

139. Corollary I. *If I is the point common to EF and GH, we have*

$$EI : IF = BG : GC, \qquad HI : IG = DF : FC.$$

HINT. Assume that the plane (P) was drawn parallel to GH.

140. Corollary II. *Two directing planes, of different orientation, of a skew quadrilateral meet its sides in four coplanar points* (§§ 136, 138).

141. Converse Theorem. *If a plane divides proportionally one pair of opposite sides of a skew quadrilateral, it also divides proportionally the other two sides.*

The proof is left to the reader.

142. Corollary. *A plane passing through the mid-points of a pair of opposite sides of a skew quadrilateral divides the other two sides in direct proportion.*

NOTE. For further theorems on transversal planes see Chapter V.

143. Theorem. *The sum of the squares of the sides of a skew quadrilateral is equal to the sum of the squares of the diagonals increased by four times the square of the segment joining the mid-points of the diagonals.*

Let E, F be the mid-points of the diagonals BD, AC of the skew quadrilateral $ABCD$. Applying the known formula for the median to the triangles ABD, CBD, EAC, successively, we have

$$2AE^2 = AB^2 + AD^2 - \tfrac{1}{2}BD^2$$
$$2CE^2 = BC^2 + CD^2 - \tfrac{1}{2}BD^2$$
$$2EF^2 = AE^2 + CE^2 - \tfrac{1}{2}AC^2.$$

Multiplying the last relation by two and adding it to the sum of the first two we obtain, after simplification,

$$4EF^2 = AB^2 + AD^2 + BC^2 + CD^2 - AC^2 - BD^2,$$

which proves the proposition.

144. Theorem. *In a skew quadrilateral the sum of the squares of the diagonals is equal to twice the sum of the squares of the bimedians.*

Let O be the point of intersection of the diagonals EG, FH of the parallelogram $EFGH$ determined by the mid-points E, F, G, H of the sides AB, BC, CD, DA of the skew quadrilateral $ABCD$ (§ 133). Applying the formula for the median to the two triangles HEF, EFG we have

$$2EO^2 = EH^2 + EF^2 - \tfrac{1}{2}FH^2$$
$$2FO^2 = EF^2 + FG^2 - \tfrac{1}{2}EG^2.$$

Multiplying each of these equalities by four and adding, we obtain, after simplification,

$$2EG^2 + 2HF^2 = AC^2 + BD^2.$$

145. Remark. The last two propositions (§§ 143, 144) are valid for a plane quadrilateral.

146. Problem. *Find the locus of the point the sum of the squares of whose distances from two opposite vertices of a skew quadrilateral is equal to the sum of the squares of the distances of the point from the other two vertices.*

Let E, F be the mid-points of the diagonals AC, BD of the skew quadrilateral $ABCD$. For any point M in space we have

$$MA^2 + MC^2 = 2ME^2 + \tfrac{1}{2}AC^2$$
$$MB^2 + MD^2 = 2MF^2 + \tfrac{1}{2}BD^2.$$

Now if M is a point of the required locus, the left hand sides of these relations are equal, hence

$$2ME^2 + \tfrac{1}{2}AC^2 = 2MF^2 + \tfrac{1}{2}BD^2,$$

or

$$ME^2 - MF^2 = \tfrac{1}{4}(BD^2 - AC^2).$$

Hence the locus is a plane perpendicular to the line joining the mid-points of the diagonals of the given quadrilateral (§ 18).

EXERCISE. Discuss the case when the diagonals are equal; when the quadrilateral becomes plane.

147. Theorem. *If two opposite sides of a skew quadrilateral are equal, they are equally inclined on the bimedian relative to the other pair of sides of the quadrilateral, and the projections of the equal sides upon this bimedian are equal to the bimedian.*

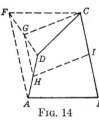

FIG. 14

In the skew quadrilateral $ABCD$ (Fig. 14) let $AB = CD$. Through C draw CF equal and parallel to BA and through the mid-point H of AD draw HG parallel to AF meeting DF in G. The line BC is parallel to AF and therefore to HG, and if I is the mid-point of BC, $IC = \tfrac{1}{2}BC = \tfrac{1}{2}AF = HG$. Hence $IHGC$ is a parallelogram, and the bimedian HI is parallel to CG. Now G is the mid-point of FD, and $CD = CF$, hence CF and CD make equal angles with CG, and their projections upon CG are equal to CG, hence the same is true about IH, which proves the proposition.

REMARK. The property is valid for a plane quadrilateral.

148. Theorem. *If the line joining the mid-points of two opposite sides of a skew quadrilateral is perpendicular to these sides:* (a) *The two angles adjacent to each of these sides are equal;* (b) *the other two sides are equal;* (c) *the diagonals are equal.*

Let M, N be the mid-points of the sides AB, CD of the skew quadrilateral $ABCD$. If the line MN is perpendicular to both AB and CD, the points A, B; C, D are symmetrical with respect to MN, hence a rotation of 180 degrees of the figure about MN will make the quadrilateral coincide with itself. The announced relations become immediately apparent.

149. Definition. The line MN is called an " axis of symmetry" of the quadrilateral $ABCD$.

A skew quadrilateral having an axis of symmetry is called an "isosceles skew trapezoid."

EXERCISES

1. The plane determined by the bimedians of a skew quadrilateral is parallel to the diagonals of the quadrilateral.

2. The line of shortest distance of the diagonals of a skew quadrilateral is perpendicular to the plane determined by the mid-points of the sides of the quadrilateral.

3. Find the locus of the point of intersection of the bimedians of the variable skew quadrilateral three of whose vertices are fixed, the fourth vertex describing a straight line, or a fixed plane, or a sphere.

4. Construct a skew quadrilateral given its sides, and two consecutive angles.

5. Construct a skew quadrilateral $ABCD$ given the four sides, the angle BAD, and the dihedral angle having DA for edge.

6. The sum of the angles of a skew quadrilateral is smaller than four right angles.

7. The sides AD, AB, CB, CD of the quadrilateral $ABCD$ are divided by the points E, F, G, H so that

$$AE : ED = AF : FB = CG : GB = CH : HD.$$

Prove that $EFGH$ is a parallelogram.

8. The locus of the point of intersection of the diagonals of a variable parallelogram inscribed in a given skew quadrilateral is the line joining the mid-points of the diagonals of this quadrilateral.

9. The line EF divides proportionally the two opposite sides AD, BC of the skew quadrilateral $ABCD$. Find a line GH perpendicular to the line EF which shall divide proportionally the sides AB, CD of $ABCD$.

10. If a line divides two opposite sides of a skew quadrilateral proportionally, the line is perpendicular to the line of shortest distance of the other two sides of the quadrilateral.

CHAPTER IV

THE TETRAHEDRON

1. The Centroid

a. Bimedians and Bialtitudes

150. Notations. Unless otherwise stated, the edges of the tetrahedron $ABCD$ will be denoted as follows: $BC = a$, $CA = b$, $AB = c$, $DA = a'$, $DB = b'$, $DC = c'$.

The mid-points of the edges BC, CA, AB will be designated by A', B', C'. The mid-points of the respectively opposite edges DA, DB, DC by A'', B'', C''.

151. Definition. A line joining the mid-points of two opposite edges of a tetrahedron will be called a *bimedian* of the tetrahedron relative to the pair of edges considered. A tetrahedron has three bimedians. They will be denoted by m_a, m_b, m_c, the bimedian m_a being relative to the edges a, a', etc.

152. Theorem. *The mid-points of two pairs of opposite edges of a tetrahedron are the vertices of a parallelogram.*

153. Theorem. *The three bimedians of a tetrahedron are concurrent and bisect each other.*

The proofs of these propositions are identical with those of the corresponding properties of the skew quadrilateral (§§ 131, 133).

154. Definition. The point common to the three bimedians of a tetrahedron is called the *centroid* of the tetrahedron. This point will be denoted by G.

155. Remark. Two pairs of opposite edges of a tetrahedron are the sides of a skew quadrilateral the diagonals of which are the third pair of edges of the tetrahedron. Conversely, the two pairs of opposite sides of a skew quadrilateral and its two diagonals are the three pairs of opposite edges of a tetrahedron. There is therefore no essential difference between these two figures. The distinction made is simply a matter of emphasis. Some properties are more readily stated with reference to one than to the other figure.

156. Theorem. *The parallels drawn through the centroid of a tetrahedron to a pair of opposite edges are harmonically separated by the two bimedians relative to the other two pairs of opposite edges.*

The bimedians $A'A''$, $B'B''$ relative to the two pairs of opposite edges DA, BC; DB, AC of the tetrahedron $ABCD$ are the diagonals of the parallelogram $A'B''A''B'$ having for vertices the mid-points of the edges BC, DA, AC, DB (§ 152). The sides $A''B'$, $A'B''$; $A'B'$, $A''B''$ are respectively parallel to the edges DC, AB of $ABCD$, and the mid-point G of the diagonals is the centroid of $ABCD$. Thus the parallels through G to DC, AB will lie in the plane $A'B''A''B'$ and be parallel to two adjacent sides of this parallelogram, hence they will be harmonically separated by the diagonals $A'A''$, $B'B''$ (C. G., p. 139).

157. Definition. A plane parallel to two opposite edges of a tetrahedron will be called a *directing plane* or a *director* of the tetrahedron.

A tetrahedron has directing planes of three different orientations.

158. Theorem. *The plane determined by two bimedians of a tetrahedron is parallel to the remaining two edges of the tetrahedron.*

Indeed, the bimedians $m_a \equiv A'A''$, $m_b \equiv B'B''$ are the diagonals of the parallelogram $A'B''A''B'$, and the edges AB, CD of $ABCD$ are respectively parallel to the sides of this parallelogram.

159. Corollary I. *The plane determined by the bimedians relative to two pairs of opposite edges of a tetrahedron is a directing plane relative to the third pair of edges of the tetrahedron.*

160. Corollary II. *The three planes determined by the three bimedians of a tetrahedron have the orientations of the three directing planes of the tetrahedron.*

161. Theorem. *A bimedian is parallel to the line of intersection of two directing planes relative to the other two pairs of opposite edges of the tetrahedron.*

The bimedians m_a, m_b are parallel to the directing plane cc' (§ 159), and the bimedians m_a, m_c are parallel to the directing plane bb', hence m_a is parallel to the two directors bb', cc', and therefore also to their line of intersection.

162. Theorem.   *A directing plane of a tetrahedron cuts this solid along a parallelogram.*

A plane parallel to the edge BD of the tetrahedron $ABCD$ will cut the planes ABD, CBD along two lines HG, EF parallel to BD. Now if the same plane is also parallel to AC, its traces HE, GF in the planes BAC, DAC are parallel to AC, hence the proposition.

163. Remark.   The parallelograms determined by the three bimedians are special cases of this theorem.   These three parallelograms are called the "median sections" of the tetrahedrons.

164. Definition.   The common perpendicular to the two opposite edges a, a' of a tetrahedron is called the **bialtitude** of the tetrahedron relative to these edges, and is denoted by d_a.   The bialtitudes d_b, d_c are relative to the pairs of edges b, b'; c, c'.

165. Theorem.   *The bialtitude relative to one pair of opposite edges of a tetrahedron is perpendicular to the two bimedians relative to the two other pairs of opposite edges.*

The bialtitude d_a is perpendicular to the director of aa' (§ 164), and the plane $m_b m_c$ has the same orientation (§ 159).

166. Corollary.   *The bimedian relative to one pair of opposite edges of a tetrahedron is perpendicular to the two bialtitudes relative to the other two pairs of opposite edges.*

Indeed, d_a is perpendicular to m_b, m_c, and d_b is perpendicular to m_c, m_a, hence m_c is perpendicular to both d_a and d_b.

167. Theorem.   *The mediators of a pair of opposite edges of a tetrahedron and the two planes perpendicular to the bimedians relative to the other two pairs of opposite edges and passing through the circumcenter of the tetrahedron are coaxal.*

The line of intersection u of the two mediators of the two opposite edges AB, CD of the tetrahedron $ABCD$ passes through the circumcenter O of $ABCD$ and is perpendicular to both AB and CD, hence to the directing plane of these two edges.

The line of intersection v of the two planes through O and perpendicular to the two bimedians $A'A''$, $B'B''$ relative to the pairs of edges DA, BC; DB, AC is perpendicular to the plane determined by these bimedians, which plane is a directing plane of the edges AB, CD (§ 159).   Thus the lines u, v pass through the same point O and are perpendicular to planes of the same orientation, hence they coincide, which proves the proposition.

168. Theorem. *The two planes passing through the circumcenter of a tetrahedron and perpendicular to two bimedians of the tetrahedron divide the third bimedian harmonically.*

The two planes through the circumcenter O of $ABCD$ and perpendicular to the bimedians m_a, m_b are coaxal with (§ 167) and separated harmonically by the two planes through O and perpendicular to the edges DC, AB (§§ 156, 39). Now these planes meet DC, AB at their mid-points C'', C', which points are the ends of the median m_c, hence the proposition.

EXERCISES

1. The line of intersection of two planes perpendicular to two opposite edges of a tetrahedron is perpendicular to the plane determined by the two bimedians relative to the remaining two pairs of opposite edges.

2. A plane passing through an edge and through the centroid of a tetrahedron divides the tetrahedron into two equivalent parts.

3. A bialtitude of a tetrahedron is bisected by the plane determined by the two bimedians relative to the other two pairs of opposite edges of the tetrahedron.

4. Construct a tetrahedron given the lengths of its bimedians and the angles these lines make with each other.

5. Construct a tetrahedron given its base and its bimedians.

6. The edges of the supplementary trihedron of the trihedron formed by the bimedians of a tetrahedron are parallel to the bialtitudes of the tetrahedron.

b. *Medians*

169. Definition. The lines joining the vertices of a tetrahedron to the centroids of the opposite faces will be referred to as the **medians** of the tetrahedron.

170. Commandino's Theorem. *The four medians of a tetrahedron meet in a point which divides each median in the ratio 1 : 3, the longer segment being on the side of the vertex of the tetrahedron.*

Let A' be the midpoint of the edge BC (Fig. 15, p. 52) of the tetrahedron $ABCD$. The centroids G_a, G_d of the faces BCD, ABC lie on the medians DA', AA' of these faces and we have

$$A'G_d : A'A = A'G_a : A'D = 1 : 3,$$

hence G_aG_d is parallel to AD and $G_aG_d : AD = 1 : 3$.

The two medians AG_a, DG_d of the tetrahedron lie in the same plane ADA', hence they meet in a point G, and we have

$$\frac{GG_d}{GD} = \frac{GG_a}{GA} = \frac{G_aG_d}{AD} = \frac{1}{3}.$$

Thus the median AG_a of $ABCD$ is divided by any other median DG_d of $ABCD$ in the ratio 1 : 3, and in turn divides that median in the same ratio, which proves the proposition.

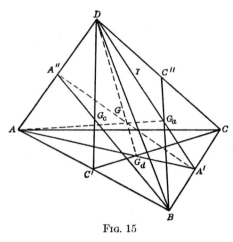

FIG. 15

OTHERWISE. Let A', A'' (Fig. 15) be the mid-points of the edges BC, AD of the tetrahedron $ABCD$. The centroid G_a of the face BCD lies on DA'. Let I be the mid-point of DG_a. The median AG_a of $ABCD$ lies in the same plane $AA'DA''$ with the bi-median $A'A''$, hence these lines meet in a point G.

The line IA'' joins the mid-points I, A'' of the sides of the triangle ADG_a, hence IA'' is parallel to AG_a and $IA'' = \frac{1}{2}AG_a$. The line G_aG passes through the mid-point G_a of the side $A'I$ of the triangle $A'A''I$ and is parallel to IA'', hence G is the mid-point of $A'A''$, and $GG_a = \frac{1}{2}IA'' = \frac{1}{4}AG_a$. But the mid-point G of $A'A''$ is the same for any bimedian of $ABCD$ (§ 153), hence the proposition is proved.

171. Remark. From the second proof of Commandino's theorem it follows that *the point common to the medians of the tetrahedron coincides with the point common to the bimedians of the solid*, i.e., with the centroid of the tetrahedron (§ 154).

The reader familiar with the theory of the center of gravity from Mechanics will readily prove the proposition by means of this theory.

172. Theorem. *The plane determined by the centroids of three faces of a tetrahedron is parallel to the fourth face of the tetrahedron.*

Let G_a, G_b, G_c, G_d denote the centroids of the faces BCD, CDA, DAB, ABC of the tetrahedron. We have seen in the proof of the preceding proposition (§ 170) that G_aG_d is parallel to AD, and we may show in a similar way that G_aG_b is parallel to AB, and again that G_bG_d is parallel to BD, hence the proposition.

173. Corollary. *The faces and the edges of the tetrahedron having for its vertices the centroids of the faces of a given tetrahedron are parallel to the faces and the edges of the given tetrahedron.*

174. Theorem. *If through the vertices of a given tetrahedron planes are drawn parallel to the opposite faces, the faces of the new tetrahedron will have for their centroids the vertices of the given tetrahedron.*

This is an immediate consequence of the preceding proposition (§ 173), if we take the tetrahedron $G_aG_bG_cG_d$ as the basic tetrahedron.

175. Definitions. The tetrahedron $G_aG_bG_cG_d$ formed by the centroids of the faces of the given tetrahedron $ABCD$ may be called the **medial** tetrahedron of the given tetrahedron $ABCD$.

The tetrahedron formed by the planes passing through the vertices of a given tetrahedron and parallel to the respective opposite faces may be called the **anticomplementary** tetrahedron of the given tetrahedron.

176. Remark. *The centroid of a tetrahedron is the homothetic center of the given tetrahedron and its medial tetrahedron, the homothetic ratio being* $-3 : 1$.

The centroid is also the homothetic center of the given tetrahedron and its anticomplementary tetrahedron, the homothetic ratio being $-1 : 3$. The last three propositions (§§ 172, 173, 174) follow immediately from this remark.

177. Problem. *Construct a tetrahedron given the directions of its four medians, and the length of one of these medians.*

Through an arbitrary point G in space draw four lines p, q, r, s having the given directions. It is assumed that no three of these lines are coplanar. It is clear that a necessary condition for the possibility of the problem is that one of these four lines, say s, shall fall within the trihedral angle determined by the remaining three. We assume that this condition is satisfied.

Let the plane rs meet the plane pq along the line u, and let A be the point on p such that GA equals to three fourths of the length of the given median. Through A draw a line meeting u in C' and q in B so that C' shall be the mid-point of AB (C. G., p. 41, § 43). Through C' draw a line meeting s in F and r in C so that $C'F : C'G = 1 : 3$. The point F is thus the centroid of the triangle ABC. Now produce FG beyond G to a point D such that $FG : GD = 1 : 3$, and the tetrahedron $DABC$ satisfies the conditions of the problem.

The solution changes but slightly, if the median of given length is to be taken on s.

178. Problem. *Construct a skew quadrilateral having its sides equal and parallel to the medians of a given tetrahedron.*

Let P be the symmetric of the vertex A of the given tetrahedron $ABCD$ with respect to the centroid G of $ABCD$, and Q the symmetric of D with respect to the mid-point U of GP.

The median DM joining the vertex D of the triangle DGQ to the mid-point M of GQ meets the median GU of DGQ in the centroid R of GDQ and we have

$$GR = \tfrac{2}{3}GU = \tfrac{1}{3}GP = \tfrac{1}{3}AG,$$

hence R coincides with the centroid of the face BCD of $ABCD$ (§ 170).   Thus the two triangles DGQ, DBC have a common vertex D and a common centroid, hence the mid-point of the base BC coincides with the mid-point M of GQ, and $GBQC$ is a parallelogram.

In the parallelogram $GDPQ$ the side PQ is equal and parallel to DG, and in the parallelogram $GBQC$ the side BQ is equal and parallel to GC, hence the sides of the skew quadrilateral $GPQB$ are parallel to the medians of $ABCD$ and equal to three fourths of these medians, respectively.   In order to find a skew quadrilateral satisfying all the conditions of the problem it suffices to construct the homothetic of $GPQB$ with respect to an arbitrary homothetic center, the homothetic ratio being $4 : 3$.

REMARK I.   Another solution of the problem is furnished by the quadrilateral $GPQC$.   The two solutions are not congruent.

REMARK II.   The two tetrahedrons P–GBQ, D–GBC have equivalent bases—each equal to half the area of the parallelogram $GBQC$—and their altitudes equal, for their vertices P, D lie on a line parallel to the common plane of their bases.   Now vol. $(D$–$GBC) =$ vol. $(G$–$BCD) = \tfrac{1}{4}$ vol. $(A$–$BCD)$

On the other hand the volume P–GBQ is equal to $(\tfrac{3}{4})^3$ of the volume of the tetrahedron (T) corresponding to the skew quadrilateral having its sides equal and parallel to the medians of $ABCD$, hence

$$\text{vol. } (T) = \tfrac{1}{4} \cdot (\tfrac{4}{3})^3 \text{ vol. } ABCD = \tfrac{16}{27} \text{ vol. } ABCD.$$

179. Theorem. *The median of a tetrahedron issued from a given vertex is smaller than the arithmetic mean of the three edges issued from this vertex.*

Let A', B', C' be the mid-points of the edges BC, CA, AB (Fig. 15) and let A'', B'', C'' be the mid-points of DA, DB, DC of the tetrahedron $ABCD$. If G is the centroid of $ABCD$, the line DG is the median of the triangle $DA'A''$ (§ 170), hence (C. G., p. 60)

$$DG < \tfrac{1}{2}(DA'' + DA'),$$

or, denoting DG_d by g_d,

$$\tfrac{3}{4}g_d < (\tfrac{1}{4}a' + \tfrac{1}{2}DA').$$

From the triangles $DB'B''$, $DC'C''$ we obtain two analogous formulas, and adding the three formulas, we have

$$\tfrac{9}{4}g_d < \tfrac{1}{4}(a' + b' + c') + \tfrac{1}{2}(DA' + DB' + DC').$$

From the triangles DBC, DCA, DAB we have

$$DA' < \tfrac{1}{2}(b' + c'), \qquad DB' < \tfrac{1}{2}(c' + a'), \qquad DC' < \tfrac{1}{2}(a' + b'),$$

hence

$$DA' + DB' + DC' < a' + b' + c'.$$

Thus

$$\tfrac{9}{4}g_d < \tfrac{1}{4}(a' + b' + c') + \tfrac{1}{2}(a' + b' + c')$$

and therefore

$$g_d < \tfrac{1}{3}(a' + b' + c').$$

180. Corollary. *The sum of the medians of a tetrahedron is smaller than two thirds of the sum of the edges of the tetrahedron.*

181. Theorem. *The sum of the medians of a tetrahedron is greater than four ninths of the sum of the edges of the tetrahedron.*

Using the same notations as in the preceding theorem (§ 179), we have in the triangle DAG

$$AG + DG > AD, \qquad \text{or} \qquad \tfrac{3}{4}(g_a + g_d) > a'.$$

Now writing five analogous relations and adding the six formulas we obtain

$$\tfrac{3}{4} \cdot 3(g_a + g_b + g_c + g_d) > a + b + c + a' + b' + c',$$

which proves the proposition.

EXERCISE. The reader may try to find upper and lower limits for the sum of the medians by making use of other triangles than those considered above, as, for instance, the triangles AGG_a, ADG_a, $A'AG_a$, and others.

182. Theorem. *The sum of the bimedians of a tetrahedron is greater than one fourth of the sum of the edges of the tetrahedron.*

Making use of the same notations (§ 179), we have from the parallelogram $A'C'A''C''$ (§ 181),

$$GA' + GC' > A'C', \qquad GA' + GC'' > A'C''$$

or

$$\tfrac{1}{2}(m_a + m_c) > \tfrac{1}{2}b, \qquad \tfrac{1}{2}(m_a + m_c) > \tfrac{1}{2}b',$$

hence

$$m_a + m_c > \tfrac{1}{2}(b + b').$$

Writing two analogous inequalities and adding we have

$$m_a + m_b + m_c > \tfrac{1}{4}(a + b + c + a' + b' + c').$$

183. Theorem. *A bimedian relative to a pair of opposite edges of a tetrahedron is smaller than the arithmetic mean of the remaining four edges.*

With the same notations as above (§ 179), we have in the parallelogram $A'C'A''C''$,

$$A'A'' < A'C' + A''C',$$

or

$$m_a < \tfrac{1}{2}(b + b').$$

Similarly

$$m_a < \tfrac{1}{2}(c + c'),$$

hence

$$m_a < \tfrac{1}{4}(b + b' + c + c').$$

184. Corollary. *The sum of the bimedians of a tetrahedron is smaller than half of the sum of the edges of the tetrahedron.*

185. Theorem. *The sum of the squares of two pairs of opposite edges of a tetrahedron is equal to the sum of the squares of the remaining two opposite edges increased by four times the square of the bimedian relative to these last edges.*

The proof is the same as the proof of the corresponding property of the skew quadrilateral (§ 143).

186. Corollary. *The sum of the squares of the edges of a tetrahedron is equal to four times the sum of the squares of its bimedians.*

187. Theorem. *The square of the median issued from a given vertex of a tetrahedron is equal to the arithmetic mean of the squares of the three edges issued from the same vertex diminished by one ninth of the sum of the squares of the remaining edges.*

Using the same notations as above and applying Stewart's theorem (C. G., p. 109) to the line DG_d in the triangle DAA' we get

$$9DG_d{}^2 = 6DA'^2 + 3DA^2 - 2AA'^2.$$

Substituting in this formula the values of the medians AA', DA' of the triangles ABC, ADC we get

$$g_d{}^2 = \tfrac{1}{3}(a'^2 + b'^2 + c'^2) - \tfrac{1}{9}(a^2 + b^2 + c^2).$$

188. Corollary. *The sum of the squares of the medians of a tetrahedron is equal to four ninths of the sum of the squares of the edges.*

EXERCISES

1. The centroid of the section of a tetrahedron by any plane parallel to a face of the tetrahedron lies on the corresponding median of the tetrahedron.

2. The centroid and the four faces of a tetrahedron divide the tetrahedron into four equivalent tetrahedrons, and the centroid is the only point having this property.

3. If the medians GA, GB, GC of the tetrahedron $ABCD$ are mutually orthogonal, prove that, with the usual notation for the edges of a tetrahedron,

$$2(a^2 + b^2) = c^2 + c'^2, \qquad 2(b^2 + c^2) = a^2 + a'^2, \qquad 2(c^2 + a^2) = b^2 + b'^2.$$

4. Construct a tetrahedron given three of its vertices, in position, and the lengths of the medians issued from these vertices.

5. If the point U is the trace of the plane $G_aG_bG_c$ on the line DG, show that $DU : UG = 8$.

6. In a given sphere to inscribe a tetrahedron given two of its vertices and the centroid. How many solutions may the problem have?

7. The line joining the centroid of a tetrahedron to the nine-point center of a face is parallel to the line joining the orthocenter of that face to the vertex opposite the face considered and is equal to one fourth of this line.

8. Construct a tetrahedron given three of its medians, both in magnitude and direction.

9. (a) The locus of a point the sum of the squares of whose distances from three given points in space is constant, is a sphere having for its center the centroid of the triangle determined by the given points. (b) Apply the result to two faces of the same tetrahedron, using the same constant in both cases, and determine the plane of the circle common to the two spheres.

10. Given a tetrahedron $ABCD$ and a point O, the four lines joining the centroids of the faces to the points which divide OA, OB, OC, OD in the same ratio $p : q$ are concurrent.

11. Consider the tetrahedron formed by the planes symmetric to the faces of a given tetrahedron with respect to the opposite vertices of this tetrahedron. The two tetrahedrons have the same centroid, and the corresponding edges are to each other as 1 : 7.

12. The algebraic sum of the distances of the vertices of a tetrahedron from any plane in space is equal, in magnitude and in sign, to four times the distance of the centroid of the tetrahedron from the plane considered.—State this proposition for a plane passing through the centroid of the tetrahedron.

13. If O, A, B, C, D are five points in space, prove that the lines drawn from the middle points of BC, CA, AB respectively parallel to the connectors of D with the middle points of OA, OB, OC meet in one point E, such that DE passes through, and is bisected by the centroid of the tetrahedron $OABC$.

c. *The Circumscribed Parallelepiped*

189. Let $A, A_1; B, B_1; C, C_1; D, D_1$ be the four pairs of diagonally opposite vertices of a parallelepiped (Fig. 16). Through one of

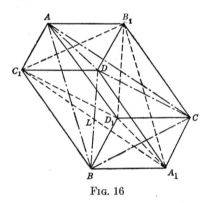

FIG. 16

its vertices, say A, draw the three diagonals AB, AC, AD of the three faces AC_1BD_1, AB_1CD_1, AB_1DC_1 which have the vertex A in common. The lines BC, CD, DB joining the other ends B, C, D of the diagonals AB, AC, AD are in turn diagonals of the faces of the parallelepiped. We have thus one diagonal in each face, and the diagonals in a pair of opposite faces are not parallel.

The tetrahedron $ABCD$ is said to be *inscribed* in the parallelepiped, and the parallelepiped is said to be *circumscribed* about the tetrahedron.

When the vertex A is chosen, the tetrahedron inscribed in the parallelepiped is uniquely determined, and we obtain the same tetrahedron $ABCD$, if we start with either of the vertices B, C, D. On the other hand, the vertices A_1, B_1, C_1, D_1 determine another tetrahedron inscribed in the parallelepiped, hence the

190. Theorem. *Two and only two tetrahedrons may be inscribed in a given parallelepiped.*

191. Definition. The two tetrahedrons inscribed in the same parallelepiped will be referred to as *twin* tetrahedrons.

The corresponding edges of twin tetrahedrons bisect each other, and corresponding faces are parallel, as is readily seen from the figure.

192. Theorem. *One and only one parallelepiped may be circumscribed about a given tetrahedron.*

The parallelepiped is obtained by drawing the pairs of parallel planes through the three pairs of opposite edges of the tetrahedron (§ 6).

193. Remark I. The three pairs of opposite faces of the parallelepiped circumscribed about a tetrahedron have the orientations of the three directing planes of the tetrahedron.

194. Remark II. A bimedian of the tetrahedron joins the midpoints of two opposite faces of the circumscribed parallelepiped, hence the bimedian is equal to the edge of the parallelepiped. Thus: *The three edges of the circumscribed parallelepiped which pass through a vertex of the tetrahedron are equal and parallel to the three bimedians of the tetrahedron.*

195. Remark III. The bialtitude relative to two opposite edges of a tetrahedron is a common perpendicular to the two faces of the circumscribed parallelepiped which contain the edges considered.

196. Remark IV. The distances of a vertex of a tetrahedron from the three faces of the circumscribed parallelepiped which do not pass through the vertex considered are equal to the three bialtitudes of the tetrahedron.

197. Note. The theorems involving the medians, the bialtitudes, and the bimedians of a tetrahedron may be derived by considering the parallelepiped circumscribed about the tetrahedron.

Conversely, these theorems may be stated as properties of the parallelepiped itself.

The reader may formulate these theorems as well as give the new proofs.

198. Theorem. *The medians of a tetrahedron lie along the diagonals of the circumscribed parallelepiped and are equal to two thirds of the respective diagonals.*

Let A, A_1; B, B_1; C, C_1; D, D_1 be the pairs of diagonally opposite vertices of the parallelepiped (P) (Fig. 16) circumscribed about the given tetrahedron $ABCD$, and let O be the point of intersection of the diagonals AA_1, CC_1 of (P).

The line CL joining the point C to the mid-point L of A_1C_1 lies in the plane of the parallelogram AC_1A_1C, hence CL meets AA_1 in the centroid M of the triangle CC_1A_1, and we thus obtain $CM : ML = 2 : 1$.

Now L is the point common to the two diagonals A_1C_1, BD of the face A_1BC_1D of (P), hence CL is a median of the face CBD of the tetrahedron, and M is the centroid of this face, i.e., the median AM of the tetrahedron lies along the diagonal $AOMA_1$ of the parallelepiped.

The segment A_1M is equal to two thirds of A_1O, hence it is equal to one third of AA_1, and therefore AM is equal to two thirds of AA_1.

REMARK.   Since the diagonals of a parallelepiped are known to be concurrent, we have here another proof of Commandino's theorem.   The proof is completed by observing that since $AM = \frac{2}{3}AA_1$, we have $AO = \frac{3}{4}AM$.

199. Corollary.   *The centroid of a tetrahedron coincides with the point of intersection of the diagonals of its circumscribed parallelepiped.*

200. Theorem.   *Two twin tetrahedrons have the same centroid and this point is a center of symmetry of the two tetrahedrons.*

Their centroids coincide with the point of intersection of the diagonals of their common circumscribed parallelepiped, and this point bisects the lines joining the pairs of corresponding vertices of the two tetrahedrons.

201. Theorem.   *If two edges of a tetrahedron are equal to their respectively opposite edges, the bimedian relative to the third pair of opposite edges coincides with the bialtitude relative to this pair of edges.*

The assumption implies that two pairs of opposite faces of the circumscribed parallelepiped (P) are rectangles, hence (P) is rectangular, and the line joining the point of intersection of the diagonals of a face of (P) which is not a rectangle to the analogous point in the opposite face of (P) is perpendicular to these faces, hence the proposition.

202. Conversely. *If a bimedian relative to one pair of opposite edges of a tetrahedron coincides with the bialtitude of this pair of edges, each of the remaining edges is equal to its opposite edge.*

Indeed this bimedian will be perpendicular to a pair of opposite faces of the circumscribed parallelepiped (P), hence (P) will be rectangular, and the diagonals in the remaining faces will be equal.

EXERCISES

1. (a) If two opposite edges of a tetrahedron are equal, the two bimedians relative to the other two pairs of opposite edges are rectangular; these bimedians are the bisectors of the angles formed by the parallels to the equal edges drawn through the centroid of the tetrahedron.

(b) If each edge of a tetrahedron is equal to its opposite edge, the bimedians of the tetrahedron form a trirectangular trihedral angle, and conversely.

2. Through the midpoints of two intersecting edges of a tetrahedron parallels are drawn to the respectively opposite edges. The point of intersection of these two parallels lies on the median of the tetrahedron issued from the vertex common to the latter two edges.

3. The triangle formed by the mid-points of three concurrent edges of a tetrahedron has for its anticomplementary triangle the face of the twin tetrahedron corresponding to the common vertex of the edges considered.

4. A face of a tetrahedron is equidistant from the four vertices of the twin tetrahedron.

5. The projection, upon a face of a tetrahedron, of the vertex of the twin tetrahedron corresponding to the face considered is the symmetric, with respect to the projection of the centroid of the tetrahedron, of the foot of the altitude relative to the face considered; the projections of the remaining three vertices of the twin tetrahedron form a triangle symmetrical to the triangle of the face considered with respect to the projection of the centroid.

6. The line joining the mid-point of an altitude of a tetrahedron to the centroid of the tetrahedron is parallel to the line joining the foot of this altitude on the respective face of the tetrahedron to the vertex of the twin tetrahedron corresponding to the face considered.

7. The harmonic conjugate of the centroid of a tetrahedron with respect to a vertex and the centroid of the opposite face coincides with the vertex of the twin tetrahedron corresponding to the face considered.

2. Altitudes

a. Special Cases

203. Theorem. *If a pair of opposite edges of a tetrahedron are rectangular, the two altitudes of the tetrahedron issued from the ends of each of these two edges are coplanar.*

If the two opposite edges BC, AD of the tetrahedron $ABCD$ are rectangular, it is possible to draw through BC a plane BMC perpendicular to AD at M. This plane is perpendicular to the two planes ADB, ADC passing through AD, hence the altitude from C to ABD and the altitude from B to ADC both lie in the plane BCM. Similarly for the altitudes issued from the ends A, D of AD.

204. Converse Theorem. *If two altitudes of a tetrahedron are coplanar, the edge joining the two vertices from which these altitudes issue is perpendicular to the opposite edge of the tetrahedron.*

Indeed, if the altitudes issued from B and C meet in a point H, the plane BHC is perpendicular to the planes ADC, ADB and therefore also to their intersection AD, which proves the proposition.

205. Corollary I. *If two altitudes of a tetrahedron intersect, the remaining two intersect also.*

206. Corollary II. *The point of intersection of two altitudes of a tetrahedron lies on a bialtitude of the tetrahedron.*

Let the altitudes issued from B, C meet in H; the altitudes issued from A and D meet in a point, say, H' (§ 205). The lines BH, CH are two altitudes of the triangle BCM, hence H is the orthocenter of this triangle, and HM is perpendicular to BC. But MH is also perpendicular to AD, hence MH is the bialtitude relative to BC, AD. Similarly for H'.

207. Definition. A parallelepiped each face of which is a rhombus shall be referred to as a *rhomboid.*

All edges of a rhomboid are equal, and, conversely, if all edges of a parallelepiped are equal, the parallelepiped is a rhomboid (or a cube, which case we exclude, unless otherwise stated).

208. Definition. A tetrahedron each edge of which is perpendicular to the opposite edge is called a **rectangular,** or **orthocentric** tetrahedron.

209. Theorem. *A tetrahedron inscribed in a rhomboid is orthocentric, and conversely.*

The diagonals of a rhombus are orthogonal, hence two opposite edges of a tetrahedron (T) inscribed in a rhomboid (R) are rectangular.

Conversely, if (T) is orthocentric, each face of the circumscribed parallelepiped (R) of (T) will have its diagonals rectangular, hence (R) will be a rhomboid.

210. Corollary. *The bimedians of an orthocentric tetrahedron are equal* (§ 207).

211. Theorem. *In an orthocentric tetrahedron the three sums of the squares of the three pairs of opposite edges are equal.*

Consider a face of the rhomboid (R) circumscribed about the given tetrahedron (T). The sum of the squares of the diagonals of this face is equal to four times the square of the edge of (R). Now these two diagonals are a pair of opposite edges of (T), and the edge of (R) is a bimedian of (T), and since the bimedians of (T) are equal (§ 210), the proposition is proved.

212. Theorem. *The four altitudes of an orthocentric tetrahedron are concurrent.*

Let $(T) \equiv ABCD$, $(T') \equiv A'B'C'D'$ be the twin tetrahedrons inscribed in the rhomboid (R) (Fig. 17). The altitude AA_h of (T) issued from A is perpendicular to the face $B'C'D'$ of (T'), for the two faces BCD, $B'C'D'$ are parallel (§ 191). But the edges AB', AC', AD' of (R) are equal (§ 207), hence AA_h passes through the circumcenter of the triangle $B'C'D'$ (§ 90), and therefore also through the circumcenter of (T'). Similarly for the other altitudes of (T). Hence the proposition.

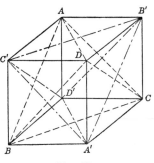

Fig. 17

213. Definition. The point common to the four altitudes of an orthocentric tetrahedron is called the **orthocenter** of the tetrahedron.

214. Corollary. *The orthocenter of an orthocentric tetrahedron is the symmetric of the circumcenter with respect to the centroid,* for the circumcenters of (T) and (T') (§ 212) are symmetrical with respect to the common centroid of these two tetrahedrons (§ 200).

215. Theorem. *In an orthocentric tetrahedron the bialtitudes pass through the orthocenter of the tetrahedron and determine in the faces the orthic triangles of these faces.*

The proposition follows immediately from an earlier proposition (§ 206).

216. Theorem. *The altitudes of an orthocentric tetrahedron pass through the orthocenters of the respective faces of the tetrahedron.*

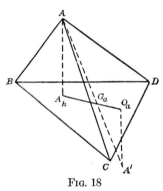

FIG. 18

The diagonal AA' (Fig. 18) of (R) (§ 212) meets the face BCD of (T) in its centroid G_a (§ 199); the perpendicular $A'O_a$ from A' upon BCD passes through the circumcenter O_a of BCD, for the edges $A'B$, $A'C$, $A'D$ of (R) are equal (§ 207). Now if A_h is the foot of the altitude AA_h from A upon BCD, we have, from similar right triangles,

$$A_hG_a : G_aO_a = AG_a : G_aA' = 2 : 1$$

(§ 198), hence A_h is the orthocenter of BCD (C. G., p. 87).

217. Theorem. *Any three vertices of an orthocentric tetrahedron and the orthocenters of the respectively opposite faces are six cospherical points. The four spheres thus obtained are equal.*

From the similar triangles of the preceding theorem (§ 216) we have

$$AA_h : A'O_a = 2 : 1.$$

Now the corresponding altitudes in (T) and (T') are equal, hence the altitudes of each of these tetrahedrons are bisected by the corresponding faces of the other tetrahedron.

Thus the point A' is equidistant from the ends of the altitudes BB_h, CC_h, DD_h of (T). But we also have

$$A'B = A'C = A'D,$$

hence the three pairs of points B, B_h; C, C_h; D, D_h lie on a sphere having for center A' and for radius an edge of (R), or a bimedian of (T) (§ 210).

The centers of the three analogous spheres are the vertices B', C', D' of (T'), and the radii are the edges of (R), hence the proposition.

218. Corollary. *In an orthocentric tetrahedron the product of the segments into which the orthocenter divides the altitudes is constant.*

NOTE. The orthocentric tetrahedron will be studied further in Chapter IX (§ 795).

EXERCISES

1. (a) If in a parallelepiped two pairs of opposite faces are rhombuses, the same is true about the third pair of faces.   (b) If in a tetrahedron two pairs of opposite edges are rectangular, the same is true about the third pair.

2. If two opposite edges of a tetrahedron are rectangular, the two sums of the squares of the remaining pairs of opposite edges are equal to each other, and conversely.

3. If three altitudes of a tetrahedron are concurrent, the fourth altitude passes through their common point, and the three pairs of opposite edges of the tetrahedron are orthogonal.

4. (a) In an orthocentric tetrahedron the square of a bimedian is equal to three sixteenths of the sum of the squares of the four medians of the tetrahedron. (b) State this proposition with reference to a rhomboid.

5. The four altitudes of an orthocentric tetrahedron form an orthocentric group the orthic trihedron of which is formed by the bialtitudes of the tetrahedron.

6. The three lines joining the mid-point of the altitude issued from one vertex of a regular tetrahedron to the remaining three vertices of the tetrahedron form a trirectangular trihedral angle.

7. If in a tetrahedron the pairs of opposite edges are rectangular, the bialtitudes of the tetrahedron are concurrent.

8. In an orthocentric tetrahedron the sum of the squares of a pair of opposite edges is equal to the square of the circumradius of a face increased by the square of the altitude of the tetrahedron relative to this face.

9. If D_h is the foot of the altitude DD_h of the orthocentric tetrahedron $DABC$, the three spheres (DD_hAB), (DD_hBC), (DD_hCA) are equal.

10. A face of an orthocentric tetrahedron is parallel to the plane formed by the three external bisectors of the face angles of the corresponding trihedral angle of the circumscribed rhomboid.

11. An altitude of an orthocentric tetrahedron is an isoclinal line of the corresponding trihedral angle of the circumscribed rhomboid.

12. The altitudes of an orthocentric tetrahedron are the orthocentric lines of the respective trihedral angles of the tetrahedron.

13. The four projections, upon a face of an orthocentric tetrahedron, of the four vertices of the twin tetrahedron are the circumcenters of the orthocentric group of triangles determined by the face considered.

14. The projection of the centroid of an orthocentric tetrahedron upon a face of this tetrahedron is the nine-point center of this face.

15. The four spheres passing through the circumcircles of the faces of an orthocentric tetrahedron and having their centers at a distance from the respective faces equal to half the corresponding altitude of the tetrahedron are equal to one another.

16. (a) If the bimedians relative to two pairs of opposite edges of an orthocentric tetrahedron are equal, the remaining two edges are orthogonal, and conversely.   (b) If the three bimedians of a tetrahedron are equal, the tetrahedron is orthocentric.   (c) The mid-points of the six edges of an orthocentric tetrahedron are cospherical; conversely, if the mid-points of the edges of a tetrahedron are cospherical the tetrahedron is orthocentric.

b. *The General Case*

219. Theorem. *The four altitudes of a tetrahedron form a hyperbolic group.*

The orthocentric line p of the trihedral angle A (§ 68) of the tetrahedron $ABCD$ lies in the plane through the edge AB and perpendicular to the plane ACD. This perpendicular plane contains also the altitude of the tetrahedron from B to the face ACD, hence p meets h_b. In a similar manner it may be shown that p meets the altitudes h_c, h_d, and p obviously meets the altitude h_a. These considerations may in turn be applied to the orthocentric lines q, r, s of the trihedral angles B, C, D of $ABCD$.

Thus any one of the four altitudes of $ABCD$ meets the four lines p, q, r, s, and since no two of these altitudes are coplanar (§ 204), they form a hyperbolic group (§ 27).

220. Remark. We have proved incidentally that *the four orthocentric lines of the four trihedral angles of a tetrahedron form a hyperbolic group* (§ 27).

221. Theorem. *Each of the four altitudes of a tetrahedron is coplanar with each of the four perpendiculars erected to the faces of the tetrahedron at their respective orthocenters.*

The altitude h_b issued from the vertex B of the tetrahedron $ABCD$ and the perpendicular t erected to the face BCD at the orthocenter H_a of the triangle BCD lie both in the plane passing through the line BH_a and perpendicular to CD.

Similarly the altitudes h_c, h_d are coplanar with t, and since t is parallel to h_a, we see that t is coplanar with each of the four altitudes of $ABCD$. The same may be shown to be true about the perpendiculars u, v, w erected to the faces CDA, DAB, ABC at their orthocenters, hence the proposition.

222. Remark. We have proved incidentally that *the perpendiculars erected to the faces of a tetrahedron at their respective orthocenters form a hyperbolic group.*

223. Theorem. *The common perpendicular of two altitudes issued from two vertices of a tetrahedron is parallel to the edge joining the remaining two vertices of the tetrahedron.*

The common perpendicular s_{ab} of the altitudes h_a, h_b issued from the vertices A, B of the tetrahedron $ABCD$ is parallel to the planes BCD, CDA, hence it is parallel to their line of inter-section CD.

224. Corollary. The six common perpendiculars of the four altitudes, taken in pairs, of a tetrahedron are parallels to the six edges of the tetrahedron.

225. Theorem. *A plane through an altitude of a tetrahedron and parallel to the shortest distance of two other altitudes passes through the orthocentric line of the trihedral angle having for its vertex the fourth vertex of the tetrahedron.*

Indeed, the plane through the altitude h_a and parallel to the common perpendicular of the altitudes h_b, h_c will contain the edge AD (§ 223) of $ABCD$ and will be perpendicular to DBC, it will therefore contain the orthocentric line s of the trihedral angle D.

226. Corollary. If through each of three altitudes of a tetrahedron planes are drawn parallel to the shortest distance of the other two of these altitudes, the three planes thus obtained will be coaxal, the axis being the orthocentric line of the trihedral angle having for its vertex the fourth vertex of the tetrahedron.

227. Problem. *Construct a tetrahedron so that three of its altitudes shall lie on three given skew lines.*

A necessary condition for the solution of the problem is that the planes drawn through each of the given lines h, i, j parallel to the common perpendicular of the remaining two lines shall pass through the same line s (§ 226).

If this condition is satisfied any point D of the line s may be taken as the vertex of the required tetrahedron.

Indeed, the plane hs is, by construction, parallel to the shortest distance u_{ij} between i and j, hence a parallel through D to u_{ij} will meet h, say, in A. Let B, C be the analogous points on i and j. The line h is perpendicular to the shortest distances u_{hi}, u_{hj} of the pairs of lines h, i; h, j; since DC, DB are respectively parallel to these shortest distances, the line h is perpendicular to DB, DC, consequently to the plane DBC. Similarly for i and j. Hence the tetrahedron $DABC$ satisfies the conditions of the problem.

Thus the problem has either no solution or an infinite number of solutions.

EXERCISES

1. The projections, upon a face of a tetrahedron, of the three altitudes of the tetrahedron issued from the vertices lying in this face, are the altitudes of the triangle of the face considered.

2. In a tetrahedron the sum of the reciprocals of any three altitudes is greater than the reciprocal of the fourth altitude.

3. The sum of the distances of the centroid of a tetrahedron from the faces of this tetrahedron is the arithmetic mean of the altitudes of the tetrahedron.

4. (a) If a, b, c are the altitudes of a triangle, and p, q, r the distances of a point inside the triangle from the sides of the triangle we have

$$(p : a) + (q : b) + (r : c) = 1.$$

(b) State and prove an analogous proposition for the tetrahedron. (c) Does the proposition hold for a point outside the triangle or the tetrahedron?

5. The perpendiculars to the four faces of a tetrahedron at their respective centroids form a hyperbolic group.

c. *The Monge Point*

228. The Monge Theorem. *The six planes through the midpoints of the edges of a tetrahedron and perpendicular to the edges respectively opposite have a point in common.*

Let (C') be the mediator of the edge AB of the tetrahedron $ABCD$, and let (C'') be the plane through the mid-point C'' of CD and perpendicular to AB. The bimedian $C'C''$ joins two points in these two planes, and these planes are parallel, hence the segment intercepted by these planes on any line passing through the mid-point G of $C'C''$ will be bisected at G. Now the plane (C') contains the circumcenter O of $ABCD$, hence (C'') meets the line GO in a point M such that $OG = GM$. But the points O and G (the centroid of $ABCD$) are independent of the particular edge AB considered, hence the proposition.

OTHERWISE. The plane (C', DC) through the mid-point C' of AB and perpendicular to CD is also perpendicular to the edge C_1D_1 of the twin tetrahedron $A_1B_1C_1D_1$ of $ABCD$ (§ 191), i.e., (C', DC) is the mediator of C_1D_1, hence this plane passes through the circumcenter O_1 of $A_1B_1C_1D_1$, which point is the symmetric of the circumcenter O of $ABCD$ with respect to the common centroid G of the two tetrahedrons (§ 200). Similarly for the other five planes, hence the proposition.

229. Definitions. The six planes perpendicular to the edges of a tetrahedron and passing through the mid-points of the respective opposite edges may be referred to as the **Monge planes** of the tetrahedron.

The point common to these planes is the **Monge point** of the tetrahedron.

The line joining the centroid and the circumcenter of a tetrahedron (and containing the Monge point) may, by analogy with the plane, be called the **Euler line** of the tetrahedron.

230. Remark I. *The Monge point of a tetrahedron is the symmetric of the circumcenter with respect to the centroid,* as is clear from the above proofs (§ 228).

231. Remark II. In an orthocentric tetrahedron the Monge point coincides with the orthocenter of the tetrahedron (§ 214).

The Monge planes of an orthocentric tetrahedron contain the edges through whose mid-points they pass.

232. Mannheim's Theorem. *The four planes determined by the four altitudes of a tetrahedron and the orthocenters of the corresponding faces pass through the Monge point of the tetrahedron.*

Let A' be the foot of the altitude AA' (Fig. 19) of the tetrahedron $ABCD$, G_a the centroid of the face BCD and G' the projection of the centroid G of the tetrahedron upon BCD. The point G' lies on $A'G_a$ and we have (§ 170)

$$A'G' : A'G_a = 3 : 4.$$

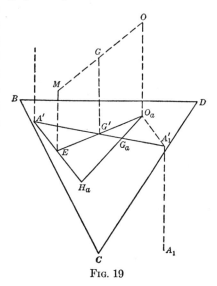

Fig. 19

Let O_a, H_a be the circumcenter and the orthocenter of the triangles BCD. These points are collinear with G_a (C. G., p. 95) and we have

$$H_aG_a : H_aO_a = 2 : 3.$$

Applying Menelaus' theorem to the triangle O_aG_aG' and the transversal $A'EH_a$ we find that G' is the mid-point of EO_a.

The point O_a is the projection upon BCD of the circumcenter O of the tetrahedron $ABCD$ and the line O_aG' is the projection of the

line OG upon BCD, hence the perpendicular EM at E to BCD will
meet OG in the symmetric M of O with respect to G. But EM
lies in the plane $AA'H_a$, hence this plane passes through M, the
Monge point of the tetrahedron (§ 228). Since the points O,
G, M do not depend upon the choice of the particular altitude AA'
considered, the proposition is proved.

OTHERWISE. With the same notations, let A_1' be the projection
upon BCD of the vertex A_1 of the twin tetrahedron (T_1) of
$(T) \equiv ABCD$. From the similar triangles we have (§ 198)

$$A'G_a : G_aA_1' = AG_a : G_aA_1 = 2 : 1.$$

We also have

$$H_aG_a : G_aO_a = 2 : 1.$$

Hence the lines $A'H_a$, $A_1'O_a$ are parallel, and the same holds for
the planes $AA'H_a$, $A_1A_1'O_a$. Furthermore, this last plane being
perpendicular to BCD contains the perpendicular to BCD at O_a,
i.e., the circumcenter O of (T) lies in $A_1A_1'O_a$.

The two planes $AA'H_a$, $A_1A_1'O_a$ are parallel and pass through
the two points A, A_1 which correspond to each other in the symmetry of which the common centroid G of (T) and (T_1) is the
center (§ 200), hence the two planes correspond to each other in
this symmetry, and since $A_1A_1'O_a$ contains the circumcenter O
of (T), the plane $AA'H_a$ contains the symmetric of O with respect
to G, i.e., the Monge point of (T).

233. Corollary. *The Monge point of a tetrahedron is equidistant
from an altitude of the tetrahedron and the perpendicular erected to
the corresponding face at its orthocenter.*

Indeed, the perpendicular to BCD at H_a (Fig. 19) lies in the
same plane with AA' and EM and is parallel to these lines. Now
the point E is the mid-point of $A'H_a$ as is readily seen by applying
Menelaus' theorem to the triangle $A'H_aG_a$ and the transversal
$EG'O_a$; hence the proposition.

234. Theorem. *The two planes passing through the Monge point
of a tetrahedron and perpendicular to two bimedians of this tetrahedron divide the third bimedian harmonically.*

The planes through the Monge point M of the tetrahedron
$ABCD$ and perpendicular to the bimedians m_a, m_b are separated
harmonically by the planes drawn through M perpendicularly to
the edges DC, AB (§ 39). Now the plane through M perpendicu-

lar to DC passes through the mid-point of AB (§ 228), and similarly for the other plane, i.e., these planes pass through the ends of the bimedian m_c, hence the proposition.

OTHERWISE. The Monge point of the given tetrahedron is the circumcenter of its twin tetrahedron (§ 228), and the two solids have the same bimedians (§ 191), hence the proposition differs only in form from the one proved before (§ 168).

EXERCISES

1. The six midpoints of the edges of a tetrahedron may be considered as determining an octahedron, four faces of which lie in the faces of the tetrahedron. The perpendiculars to these four faces of the octahedron at their respective orthocenters have a point in common, and the remaining four faces of the octahedron enjoy a similar property.

2. Consider the four segments in the faces of a tetrahedron determined by the orthocenter of each face and the foot of the altitude of the tetrahedron corresponding to this face. The mediators of these four segments have a point in common.

3. The center of the sphere determined by the mid-points of the medians of a tetrahedron lies on the Euler line of the tetrahedron.

3. Bisecting Planes of Dihedral Angles

235. Gergonne's Theorem. *The internal (external) bisecting plane of a dihedral angle of a tetrahedron divides the opposite edge in the ratio of the areas of the adjacent faces.*

Let E be the trace on CD of the internal bisecting plane of the dihedral angle AB of the tetrahedron $ABCD$. The point E being equidistant from the faces ABC, ABD, the two tetrahedrons $E{-}ABC$, $E{-}ABD$ have equal altitudes, hence

vol. $ABCE$: vol. $ABDE$ = area ABC : area ABD.

Now these tetrahedrons also have a common base ABE, hence their volumes are to each other as the distances of the points C, D from the plane ABE, and these distances, in turn, are to each other as the segments CE, DE, hence the proposition.

The reader will readily modify the above proof to fit the case of the external bisecting plane of the dihedral angle.

236. Theorem. *The point where an edge of a tetrahedron is met by the external bisecting plane of the opposite dihedral angle is collinear with the two points in which the two edges coplanar with the first are met by the internal bisecting planes of the dihedral angles respectively opposite these edges.*

The proof of this proposition is readily obtained by applying the preceding theorem (§ 235) and the theorem of Menelaus.

OTHERWISE. This follows also from the property of the bisecting planes of the dihedral angles of a trihedron (§ 114).

237. Cesaro's Theorem. *The three points determined on three coplanar edges of a tetrahedron by the external bisecting planes of the opposite dihedral angles are collinear.*

This line belongs to the plane determined by the three points in which the remaining three (concurrent) edges of the tetrahedron are met by the internal bisecting planes of the respectively opposite dihedral angles.

The first part of the proposition may be proved the same way as the preceding theorem (§ 236). The second part is a consequence of the first part and the preceding theorem (§ 236).

238. Theorem. *The external bisecting planes of the six dihedral angles of a tetrahedron meet the respective opposite edges in six coplanar points.*

The external bisecting planes of the three dihedral angles DA, DB, DC meet the edges BC, CA, AB in three points lying on the same line s, by Cesaro's theorem. We shall have analogous lines p, q, r in the faces BCD, CDA, DAB. Now each of the four lines p, q, r, s meets the remaining three, for s and p, for instance, have in common the trace of the external bisecting plane of the dihedral angle DC on the edge AB. But the four lines are not concurrent, hence they are coplanar.

EXERCISES

1. The internal (external) bisecting plane of the dihedral angle AB of the tetrahedron $ABCD$ divides the edge CD in the ratio of the distances of C, D from AB.

2. The bisecting planes of the dihedral angles of a tetrahedron determine pairs of points on the respectively opposite edges, in all twelve points. These points lie by sixes in how many planes? by threes on how many lines?

4. The Spheres Touching the Four Faces of a Tetrahedron

a. The Inscribed Sphere

239. Theorem. *The internal bisecting planes of the six dihedral angles of a tetrahedron have a point in common.*

The three internal bisecting planes of the three dihedral angles of the trihedral angle D of the tetrahedron $DABC$ pass through the internal axis of this trihedral angle (§ 112). The point of intersection I of this axis with the internal bisecting plane of one of the remaining three dihedral angles of $DABC$, say AB, lies within the tetrahedron and is equidistant from the faces of $DABC$, hence I belongs also to the internal bisecting planes of the dihedral angles BC and CA.

240. Remark. The point I is common to the four internal axes of the four trihedral angles of $DABC$.

241. Corollary. The point I is the center of a sphere (I) which touches the four faces of $DABC$ and which lies within the tetrahedron.

This sphere (I) is the *inscribed sphere* of the tetrahedron.

242. Construction of the Point of Contact of a Face of a Tetrahedron with the Inscribed Sphere. If the face DAB of the tetrahedron $DABC$ (Fig. 20) revolves about AB until it coincides with ABC so as to crush the inscribed sphere (I) of $DABC$ (i.e., so that the vertex D falls on the same side of AB as C), the point of contact of (I) with DAB will coincide with the point of contact X of (I) with ABC.

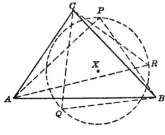

Fig. 20

If P is the new position of D, when DAB coincides with ABC, and Q, R are the analogous points for the faces DBC, DCA, the segments PX, QX, RX are equal, for the lengths of the three tangents from D to the sphere (I) are equal. Hence X is the circumcenter of the triangle PQR. Now given the base ABC and the lengths of the three edges DA, DB, DC of $DABC$, the points P, Q, R, in the plane ABC, are readily constructed, hence the point X.

243. Lemma. *Any given segment of the line of intersection of two planes which are tangent to the same sphere subtends equal angles at the two points where the planes touch this sphere.*

Let AB be a segment on the line of intersection AB of the two planes ABT, ABT' which touch the same sphere at the points T, T', respectively. We have (§ 384)

$$AT = AT', \qquad BT = BT',$$

hence the triangles ATB, $AT'B$ are congruent, and therefore angle $ATB = AT'B$.

244. Theorem. *The four angles subtended by two opposite edges of a tetrahedron at the points of contact of the faces with the inscribed sphere are equal.*

The common edge a of the two faces ABC, DBC of the tetrahedron $DABC$ subtends the same angle u at the two points of contact of these two faces with the inscribed sphere of $DABC$, according to the preceding lemma (§ 243). Let v, w, u', v', w' be the analogous angles corresponding to the edges b, c, a', b', c' Thus we have in the four faces of $DABC$

$$2\pi = u + v + w = u + v' + w' = u' + v + w' = u' + v' + w$$

hence

$$v + w = v' + w', \qquad v + w' = v' + w,$$

therefore

$$v = v', \qquad w = w',$$

and also

$$u = u'.$$

245. Corollary. *In a tetrahedron the three angles subtended by the edges of a face at the point of contact of this face with the inscribed sphere are the same in the four faces of the tetrahedron.*

b. *The Existence and Distribution of the Escribed Spheres*

246. If the faces of a tetrahedron are considered to be indefinitely produced, these planes divide space into fifteen regions, as follows (Fig. 21).

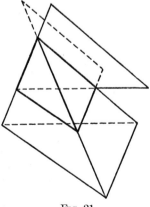

(a) The region occupied by the tetrahedron itself.

(b) The region formed by one face of the tetrahedron and the other three faces produced, or, in other words, the region left when from a trihedral angle of the tetrahedron we remove the tetrahedron itself. There are four such regions, one relative to each face of the tetrahedron, or relative to each vertex. We shall refer to these regions as the *truncs* of the tetrahedron, and

Fig. 21

distinguish them from one another by the particular vertex, or face of the tetrahedron to which each of them belongs.

(c) The region formed by the vertical angle of a dihedral angle and the other two faces produced, or, in other words, by an edge of the tetrahedron and the four edges, produced, which pass through the ends of the edge considered. There are six such regions. We shall refer to them as the *roofs* (German *Dach*, French *comble*) of the tetrahedron. The edge to which a given roof corresponds is the *ridge* of the roof.

(d) The regions formed by the vertical trihedral angles of the trihedral angles of the tetrahedron. There are four such regions. Each is formed by three of the faces of the tetrahedron.

247. The point *I* which we found (§ 239) is equidistant from the four faces of the tetrahedron *DABC*. We shall now consider, in general, the

PROBLEM. *To find a point equidistant from the four faces of a tetrahedron.*

The locus of the points equidistant from the three faces of the trihedral angle *D* of the given tetrahedron *DABC* consists of the four axes of this angle (§ 118). A point equidistant from the four faces of *DABC* must lie on one of these axes, and in one of the two bisecting planes of the dihedral angle *BC* of *DABC*. Now the four lines may meet the two bisecting planes in eight points. Hence: *The problem may have eight solutions.*

The problem cannot have other solutions than these eight, for any point satisfying the conditions of the problem must lie on one of the four axes of the trihedral angle *D*, and in one of the two bisecting planes of the dihedral angle *BC*.

248. Remark I. Each of the eight points thus found (§ 247) may be taken for the center of a sphere tangent to the four faces of *DABC*. Thus, besides the inscribed sphere, a tetrahedron may have seven other spheres which touch, each, the four faces of the tetrahedron. We shall refer to these spheres as the *escribed* spheres of the tetrahedron.

249. Remark II. The four trihedral angles of the tetrahedron have $4 \times 4 = 16$ axes, and an axis contains two of the eight points (§ 247), hence each point lies on $2 \times 16 : 8 = 4$ axes.

Again, the six dihedral angles have $6 \times 2 = 12$ bisecting planes,

76   MODERN PURE SOLID GEOMETRY

and a bisecting plane contains four of the points, hence each point lies in $4 \times 12 : 8 = 6$ bisecting planes.

250. Theorem. *Each of the four truncs of a tetrahedron contains an escribed sphere.*

Let P be the trace in the plane ABC of the line DI joining the incenter I of the tetrahedron $DABC$ to the vertex D (Fig. 22). Consider the three tetrahedrons $DPAB$, $DPBC$, $DPCA$, and the internal bisecting planes ABI, BCI, CAI of the dihedral angles AB, BC, CA. If A, B, C, D denote the areas of the faces of $ABCD$, we have (§ 235)

$$\frac{DI}{IP} = \frac{C}{PAB} = \frac{A}{PBC} = \frac{B}{PCA} = \frac{C + A + B}{D}.$$

Now $A + B + C$ is always greater than D, hence DI is greater than IP, i.e., the mid-point of DP lies on DI and is distinct from

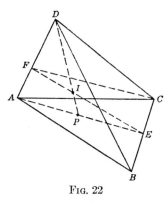

FIG. 22

I. Hence the harmonic conjugate I_d of I with respect to D, P may be constructed and lies in the trunc of $DABC$ relative to D. But this harmonic conjugate is the intersection of the axis DI with the external bisecting plane of either of the dihedral angles BC, CA, AB. Hence I_d is the center of a sphere (I_d) which touches the four faces of $DABC$ and which is located in the trunc of $DABC$ relative to D.

Similarly the truncs of $DABC$ relative to the vertices A, B, C contain, respectively, the escribed spheres (I_a), (I_b), (I_c).

251. Theorem. *Of the two roofs of a tetrahedron having for ridges two opposite edges of the tetrahedron only one may contain an escribed sphere of the tetrahedron.*

Let E, F be the traces on BC, DA (Fig. 22) of the internal bisecting planes of the dihedral angles AD, BC of the tetrahedron $DABC$.

Now consider the tetrahedrons $ABEF$, $CDEF$; $ACEF$, $BDEF$ and the internal bisecting planes ABI, CDI, ACI, BDI of the dihedral angles AB, CD, AC, BD. We have (§ 235)

$$\frac{EI}{IF} = \frac{\text{area } ABE}{\text{area } ABF} = \frac{CDE}{CDF} = \frac{ACE}{ACF} = \frac{BDE}{BDF} = \frac{D+A}{B+C}.$$

The harmonic conjugate I' of I with respect to E, F necessarily lies either in the roof having for ridge the edge DA, or in the roof having for ridge the edge BC. From the proportion just established it follows that I' will lie in the first roof, if $D + A$ is greater than $B + C$, otherwise it will lie in the second roof.

Now the harmonic conjugate of I with respect to E, F is the trace on EF of the external bisecting plane of either of the dihedral angles AB, CD, AC, BD. Hence I' is the center of an escribed sphere (I') of $DABC$ lying in one of the roofs BC, DA.

Similarly there may be an escribed sphere (I'') in one of the two roofs CA, DB, and an escribed sphere (I''') in one of the two roofs AB, DC.

252. Discussion. (a) The point I' (§ 251), and consequently the sphere (I'), may be constructed, if the two sums $A + D$, $B + C$ are unequal. In case of equality of these two sums, the sphere (I') ceases to exist (vanishes at infinity).

(b) The sphere (I'') will vanish, if $A + C = B + D$. Both spheres (I') and (I'') will vanish, if we have

$$A + D = B + C, \qquad A + C = B + D,$$

which implies that

$$A = B, \qquad C = D.$$

This last condition for the vanishing of the two spheres (I'), (I'') may be put in a simpler form. Since $A = B$, the internal bisecting plane of the dihedral angle CD passes through the mid-point C' of AB (§ 235). Similarly the internal bisecting plane of the dihedral angle AB passes through the mid-point C'' of DC. The common line of these two bisecting planes is thus the bimedian $C'C''$ of $DABC$ relative to the pair of edges AB, CD. It may be shown that (§ 303) $C'C''$ is in this case also the bialtitude of AB, CD, hence $AD = BC$, $AC = BD$ (§ 202).

Similar results are obtained if the spheres (I'), (I'''), or the spheres (I''), (I''') vanish.

(c) All three spheres (I'), (I''), (I''') vanish, if

$$A + B = C + D, \qquad A + C = B + D, \qquad A + D = B + C.$$

It is readily seen that this implies the equalities $A = B = C = D$, and the tetrahedron is isosceles (§ 290).

253. Resumé. A tetrahedron always has an inscribed sphere, and an escribed sphere in each of its four truncs. To fix the ideas let us suppose now that

$$A \geqslant B \geqslant C \geqslant D.$$

(1) There will be an escribed sphere in the roof AB, unless $A = B = C = D$, i.e., unless the tetrahedron is isosceles (§ 252).

(2) There will be a sphere in the roof AC, unless $A = B, C = D$, i.e., unless $AC = BD$, $BC = AD$.

(3) There will be a sphere in one of the two roofs AD, BC, unless $A + D = B + C$.

c. *Relative Position of the Centers to Each Other*

254. Notation. It has already been indicated (§§ 239, 250, 251) that the center of the inscribed sphere of the tetrahedron $DABC$ will be denoted by I, while the centers of the four spheres belonging to the four truncs A, B, C, D will be denoted by I_a, I_b, I_c, I_d, respectively. The center of the sphere located in one of the two roofs DA, BC will be denoted by I', while the centers I'', I''' will denote those lying in the roofs DB, CA; DC, AB, respectively. The spheres themselves will be indicated by their centers, in parentheses.

255. Let u, v, w be the internal bisecting planes of the dihedral angles having for edges BC, CA, AB of the tetrahedron $DABC$, and let x, y, z be the analogous planes corresponding to the edges DA, DB, DC. The external bisecting planes of these six dihedral angles will be denoted by u', v', w', x', y', z'.

In the table below are listed the bisecting planes passing through the center of each sphere touching the faces of the tetrahedron (§ 249)

	1.				2.		
I	(u, x),	(v, y),	(w, z)	I_a	(u', x),	(v, y'),	(w, z')
I'	(u, x),	(v', y'),	(w', z')	I_b	(u, x'),	(v', y),	(w, z')
I''	(u', x'),	(v, y),	(w', z')	I_c	(u, x'),	(v, y'),	(w', z)
I'''	(u', x'),	(v', y'),	(w, z)	I_d	(u', x),	(v', y),	(w', z)

In this table the eight centers are divided into two groups. The first group contains the incenter and the centers of the spheres located in the roofs of the tetrahedron, while the second group comprises the centers of the spheres situated in the truncs of the tetrahedron.

(a) Through each point of the first group pass an even number of external bisecting planes of the dihedral angles of the tetrahedron, while through each point of the second group pass an odd number of such planes.

(b) The line joining two centers belonging to the same group meets a pair of opposite edges of the tetrahedron.

Thus, for instance, the two centers I_a, I_d of the second group lie both in each of the two planes u', x, hence the line $I_a I_d$ meets the edges DA, BC.

(c) The line joining a center of one group to a center of the other group passes through a vertex of the tetrahedron.

Thus, for instance, the two points I', I_c both lie in each of the three planes u, y', w', hence the line $I' I_c$ coincides with one of the axes of the trihedral angle having B for its vertex.

256. Corollary. The two tetrahedrons (§ 254) $(U) \equiv II'I''I'''$, $(V) \equiv I_a I_b I_c I_d$ are such that each of their twelve edges meets a pair of opposite edges of $DABC$, and if we take any vertex of (U) and a vertex of (V), the two points are collinear with a vertex of $DABC$.

The sixteen lines joining the vertices of (U) to the vertices of (V) and the twelve edges of these two tetrahedrons together account for the $8 \times 7 : 2 = 28$ lines determined by the eight centers.

257. Remark. *If the incenter I is known, the remaining centers may be constructed as harmonic conjugates of I.*

The center of a sphere belonging to a trunc, say I_d, is the harmonic conjugate of I with respect to D and the trace of DI in the face ABC.

To construct the center of a sphere belonging to a roof, it suffices to draw through I the line meeting the corresponding pair of edges of the tetrahedron (§ 251), and to find the harmonic conjugate of I with respect to the two points where the line meets the two edges.

If instead of I we have given any of the other centers, we begin by constructing I, and then continue as above.

258. If we group the eight spheres touching the faces of the tetrahedron $DABC$ in the same way in which we grouped their

centers (§ 255), a sphere of one group will be homothetic with
every sphere of the other group, the homothetic center being in
each case a vertex of $DABC$, namely the vertex of $DABC$ collinear with the centers of the two spheres considered [§ 255 (c)].
In the following table are given the pairs of homothetic spheres
and their homothetic centers.

A	$(I), (I_a)$;	$(I'), (I_d)$;	$(I''), (I_c)$;	$(I'''), (I_b)$
B	$(I), (I_b)$;	$(I'), (I_c)$;	$(I''), (I_d)$;	$(I'''), (I_a)$
C	$(I), (I_c)$;	$(I'), (I_b)$;	$(I''), (I_a)$;	$(I'''), (I_d)$
D	$(I), (I_d)$;	$(I'), (I_a)$;	$(I''), (I_b)$;	$(I'''), (I_c)$

EXERCISE.   (a) The four points I, I', I'', I''' may be divided into a group of
two pairs of points in three different ways.   The two lines determined by the
two pairs of points of one group meet the same pair of opposite edges of the
tetrahedron $DABC$.   (b) State and prove a similar proposition about the
points I_a, I_b, I_c, I_d.

d. *The Points of Contact with the Faces*

259. The method used to construct the point of contact of a
face of the tetrahedron with the inscribed sphere (§ 242) may be
applied to the escribed spheres of the tetrahedron.

Consider the face ABC of the tetrahedron $DABC$.   If we revolve the faces DAB, DBC, DCA about the edges AB, BC, CA

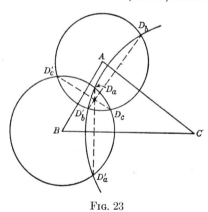

until they coincide with ABC
and so as to crush the escribed sphere considered, the
points of contact of these
faces with the sphere will all
fall upon the point of contact T of ABC with this
sphere, and since the distances of D from the three
points of contact are equal,
the three new positions of
D in ABC will be equidistant from T, hence T is
the circumcenter of the tri-

FIG. 23

angle formed by the three new positions of D.

These considerations lead to the following construction.
With the vertices A, B, C (Fig. 23) as centers, and the edges AD,

BD, CD as radii we draw, in the plane ABC, the three circles (A), (B), (C).   Let D_c, $D_c{}'$; D_a, $D_a{}'$; D_b, $D_b{}'$ be the pairs of points of intersection of the pairs of circles (A), (B); (B), (C); (C), (A), the points D_c and C lying on the same side of the line of centers AB, and similarly for the other points.   These six points are the possible positions of D in the plane ABC, when the faces DAB, DBC, DCA are revolved about the respective edges.

260. If we denote the points of contact of ABC with the spheres (I), (I_a), (I_b), (I_c), (I_d), (I'), (I''), (I''') respectively by J, J_a, J_b, J_c, J_d, J', J'', J''', the following table gives the triangles of which these points are respectively the circumcenters.

J	$D_aD_bD_c$	J_d	$D_a{}'D_b{}'D_c{}'$
J'	$D_aD_b{}'D_c{}'$	J_a	$D_a{}'D_bD_c$
J''	$D_a{}'D_bD_c{}'$	J_b	$D_aD_b{}'D_c$
J'''	$D_a{}'D_b{}'D_c$	J_c	$D_aD_bD_c{}'$

Similar tables may be constructed for the other faces of the tetrahedron.

261. Remark. The five triads of points $D_aD_bD_c$; $D_a{}'D_b{}'D_c{}'$; $D_a{}'D_bD_c$; $D_aD_b{}'D_c$; $D_aD_bD_c{}'$ always represent proper triangles, therefore the points J, J_a, J_b, J_c, J_d may always be constructed, and from this we infer that the corresponding spheres always exist.

Of the three triads $D_aD_b{}'D_c{}'$, $D_a{}'D_bD_c{}'$, $D_a{}'D_b{}'D_c$, either one, or two, or all three may happen to represent three collinear points. When this takes place, the corresponding sphere vanishes.   It is thus possible to obtain in this manner the results we arrived at before, in a different way (§ 253).

262. Theorem. *The four lines* JJ_d; $J'J_a$; $J''J_b$; $J'''J_c$ (§ 260) *are concurrent.*

Indeed, the centers of the corresponding pairs of spheres lie on the four axes of the trihedral angle D of $DABC$, hence the pairs of points of contact are collinear with the foot of the altitude of $DABC$ issued from D.

263. Theorem. *The pairs of points* J, J_d; J', J_a; J'', J_b; J''', J_c *are isogonal conjugates with respect to the triangle* ABC.

Consider, for instance, the two points J, J_d.   Let X, X'; Y, Y'; Z, Z' be the projections of these two points upon the edges BC, CA, AB.

The angles IXJ, $I_dX'J_d$ are the plane angles of the complementary dihedral angles (BCA, BCI), (BCA, BCI_d), hence the two triangles IJX, $I_dX'J_d$ are similar, and we have

$$IJ : J_dX' = JX : I_dJ_d,$$

or

$$IJ \cdot I_dJ_d = JX \cdot J_dX' = JY \cdot J_dY' = JZ \cdot J_dZ',$$

hence the proposition (C. G., pp. 240–241).

EXERCISES

1. The six projections of the two centers I, I_a upon the sides of the triangle BCD lie on a sphere having II_a for diameter. Generalize.

2. (a) The radical center of the circles (A), (B), (C) (§ 259) is the foot H of the altitude from D upon ABC. (b) The point H is the center of similitude of the circles $D_aD_bD_c$, $D_a'D_b'D_c'$. Find other pairs of circles having H for center of similitude.

e. *Relations between the Radii*

264. Notations. The radii of the eight spheres (I), (I_a), (I_b), (I_c), (I_d), (I'), (I''), (I''') of the tetrahedron $ABCD$ will be denoted, respectively, by r, r_a, r_b, r_c, r_d, r', r'', r'''.

265. Let A, B, C, D denote the areas of the faces BCD, CDA, DAB, ABC, and V the volume of the tetrahedron $ABCD$. We have

$$\text{vol. } IBCD + \text{vol. } ICDA + \text{vol. } IDAB + \text{vol. } IABC = \text{vol. } ABCD$$

or

$$r(A + B + C + D) = 3V.$$

Again,

$$\text{vol. } I_dBCD + \text{vol. } I_dCDA + \text{vol. } I_dDAB - \text{vol. } I_dABC$$
$$= \text{vol. } ABCD$$

or

$$r_d(A + B + C - D) = 3V,$$

and similarly for r_a, r_b, r_c.

If we put $A + B + C + D = 2S$, we thus obtain

$$(1) \quad 3V = 2rS = 2r_a(S - A) = 2r_b(S - B)$$
$$= 2r_c(S - C) = 2r_d(S - D).$$

If we arrange the areas of the faces of $DABC$ in order of magnitude, and, to fix the ideas, assume that $A > B > C > D$, it follows from (1) that we also have $r_a > r_b > r_c > r_d > r$.

266. We derive from (1) (§ 265)

$$\frac{1}{r} - \frac{1}{r_a} = \frac{2S}{3V} - \frac{2(S-A)}{3V} = \frac{2A}{3V};$$

hence

(1')
$$A = \frac{3V}{2}\left(\frac{1}{r} - \frac{1}{r_a}\right),$$

and similarly

(2)
$$B = \frac{3V}{2}\left(\frac{1}{r} - \frac{1}{r_b}\right),$$

(3)
$$C = \frac{3V}{2}\left(\frac{1}{r} - \frac{1}{r_c}\right),$$

(4)
$$D = \frac{3V}{2}\left(\frac{1}{r} - \frac{1}{r_d}\right).$$

267. Adding the last four relations (§ 266), we get

$$2S = \frac{3V}{2}\left(\frac{4}{r} - \frac{1}{r_a} - \frac{1}{r_b} - \frac{1}{r_c} - \frac{1}{r_d}\right);$$

hence, taking into account the relation $3V = 2rS$,

(5)
$$\frac{2}{r} = \frac{1}{r_a} + \frac{1}{r_b} + \frac{1}{r_c} + \frac{1}{r_d}.$$

268. If the magnitudes of the faces of the tetrahedron $DABC$ remain arranged as before (§ 265), there is a sphere (I''') in the roof AB, and another escribed sphere (I'') in the roof AC. For the radius r''' of the first sphere we have

$$3V = r'''(A + B - C - D) = 2r'''(S - C - D),$$

and for the radius of the second sphere we have

$$3V = r''(A + C - B - D) = 2r''(S - B - D);$$

hence

(6)
$$r'' = \frac{3V}{2(S - B - D)},$$

(7)
$$r''' = \frac{3V}{2(S - C - D)}.$$

There is also a sphere (I') in one of the roofs DA, BC, but there is doubt in which of the two roofs this sphere lies, for the assumptions made about the relative magnitudes of the areas of the faces of $DABC$ (§ 265) still leave undecided the question which of the two sums $A + D$, $B + C$ is the greater.   We allow for both possibilities by writing

$$3V = \pm r'(B + C - A - D) = \pm 2r'(S - A - D)$$

or

(8) $$r' = \pm \frac{3V}{2(S - A - D)}.$$

269. From the formulas (§ 265),

$$3V = 2r_c(S - C) = 2r_d(S - D),$$

we get

$$\frac{3V}{2}\left(\frac{1}{r_c} + \frac{1}{r_d}\right) = S - C + S - D,$$

and from the formulas (§ 268),

$$3V = 2rS = 2r'''(S - C - D),$$

we get

$$\frac{3V}{2}\left(\frac{1}{r} + \frac{1}{r'''}\right) = S + S - C - D;$$

hence

(9) $$\frac{1}{r'''} = \frac{1}{r_c} + \frac{1}{r_d} - \frac{1}{r}.$$

In an analogous way we obtain

(10) $$\frac{1}{r''} = \frac{1}{r_b} + \frac{1}{r_d} - \frac{1}{r},$$

(11) $$\pm\frac{1}{r'} = \frac{1}{r_a} + \frac{1}{r_d} - \frac{1}{r}.$$

If r' in the formula (11) is considered positive, we obtain by adding the relations (9), (10), (11), and taking into account (5),

(12) $$\frac{1}{r} + \frac{1}{r'} + \frac{1}{r''} + \frac{1}{r'''} = \frac{2}{r_d}.$$

If, on the contrary, r' is negative, we obtain, in a similar manner,

(13) $$\frac{1}{r} + \frac{1}{r'} + \frac{1}{r''} + \frac{1}{r'''} = \frac{2}{r} - \frac{2}{r_a}.$$

270. The ambiguity of the sign of r' (§ 269) disappears if we consider the square of r'. Thus squaring (9), (10), (11) and adding, we obtain, after using (5) and simplifying,

(14) $$\frac{1}{r^2} + \frac{1}{r'^2} + \frac{1}{r''^2} + \frac{1}{r'''^2} = \frac{1}{r_a^2} + \frac{1}{r_b^2} + \frac{1}{r_c^2} + \frac{1}{r_d^2}.$$

271. If h_a, h_b, h_c, h_d denote the altitudes of the tetrahedron $ABCD$, we have

$$A = 3V : h_a, \qquad B = 3V : h_b, \qquad C = 3V : h_c, \qquad D = 3V : h_d.$$

If these values for the areas of the faces are compared with those obtained before (§ 266), we have, using (9), (10), (11),

$$(15) \qquad \frac{2}{h_d} = \frac{1}{r} - \frac{1}{r_d} = \frac{1}{r_a} \pm \frac{1}{r'} = \frac{1}{r_b} - \frac{1}{r''} = \frac{1}{r_c} - \frac{1}{r'''},$$

and similarly for the other altitudes.

272. We have

$$3V = r(A + B + C + D) = Ah_a = Bh_b = Ch_c = Dh_d,$$

hence

$$3V = A : \frac{1}{h_a} = B : \frac{1}{h_b} = C : \frac{1}{h_c} = D : \frac{1}{h_d}$$
$$= (A + B + C + D):\left(\frac{1}{h_a} + \frac{1}{h_b} + \frac{1}{h_c} + \frac{1}{h_d} \right).$$

Thus

$$(16) \qquad \frac{1}{h_a} + \frac{1}{h_b} + \frac{1}{h_c} + \frac{1}{h_d} = \frac{1}{r}.$$

From (16), (5), and (13) we get

$$(17) \qquad 2\left(\frac{1}{h_a} + \frac{1}{h_b} + \frac{1}{h_c} + \frac{1}{h_d} \right) = \frac{1}{r_a} + \frac{1}{r_b} + \frac{1}{r_c} + \frac{1}{r_d}$$
$$= \frac{1}{r} + \frac{1}{r'} + \frac{1}{r''} + \frac{1}{r'''} + \frac{2}{r_a}.$$

273. From the relations

$$3V = Ah_a = Bh_b = Ch_c = Dh_d$$

we have

$$\frac{1}{h_a^2} + \frac{1}{h_b^2} + \frac{1}{h_c^2} + \frac{1}{h_d^2} = \frac{A^2 + B^2 + C^2 + D^2}{9V^2}.$$

Again from the formulas (1) we have

$$\frac{1}{4}\left(\frac{1}{r_a^2} + \frac{1}{r_b^2} + \frac{1}{r_c^2} + \frac{1}{r_d^2} \right)$$
$$= \frac{(S - A)^2 + (S - B)^2 + (S - C)^2 + (S - D)^2}{9V^2}$$
$$= \frac{4S^2 - 2S(A + B + C + D) + A^2 + B^2 + C^2 + D^2}{9V^2}.$$

Now $A + B + C + D = 2S$ (§ 265), hence

$$\frac{1}{h_a{}^2} + \frac{1}{h_b{}^2} + \frac{1}{h_c{}^2} + \frac{1}{h_d{}^2} = \frac{1}{4}\left(\frac{1}{r_a{}^2} + \frac{1}{r_b{}^2} + \frac{1}{r_c{}^2} + \frac{1}{r_d{}^2}\right)$$

$$= \frac{1}{4}\left(\frac{1}{r^2} + \frac{1}{r'^2} + \frac{1}{r''^2} + \frac{1}{r'''^2}\right).$$

EXERCISES

1. Show that

$$\frac{1}{r_a} = \frac{1}{h_b} + \frac{1}{h_c} + \frac{1}{h_d} - \frac{1}{h_a}$$

and similarly for r_b, r_c, r_d.

2. Show that

$$\frac{1}{r} = \frac{1}{r_a} + \frac{1}{r_b} + \frac{1}{r'''} = \frac{1}{r_a} + \frac{1}{r_c} + \frac{1}{r''} = \frac{1}{r_a} + \frac{1}{r_d} + \frac{1}{r'}.$$

HINT. Use (5), (9), (10), (11).

3. Show that

$$\frac{3V}{2}\left(\frac{1}{r} - \frac{1}{r_d}\right) = \frac{3V}{2}\left(\frac{1}{r_c} - \frac{1}{r'''}\right) = \frac{3V}{2}\left(\frac{1}{r_b} - \frac{1}{r''}\right) = \frac{3V}{2}\left(\frac{1}{r_a} - \frac{1}{r'}\right) = D,$$

and similarly for A, B, C.   HINT.   Use (9), (10), (11), and (1'), (2), (3), (4).

5. Volume of Tetrahedron

274. Theorem.   *The volume of a tetrahedron is equal to one third of the volume of the circumscribed parallelepiped.*

Let A, A_1; B, B_1; C, C_1; D, D_1 be the pairs of opposite vertices of the parallelepiped (P) circumscribed about the tetrahedron $ABCD$ (Fig. 16).   The volume of (P) consists of the volume V of $ABCD$ and of the volumes of the four tetrahedrons A_1–BCD, B_1–CDA, C_1–DAB, D_1–ABC.   Now the two tetrahedrons A–BCD, A_1–BCD have the same base BCD, hence the ratio of their volumes is equal to the ratio of their altitudes, which ratio is equal to $AG_a : A_1G_a = 2 : 1$ (§ 198), hence

$$\text{vol. } A_1\text{–}BCD = \tfrac{1}{2}V.$$

Similarly

$$\text{vol. } B_1\text{–}CDA = \text{vol. } C_1\text{–}DAB = \text{vol. } D_1\text{–}ABC = \tfrac{1}{2}V.$$

Thus

$$\text{vol. } (P) = V + 4\cdot\tfrac{1}{2}\cdot V = 3V.$$

275. Theorem.   *The volume of a tetrahedron is equal to one sixth of the product of two opposite edges times the sine of the angle between these edges and times the shortest distance between these edges.*

The angle (cc') between the two opposite edges c, c' of the tetrahedron (T) is equal to the angle between the two diagonals of the corresponding face (F) of the circumscribed parallelepiped (P) (Fig. 16), and the area of (F) is equal to $\frac{1}{2}cc' \sin (cc')$. The bialtitude relative to c, c' is equal to the distance between (F) and the opposite face in (P). Now the volume of (T) is equal to one third the volume of (P) (§ 274), hence the proposition.

276. Steiner's Theorem. *If two opposite edges of a tetrahedron move on two fixed skew lines in any way whatever but remain fixed in length, the volume of the tetrahedron remains constant.*

Since the two skew lines are fixed the angle between the two moving edges, as well as the shortest distance between them, remains fixed, hence the proposition (§ 275).

OTHERWISE. Steiner's Theorem, however, may be proved without reference to the above formula for the volume of the tetrahedron (§ 275). Let s, s' be the two fixed skew lines, AB, $A'B'$ two positions of the edge moving on s, and CD, $C'D'$ two positions of the edge moving on s' (Fig. 24).

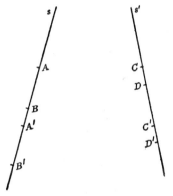

Fig. 24

The areas of the two triangles BCD, $BC'D'$, in the plane B–s' are equivalent as having equal bases and equal altitudes, hence the two tetrahedrons $ABCD$, $ABC'D'$ are equivalent, for they have equivalent bases and a common altitude, namely the distance of A from the plane B–s'.

Similarly the two tetrahedrons $C'D'AB$, $C'D'A'B'$ are equivalent, hence $ABCD$ is equivalent to $A'B'C'D'$, and this proves the proposition.

277. Theorem. *The volume of a tetrahedron is equal to two thirds of the product of the areas determined by the tetrahedron in the two planes passing through a bimedian and the corresponding two edges, multiplied by the sine of the angle between these planes and divided by the bimedian considered.*

Let E, F be the mid-points of the opposite edges CD, AB of the tetrahedron $ABCD$, and CK, CL the perpendiculars from C to the line EF and to the plane ABE, respectively (Fig. 25). If V denotes the volume of $ABCD$, we have

$$V = 2 \text{ vol. } (E\text{–}ABC) = 2 \text{ vol. } (C\text{–}ABE) = \tfrac{2}{3}CL \cdot \text{area } ABE.$$

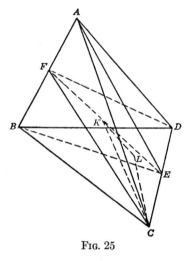

Now the angle CKL is the plane angle (u) (or its supplement) of the dihedral angle between the planes ABE, CDF, and we have

$$CL = CK \cdot \sin (u).$$

On the other hand we have

$$\text{area } CDF = EF \cdot CK,$$

hence

$$CL = \text{area } CDF \cdot \sin (u) : EF.$$

Substituting this value of CL into the formula for V, we get

$$V = \tfrac{2}{3} \text{ area } ABE \cdot \text{area } CDF \cdot \sin (u) : EF.$$

Fig. 25

278. Theorem. *The volume of a tetrahedron is equal to one sixth of the product of two altitudes of the tetrahedron multiplied by the ratio of the edge joining the remaining two vertices of the tetrahedron to the sine of the dihedral angle of this edge.*

Let h_d and k be the perpendiculars from D to the face ABC and to the edge BC. If (a) denotes the dihedral angle having BC for edge and h_a the altitude of $ABCD$ issued from A, we have, successively,

$$\sin (a) = \frac{h_d}{k} = \frac{h_d \cdot BC}{k \cdot BC} = \frac{h_d \cdot BC}{2 \cdot \text{area } BCD} = \frac{h_a \cdot h_d \cdot BC}{6 \text{ vol. } ABCD},$$

hence

$$\text{vol. } ABCD = \tfrac{1}{6} h_a \cdot h_d \cdot \frac{BC}{\sin (a)}.$$

279. Corollary. *In a tetrahedron the product of the ratios of two opposite edges to the sines of their dihedral angles is constant.*

Denoting by (a') the dihedral angle AD, we have (§ 278)

$$\frac{BC}{\sin (a)} = \frac{6V}{h_a h_d}, \qquad \frac{AD}{\sin (a')} = \frac{6V}{h_b h_c},$$

hence

$$\frac{BC \cdot AD}{\sin (a) \cdot \sin (a')} = \frac{36V^2}{h_a h_b h_c h_d}$$

and, since the right hand side of this equality does not depend upon the particular pair of edges considered, the proposition is proved.

280. Theorem. *If a plane divides two opposite edges of a tetrahedron in a given ratio, it divides the volume of the tetrahedron in the same ratio.*

Suppose that in the tetrahedron $ABCD$ we have (Fig. 26)

$$AE : ED = BF : FC = m : n,$$

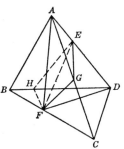

and that a plane passing through EF meets the two opposite edges AC, BD in the points G, H.

Fig. 26

The two parts into which the plane $EFGH$ divides the tetrahedron $ABCD$ consist respectively of the two quadrangular pyramids $A–FGEH$, $D–FGEH$, and the two triangular pyramids $A–BFH$ and $D–CFG$.

The two quadrangular pyramids have the same base, hence their volumes are to each other as their altitudes, and this ratio in turn is equal to the ratio of the segments AE, ED, hence

(1)   vol. $AFGEH$: vol. $DFGEH = m : n$.

The tetrahedrons $ABHF$, $ABCD$ have the trihedral angle B in common, hence

$$\frac{\text{vol.}\, BAFH}{\text{vol.}\, BACD} = \frac{BA \cdot BH \cdot BF}{BA \cdot BD \cdot BC} = \frac{BH \cdot m}{BD(m+n)}.$$

Similarly,

$$\frac{\text{vol.}\, CDGF}{\text{vol.}\, CDAB} = \frac{CD \cdot CG \cdot CF}{CD \cdot CA \cdot CB} = \frac{CG \cdot n}{CA(m+n)}.$$

From the skew quadrilateral $ABCD$ we have (§ 141)

$$BH : BD = CG : CA,$$

hence

(2)   vol. $BAFH$: vol. $CDFG = m : n$.

Thus, from (1) and (2),

$$\frac{m}{n} = \frac{\text{vol. } AFGEH}{\text{vol. } DFGEH} = \frac{\text{vol. } BAFH}{\text{vol. } CDGF} = \frac{\text{vol. } ABEGFH}{\text{vol. } CDEGFH}.$$

281. Corollary. *Any plane passing through a bimedian of a tetrahedron bisects the volume of the tetrahedron.*

EXERCISE. The reader may give a direct proof of this proposition (§ 281), modelled upon the proof above (§ 280).

EXERCISES

1. Draw a plane through a given point (or parallel to a given line) so that the plane shall divide the volume of a given tetrahedron into two equivalent parts.

2. Through a line given in a face of a given trihedron to draw a plane forming with the faces of this trihedron a tetrahedron of given volume.

3. The volume of the medial tetrahedron of a given tetrahedron is equal to one twenty-seventh of the volume of the given tetrahedron.

4. (a) If through a point lines are drawn equal in magnitude and direction to any two medians of a triangle, the area of the triangle thus formed is independent of the choice of the medians. (b) State and prove an analogous proposition for the tetrahedron.

5. The volume of the tetrahedron whose vertices are any vertex of a given tetrahedron and the centroids of the faces meeting in this vertex, is two twenty-sevenths of the volume of the given tetrahedron.

6. The volume of a tetrahedron is equal to one third of an edge times the area obtained by projecting the tetrahedron upon a plane perpendicular to the edge considered. HINT. Use the formula for the volume of a right truncated prism.

7. The six mid-points of the edges of a given tetrahedron determine an octahedron whose volume is equal to one half the volume of the given tetrahedron.

8. Calculate the volume common to two twin tetrahedrons.

9. If a parallelepiped varies so that two non-parallel diagonals of a pair of opposite faces move, in any way whatever, and independently of each other, along two fixed skew lines, without changing their respective lengths, the volume of the parallelepiped remains fixed.

10. Given three non-coplanar parallel lines, a segment AB of given length is laid off on the first given line, and the points C, D are marked on the second and third given lines, respectively. Show that the volume of the tetrahedron $ABCD$ remains constant, if the segment AB and the points C, D move in any way whatever on their respective lines.

11. If $ABCD$ be a tetrahedron, p, q, r, s its altitudes, then denoting by (AB) etc. the different dihedral angles between the faces which intersect in AB, prove that

sin (AB) : sin (BC) : sin (CA) : sin (AD) : sin (BD) : sin (CD)

$$= \frac{AB}{pq} : \frac{BC}{qr} : \frac{CA}{rp} : \cdots.$$

12. The volume of a tetrahedron is equal to the area determined by the tetrahedron in a plane passing through two bimedians (i.e., medial section) times two thirds of the bialtitude relative to the third pair of opposite edges of the tetrahedron. HINT. Consider the circumscribed parallelepiped.

13. If through a point in space lines are drawn equal in magnitude and direction to the three bimedians of a given tetrahedron, the volume of the tetrahedron thus formed is equal to one half the volume of the given tetrahedron.

14. With a given point as center to describe a sphere so that the tetrahedron determined by the points of intersection of this sphere with two given skew lines shall have a given volume.

6. Special Tetrahedrons

a. The Trirectangular Tetrahedron

282. Definition. A tetrahedron having a trihedral angle all the face angles of which are right angles will be called a *trirectangular* tetrahedron, and this trihedral angle will be called the *right angle* of the tetrahedron.

The face opposite the vertex of the right angle will be referred to as the *base* of the tetrahedron, and the edges issued from the right angle will be called the *legs* of the tetrahedron.

The perpendicular from the vertex of the right angle to the base will be called the *altitude* of the tetrahedron.

283. Theorem. *In a trirectangular tetrahedron the foot of the altitude is the orthocenter of the base.*

Let H be the foot of the altitude DH of the trirectangular tetrahedron $DABC$. The edge DC being perpendicular to the plane DAB, and therefore to AB, a plane CDR may be drawn through CD perpendicular to AB, say, at R. The two planes CDR, ABC thus being perpendicular, the plane CDR contains the altitude DH and cuts ABC along the altitude CR of the triangle ABC, hence H lies on CR. Likewise for the other two altitudes of ABC, hence the proposition.

284. Lemma. *The sum of the squares of the reciprocals of the legs of a right triangle is equal to the square of the reciprocal of the altitude on the hypotenuse.*

Let x, y be the legs, and u, v the segments, adjacent to x, y, into which the hypotenuse z of the given right triangle is divided by the altitude h to z. We have

$$u + v = z, \qquad h^2 = uv, \qquad x^2 = uz, \qquad y^2 = vz,$$

hence

$$\frac{1}{x^2} + \frac{1}{y^2} = \frac{1}{uz} + \frac{1}{vz} = \frac{1}{z} \cdot \frac{u+v}{uv} = \frac{1}{h^2}.$$

285. Theorem. *The sum of the squares of the reciprocals of the legs of a trirectangular tetrahedron is equal to the square of the reciprocal of the altitude of the tetrahedron.*

Let $DA = a$, $DB = b$, $DC = c$ be the legs and $DH = h$ the altitude of the trirectangular tetrahedron $DABC$. If DR is the perpendicular from D to AB, we have in the right triangle DAB (§ 284)

$$\frac{1}{DR^2} = \frac{1}{a^2} + \frac{1}{b^2}.$$

Now CD is perpendicular to the plane DAB and DR is perpendicular to AB, hence CR is perpendicular to AB, and therefore DH is the altitude of the right triangle DCR. Thus (§ 284),

$$\frac{1}{h^2} = \frac{1}{DR^2} + \frac{1}{c^2}.$$

Replacing DR by its value we obtain the announced relation.

286. Theorem. *The square of the area of the base of a trirectangular tetrahedron is equal to the sum of the squares of the areas of its other three faces.*

Let DH be the altitude of the trirectangular tetrahedron $DABC$. The three triangles DAB, HAB, CAB have the same base AB, hence, denoting by R the foot of the perpendicular from D to AB,

area DAB : area HAB : area $CAB = DR : HR : CR$.

Now (§ 285)

$$DR^2 = HR \cdot CR,$$

hence

area DAB^2 = area $HAB \cdot$ area CAB

and similarly

area $DBC^2 = HBC \cdot ABC$,   area $DCA^2 = HCA \cdot BCA$.

Thus

$DAB^2 + DBC^2 + DAC^2$
$$= (HAB + HBC + HCA) \cdot ABC = ABC^2.$$

287. Theorem. *The median of a trirectangular tetrahedron issued from the right angle passes through the circumcenter of the* *tetrahedron and is equal to two thirds of the circumradius of the tetrahedron.*

Let A_1, B_1, C_1 be the symmetrics of the vertex D of the right angle of the trirectangular tetrahedron $DABC$ with respect to the mid-points A', B', C' of the edges BC, CA, AB (Fig. 27). The points A_1, B_1, C_1, D, A, B, C are seven vertices of a rectangular parallelepiped (P), the eighth vertex D_1 of which is diagonally opposite to D on (P).

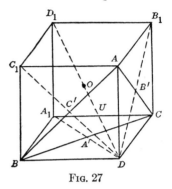

Fig. 27

The circumcenter O of $DABC$ is also the circumcenter of (P), hence O is the mid-point of the diagonal DD_1 of (P). Now the tetrahedron D_1–ABC is inscribed in (P), hence D_1D passes through the centroid U of ABC (§ 198), and DU is equal to one third of DD_1, hence DU is equal to two thirds of DO.

288. Corollary I. *The circumcenter of a trirectangular tetrahedron is the symmetric of the vertex of the right angle with respect to the centroid of the tetrahedron.*

289. Corollary II. *The altitude of a trirectangular tetrahedron is equal to one third of the chord intercepted on this line by the circumsphere of the tetrahedron.*

Indeed, if we produce the altitude DH until it meets the circumsphere in E, we have, from the similar right triangles DED_1, DHU,

$$DH : DE = DU : DD_1 = 1 : 3.$$

EXERCISES

1. The Monge point of a trirectangular tetrahedron coincides with the vertex of the right angle of the tetrahedron.

2. The distance of the base of a trirectangular tetrahedron from the circumcenter is equal to half the altitude of the tetrahedron.

3. If two face angles of a trihedral angle of a tetrahedron are right angles, and the foot of the altitude from the vertex of this trihedral angle upon the opposite face is the orthocenter of this face, the tetrahedron is trirectangular.

4. In a trirectangular tetrahedron we have, with the usual notations for the radii of the spheres touching the faces of the tetrahedron,

$$\frac{1}{r_a - r} = \frac{1}{r_d + r'} + \frac{1}{r_e + r''} + \frac{1}{r_b + r'''}$$

$$\frac{1}{rr_a} = \frac{1}{r_dr'} + \frac{1}{r_er''} + \frac{1}{r_br'''}.$$

HINT. Use § 286.

5. The medial triangle of the base of a trirectangular tetrahedron and the vertex of the right angle determine a tetrahedron in which opposite edges are equal.

6. If a, b, c are the lengths of the edges of the base of a trirectangular tetrahedron the square of the length of one leg is given by the formula

$$\tfrac{1}{2}(a^2 + b^2 - c^2),$$

and similarly for the other two legs.

7. In a trirectangular tetrahedron the square of the median to the base is equal to (a) one ninth of the sum of the squares of the legs; (b) one eleventh of the sum of the squares of the remaining three medians.

8. If H is the foot of the altitude DH of the trirectangular tetrahedron $DABC$, the area of the triangle DBC is the mean proportional between the areas of the triangles ABC and HBC.

9. Given the tetrahedron $DABC$, trirectangular at D, the power of the vertex A with respect to the circle having BC for diameter is equal to the square of DA.

10. The three projections of a point upon the faces of a trirectangular trihedral angle form a triangle such that the sum of the angles which its sides subtend at the vertex of the trihedral angle is equal to two right angles.

11. In a trirectangular tetrahedron the squares of the legs are proportional to the cotangents of the respective angles of the base of the tetrahedron.

12. The square of the circumdiameter of a trirectangular tetrahedron is equal to the sum of the squares of the legs.

13. Given the trirectangular tetrahedron $OABC$, with the right angle at O, the perpendicular erected to the base ABC at the centroid G meets the faces OAB, OBC, OCA in the points C', A', B'. Show that

$$GA' : GB' : GC' = OA^2 : OB^2 : OC^2.$$

b. *The Isosceles Tetrahedron*

290. Definition. A tetrahedron in which each edge is equal to its opposite will be referred to as an *isosceles* tetrahedron.

291. Theorem. *The parallelepiped circumscribed about an isosceles tetrahedron is rectangular, and, **conversely,** a tetrahedron inscribed in a rectangular parallelepiped is isosceles.*

If two opposite edges of a tetrahedron (T) are equal, each of the two corresponding faces of the circumscribed parallelepiped (P) has equal diagonals, and therefore is rectangular.

CONVERSELY, if (P) has a pair of rectangular faces, the diagonals in each of these two faces are equal, hence the inscribed tetrahedron has two opposite edges which are equal to each other.

292. Remark. In a parallelepiped all three pairs of opposite faces may be rectangles, or only two of these pairs, or just one pair, hence in a tetrahedron each edge may be equal to its opposite, or this may hold only for two pairs of opposite edges, or just for one pair.

293. Theorem. *The faces of an isosceles tetrahedron are congruent triangles.*

294. Theorem. *The four altitudes of an isosceles tetrahedron are equal.*

The proofs of these propositions are left to the reader.

295. Theorem. *In an isosceles tetrahedron the medians are equal, and,* **conversely,** *if the medians are equal, the tetrahedron is isosceles.*

The circumscribed parallelepiped (P) of the tetrahedron (T) is rectangular (§ 291), hence its diagonals are equal, and the medians of (T) are equal to two thirds of these diagonals (§ 198).

CONVERSELY, if the medians of (T) are equal, the same holds for the diagonals of (P), hence (P) is rectangular.

296. Theorem. *The bimedians of an isosceles tetrahedron coincide with the bialtitudes and form a trirectangular trihedral angle.*

The bimedians of any tetrahedron (T) are parallel to the edges of its circumscribed parallelepiped (P). When (T) is isosceles, (P) is rectangular (§ 291), and the proposition follows immediately.

297. Theorem. *If two of the bimedians of a tetrahedron coincide with the respective bialtitudes, the tetrahedron is isosceles.*

Given the tetrahedron $(T) \equiv ABCD$ and its circumscribed parallelepiped (P), if the bimedian $A'A''$ is perpendicular to the edges AD, BC, it is also perpendicular to the faces AB_1DC_1, A_1BD_1C of (P), hence (P) is a right parallelepiped, and we have $AB = CD$, $AC = BD$. Now if the bimedian $B'B''$ is also perpendicular to the respective edges AC, BD, we have, in addition, $AD = BC$, hence the proposition.

298. Theorem. *In an isosceles tetrahedron the circumcenter and the centroid coincide, and* **conversely,** *if in a tetrahedron the circumcenter and the centroid coincide, the tetrahedron is isosceles.*

The medians of an isosceles tetrahedron being equal (§ 295), the centroid is equidistant from the vertices of the tetrahedron. CONVERSELY, if the centroid is equidistant from the vertices, the medians are equal, hence the tetrahedron is isosceles (§ 295).

299. Theorem. *The Monge point of an isosceles tetrahedron coincides with the centroid, and,* **conversely,** *if the Monge point of a tetrahedron coincides with the centroid, the tetrahedron is isosceles.*

In an isosceles tetrahedron the circumcenter coincides with the centroid (§ 298), hence the same is true about the Monge point (§ 230).

CONVERSELY, if the Monge point coincides with the centroid, the circumcenter also coincides with the centroid (§ 230), hence the tetrahedron is isosceles (§ 298).

300. Theorem. *In an isosceles tetrahedron the incenter coincides with the centroid.*

The distance of the centroid G of the tetrahedron (T) from a face is equal to one fourth of the corresponding altitude. Now if (T) is isosceles its altitudes are equal (§ 244), and G is equidistant from the faces of (T), hence G is also the incenter of (T).

OTHERWISE. The bisecting plane of a dihedral angle of a tetrahedron (T) divides the opposite edge in the ratio of the areas of the two adjacent faces (§ 235). If (T) is isosceles, these areas are equal, hence the bisecting plane passes through the mid-point of the opposite edge, and thus contains the corresponding bimedian, hence also the centroid G. The point G thus lies in the six bisecting planes and therefore coincides with the centroid.

301. Corollary I. The inradius of an isosceles tetrahedron is equal to one fourth of the altitude of the tetrahedron.

302. Corollary II. *The points of contact of the faces of an isosceles tetrahedron with its inscribed sphere are the circumcenters of these faces.*

For in an isosceles tetrahedron the centroid is also the incenter (§ 300) and the circumcenter (§ 298) of the tetrahedron.

303. Converse Theorem. *If the incenter of a tetrahedron coincides with the centroid, the tetrahedron is isosceles.*

If the centroid G coincides with the incenter, the plane ABG of the tetrahedron $(T) \equiv ABCD$ is the internal bisecting plane of the dihedral angle (AB) having AB for its edge, and since ABG passes through the mid-point C'' of DC, the external bisecting plane (U) of (AB) is parallel to CD (§ 37). Similarly the external bisecting plane (V) of the dihedral angle (CD) is parallel to AB, hence the two planes (U), (V) are parallel to each other, for they are both parallel to the same directing plane of (T).

The internal bisecting plane CDG of (CD) is perpendicular to (V), hence also to (U), and since ABG is also perpendicular to (U), the line of intersection $C'GC''$ of the two planes ABG, CDG is perpendicular to (U), and therefore to AB. Similarly the bimedian $C'GC''$ is perpendicular to CD, i.e., this bimedian is also a bialtitude. Similarly for the other two bimedians of (T). Hence the proposition (§ 297).

304. Theorem. *If the circumcenter and the incenter of a tetrahedron coincide, the tetrahedron is isosceles.*

If the incenter coincides with the circumcenter of the tetrahedron $ABCD$, the faces of $ABCD$ are equidistant from the circumcenter, hence the circumcircles of the four faces are equal. Now equal chords subtend equal angles in equal circles, hence

$$\text{angle } BAC = BDC = u, \qquad \text{angle } ACD = ABD = u',$$
$$\text{angle } ABC = ADC = v, \qquad \text{angle } DAB = DCB = v',$$
$$\text{angle } BCA = BDA = w, \qquad \text{angle } DAC = DBC = w'.$$

But

$$180° = u + v + w = u' + v' + w = u + v' + w' = u' + v + w',$$

hence

$$v + w = v' + w', \qquad v + w' = v' + w$$

and $v = v'$, $w = w'$, so that $u = u'$.

Thus the faces of $ABCD$ are equiangular, hence they are similar, and since they have two-by-two a side in common, these triangles are congruent, and consequently the opposite edges of $ABCD$ are equal.

305. Consequence. The preceding theorems (§§ 298, 299, 303, 304) may be summarized as follows: *Consider the centroid, the circumcenter, the incenter, and the Monge point of a tetrahedron. If any two of these points coincide, the remaining two points coincide with them, and the tetrahedron is isosceles.*

306. Theorem. *If the altitudes of a tetrahedron are equal, the tetrahedron is isosceles.*

In any tetrahedron (T) the distance of the centroid G from a face is equal to one fourth of the altitude corresponding to this face. Hence if the four altitudes are equal, G is equidistant from the faces of (T), and therefore coincides with the incenter of (T), which proves the proposition (§ 305).

307. Corollary. *If the faces of a tetrahedron are equivalent the tetrahedron is isosceles.*

For the equivalence of the faces implies the equality of the altitudes.

308. Theorem. *The foot of the perpendicular dropped upon a face of an isosceles tetrahedron from the corresponding vertex of the twin tetrahedron is the orthocenter of this face.*

If $(T) \equiv ABCD$ is an isosceles tetrahedron, and (T') its twin, the vertex A_1 of (T') which corresponds to the face BCD of (T) and the vertex A of (T) are diagonally opposite vertices on the parallelepiped (P) circumscribed about both (T) and (T'). Now (P) is rectangular (§ 291), hence the tetrahedron A_1BCD is trirectangular and BCD is its base, hence the proposition (§ 283).

309. Theorem. *The foot of the altitude dropped from a vertex of an isoscles tetrahedron upon the corresponding face is the symmetric of the orthocenter of this face with respect to its circumcenter.*

The centroid G of the isosceles tetrahedron (T) bisects the line joining the vertex A of (T) to the corresponding vertex A_1 of the twin tetrahedron (§ 191), hence the projections of A and A_1 upon any plane, and in particular upon BCD, are symmetrical with respect to the projection of G. Now the projection of A_1 upon BCD is the orthocenter of BCD (§ 308), and the projection of G upon BCD is its circumcenter (§ 302), hence the proposition.

310. Theorem. *The projections upon a face of an isosceles tetrahedron of the three vertices of the twin tetrahedron which do not correspond to the face considered lie on the circumcircle of this face and form a triangle symmetric to the face considered with respect to the circumcenter of this face.*

Consider the face BCD of the isosceles tetrahedron (T) $\equiv ABCD$ and the twin tetrahedron $(T') \equiv A_1B_1C_1D_1$. The line BB_1 is bisected by the common centroid G of the two tetrahedrons.

Now the projection of G upon BCD is the circumcenter of BCD, hence the projection of B_1 upon BCD is the diametric opposite of B on the circumcircle of BCD, etc.

311. Remark. *The triangle thus obtained (§ 310) has for its orthocenter the foot of the altitude upon the face considered.*

Indeed, on account of the symmetry, the orthocenter of this triangle is the symmetric of the orthocenter of BCD with respect to the circumcenter of BCD, hence the proposition (§ 309).

312. Theorem. *The four faces of an isosceles tetrahedron are equidistant from any one of the vertices of the twin tetrahedron of the given tetrahedron.*

The centroid G of the given isosceles tetrahedron $(T) \equiv ABCD$ is the mid-point of the line joining the vertex A of (T) to the corresponding vertex A_1 of its twin tetrahedron (T) (§ 200), hence the distance of A_1 from any face of (T) passing through A is equal to twice the distance of G from the same face.

Furthermore, we have, denoting by G_a the centroid of the face BCD (§ 170)

$$3 : 1 = AG : GG_a = GA_1 : GG_a,$$

hence

$$A_1G_a : GG_a = -2 : 1,$$

hence here again the distance of A_1 from BCD is equal to twice the distance of G from this face.

Now (T) being isosceles, G is equidistant from the faces of (T) (§ 300), hence the proposition.

OTHERWISE. We have

$$AG = GA_1, \quad AG : GG_a = 3 : 1, \quad AG : AG_a = 3 : 4,$$

hence

$$AA_1 : AG_a = 6 : 4 = 3 : 2$$

or

$$AA_1 : (AA_1 - AG_a) = AA_1 : A_1G_a = 3 : (3 - 2) = 3 : 1,$$

i.e., the point A_1 is the harmonic conjugate of G with respect to A and G_a.

Now the internal bisector of the dihedral angle having BC for its edge passes through G (§ 303), hence the external bisector of this angle will pass through A_1, therefore this point is equidistant from the faces BCA, BCD. Similarly for the edges CD, DB. Hence the proposition.

313. Corollary. *Given an isosceles tetrahedron, the diametric opposites of its vertices on its circumsphere are the centers of four spheres touching the faces of the tetrahedron. The four spheres are equal and their radii are equal to twice the radius of the inscribed sphere of the tetrahedron.*

Indeed, in an isosceles tetrahedron the circumcenter and the incenter coincide with the centroid (§ 300), and the circumsphere of the tetrahedron is also the circumsphere of its twin (§ 298).

314. Remark. The four spheres thus obtained (§ 313) are the *escribed spheres* of the isosceles tetrahedron.

315. Theorem. *The point of contact of a face of an isosceles tetrahedron with the escribed sphere relative to this face is the orthocenter of this face.*

The point of contact of the face with the escribed sphere is the projection upon the face of the center of the sphere. Now this center is the vertex of the twin tetrahedron relative to the face considered (§ 313), hence the proposition (§ 308).

316. Theorem. *The lines joining the vertices of an isosceles tetrahedron to the Gergonne points of the opposite faces form a hyperbolic group.*

In the given isosceles tetrahedron $ABCD$ let $DA = BC = a$, $DB = CA = b$, $DC = AB = c$, and let X, Y, Z be the points of contact of the sides BC, CA, AB with the incircles of the triangles DBC, DCA, DAB, respectively. The Gergonne points A', B', C' of these three triangles lie, respectively, on the lines DX, DY, DZ.

If $2p = a + b + c$, we have (C. G., p. 74) $BX = p - c$. On the other hand, if X' is the point of contact of BC with the excircle relative to BC in the triangle ABC, we have (C. G., p. 75) $BX' = p - c$, hence X' coincides with X. Similarly for Y and Z. Consequently the lines AX, BY, CZ meet in a point N (C. G., p. 130).

The lines AA', BB', CC' lie in the planes DAX, DBY, DCZ, hence these three lines are met by the line DN.

Similarly for the other vertices of $ABCD$. Hence the theorem.

317. Corollary. The point N is often referred to as the *Nagel point* of the triangle ABC. We may thus complete the proposition as follows: *The lines joining the vertices of an isosceles* *tetrahedron to the Gergonne point and the Nagel point of the respectively opposite faces form two supplementary hyperbolic groups.*

318. Problem.   *Construct an isosceles tetrahedron DABC so that its base ABC shall be similar to a given triangle, its edge DA shall lie on a given line, the opposite edge BC shall pass through a given point, and that the directing plane of DA, BC shall have a given orientation.*

On the given triangle LMN as base construct an isosceles tetrahedron $OLMN$.   This tetrahedron is similar to the required tetrahedron, hence the angle between OL and MN is equal to the angle between DA and BC.   Thus if we pass through the given indefinite line DA a plane having the given orientation and in that plane draw a line making with DA an angle equal to the angle between OL and MN, the parallel through the given point, P, to the line so constructed will be the line on which BC must lie. The bialtitude FE of $DABC$ is thus known, and if QR is the bialtitude relative to the edges OL, MN of $OLMN$, the vertices D, A, B, C may be constructed from the proportions

$$FE : QR = FD : QO = FA : QL = EB : RM = EC : RN.$$

EXERCISES

1. Construct an isosceles tetrahedron given its base.

2. In an isosceles tetrahedron the sum of the face angles of any trihedral angle is equal to two right angles.

3. If the perimeters of the four faces of a tetrahedron are equal the tetrahedron is isosceles.

4. If in a tetrahedron the sum of the areas of any two faces is equal to the sum of the areas of the remaining two faces, the tetrahedron is isosceles.

5. In an isosceles tetrahedron the internal (external) bisectors of the two face angles opposite a given edge meet this edge in two points symmetrical with respect to the mid-point of this edge.

6. The external bisecting plane of a dihedral angle of an isosceles tetrahedron is parallel to the edge opposite the edge considered.

7. The external bisecting planes of the dihedral angles of an isosceles tetrahedron are the faces of the parallelepiped circumscribed about the tetrahedron.   Conversely.

8. The points of contact of a face of an isosceles tetrahedron with the three escribed spheres not relative to this face lie on the circumcircle of this face and form a triangle symmetric to the triangle of the face considered with respect to the circumcenter of this triangle.   The orthocenter of the triangle formed by the points of contact is the foot of the altitude corresponding to the face considered.

9. An isosceles tetrahedron and its twin tetrahedron have the same inscribed sphere.

10. An altitude of an isosceles tetrahedron is equal to two thirds of the chord intercepted on this line by the circumsphere of the tetrahedron.

11. The sum of the squares of the reciprocals of the three bialtitudes of an isosceles tetrahedron is equal to four times the square of the reciprocal of the altitude of the tetrahedron.

12. (a) If each edge of a tetrahedron subtends equal angles at the remaining two vertices of the tetrahedron, the tetrahedron is isosceles. (b) What is the minimum number of edges that must satisfy the above condition in order that the conclusion shall remain valid?

13. The sum of the squares of the distances of a point from the vertices of an isosceles tetrahedron is equal to four times the square of the distance of the point from the circumcenter increased by four times the square of the circumradius of the tetrahedron.

14. The four trihedral angles of an isosceles tetrahedron are congruent.

15. In an isosceles tetrahedron two opposite dihedral angles are equal.

16. An isosceles tetrahedron may be made to coincide with itself in four different ways.

17. The four circumcenters of the faces of an isosceles tetrahedron are the vertices of an isosceles tetrahedron having the same centroid as the given tetrahedron. Show that a similar proposition may be stated about any four homologous points of the four faces of an isosceles tetrahedron.

18. If a, b, c are the edges of an isosceles tetrahedron, and if R, V, r, h, S denote the circumradius, the volume, the inradius, the altitude, and the area of a face of the tetrahedron, we have

$$8R^2 = a^2 + b^2 + c^2,$$
$$72V^2 = 128S^2r^2 = 8S^2h^2 = (b^2 + c^2 - a^2)(c^2 + a^2 - b^2)(a^2 + b^2 - c^2).$$

7. Miscellaneous Propositions

319. Definition.   The planes passing through the vertices of a tetrahedron $ABCD$ and tangent to the circumsphere (O) at these points form a tetrahedron $A'B'C'D'$ called the *tangential* tetrahedron of the given tetrahedron.

To a face, say ABC, of $ABCD$ corresponds the face $A'B'C'$ of $A'B'C'D'$ which touches (O) at the vertex D opposite ABC, and to the vertex D corresponds the vertex D' common to the faces $D'A'B'$, $D'B'C'$, $D'C'A'$, tangent to (O) at C, A, B, respectively.

To an edge, say AB, of $ABCD$ corresponds the edge $A'B'$ common to the planes $A'B'C'$, $A'B'D'$ which are tangent to (O) at D and C respectively.

320. Theorem.   *The four lines of intersection of the faces of a tetrahedron with the corresponding faces of its tangential tetrahedron form a hyperbolic group.*

The plane ABC of the given tetrahedron $ABCD$ (Fig. 28) cuts the faces $B'C'D'$, $C'D'A'$, $D'A'B'$ of the tangential tetrahedron $A'B'C'D'$ along the tangents to the circumcircle of the triangle ABC at the points A, B, C. These tangents meet the sides BC, CA, AB of ABC in three points P, Q, R which are collinear (C. G., p. 124). Now the points P, Q, R belong, respectively, to the lines of intersection of pairs of planes BCD, $B'C'D'$; CDA, $C'D'A'$; DAB, $D'A'B'$, hence these three lines meet the face ABC in three collinear points. Likewise for the other faces, hence the proposition (§ 27).

The special case, when the four lines are coplanar, will be considered later (§ 846).

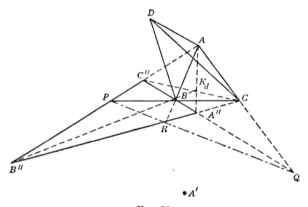

Fig. 28

321. Remark. The line PQR (§ 320) is the Lemoine axis of ABC (C. G., p. 229), hence: *The four Lemoine axes of the faces of a tetrahedron form a hyperbolic group, supplementary to the hyperbolic group formed by the lines of intersection of the faces of the tetrahedron with the corresponding faces of its tangential tetrahedron.*

322. Theorem. *The lines joining the vertices of a tetrahedron to the corresponding vertices of its tangential tetrahedron are hyperbolic.*

Let A'', B'', C'' (Fig. 28) be the vertices of the triangle circumscribed about the circle ABC (§ 320). These points are the traces, in the plane ABC, of the edges $D'A'$, $D'B'$, $D'C'$ of the tangential tetrahedron $A'B'C'D'$. Now the lines $A''A$, $B''B$, $C''C$ meet in the Gergonne point K_d of $A''B''C''$ (C. G., p. 129), hence each of the three lines AA', BB', CC' intersects $D'K_d$.

Similarly for the other vertices of $A'B'C'D'$.   Hence the proposition (§ 27).

323. Remark.   The point K_d is the symmedian point of the triangle ABC (C. G., p. 229), hence: *The supplementary system of these four lines* (§ 322) *contains the four lines which join the vertices of the tangential tetrahedron to the symmedian points of the respective faces of the given tetrahedron.*

324. Theorem.   *The lines joining the vertices of a tetrahedron to the symmedian points of the opposite faces are hyperbolic.*

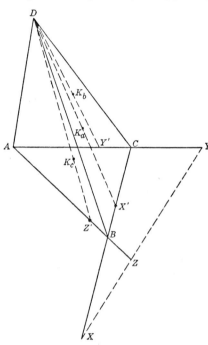

Let X, Y, Z be the traces of the tangent plane to the circumsphere of $DABC$ at D on the edges BC, CA, AB (Fig. 29).   The point X is also the trace on BC of the tangent to the circumcircle of DBC at D, hence the harmonic conjugate X' of X with respect to B, C is the trace on BC of the line DK_a joining D to the symmedian point K_a of the triangle DBC (C. G., p. 227).   Similarly for the analogous lines DK_b, DK_c.

Now the lines AX', BY', CZ' meet in the same point, namely in the trilinear pole P of XYZ with respect to the triangle ABC, hence AK_a, BK_b, CK_c are each met by the line DP, and

FIG. 29

the line DP obviously meets the line DK_d.

Similarly for the other vertices.   Hence the proposition.

325. Theorem.   *The lines joining the vertices of a tetrahedron to the points of contact of the opposite faces with the inscribed sphere of the tetrahedron form a hyperbolic group.*

This is a different form of the preceding proposition (§ 324), in which we consider $A'B'C'D'$ as the basic tetrahedron.

326. Theorem. *If the lines joining corresponding vertices of two tetrahedrons form a hyperbolic group, the same is true about the four lines of intersection of the pairs of corresponding faces of the two tetrahedrons.*

Let X, Y, Z (Fig. 30) be the traces of the face ABC of the tetrahedron $ABCD$ on the edges $D'A'$, $D'B'$, $D'C'$ of the tetrahedron $A'B'C'D'$. By hypothesis, there is a line through D' meeting the lines AA', BB', CC', hence the planes $AA'D'$, $BB'D'$, $CC'D'$ have a line in common, and therefore the lines AX, BY, CZ are concurrent. Thus the pairs of sides AB, XY; BC, YZ; CA, ZX of the triangles ABC, XYZ meet in three collinear points R, P, Q (C. G., p. 133).

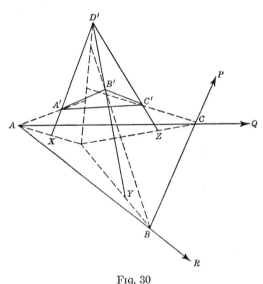

Fig. 30

Now the points R, P, Q belong, respectively, to the lines of intersection of the pairs of planes DAB, $D'A'B'$; DBC, $D'B'C'$; DCA, $D'C'A'$, hence the line PQR meets the four lines of intersection of the pairs of corresponding faces of the tetrahedrons $ABCD$, $A'B'C'D'$. In a similar way it may be shown that there are three other lines having the same property, hence the proposition.

327. Converse Theorem. *If the four lines of intersection of the pairs of corresponding faces of two tetrahedrons form a hyperbolic* *group, the same is true about the four lines joining the pairs of corresponding vertices of the tetrahedrons.*

The proof is obtained by retracing the steps of the proof of the direct theorem.

328. Theorem. *If the four planes determined by a given line and the four vertices of a tetrahedron are harmonic, the four points determined on this line by the four faces of the tetrahedron are also harmonic, and conversely.*

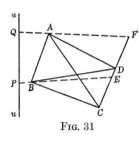

Fig. 31

Let P, Q, R, S (Fig. 31) be the traces on the given line u of the faces BCD, CDA, DAB, ABC of the tetrahedron $ABCD$. Let E, F be the points of intersection of the pairs of coplanar lines PB, CD; QA, CD.

The two pairs of planes uA, uB; uC, uD are harmonic, by assumption, hence their traces F, E; C, D on the line CD are two pairs of harmonic points. Thus the pencil of planes $AB(FECD)$ is harmonic, and therefore the traces Q, P; S, R on the line u are harmonic, which proves the proposition.

The converse is proved by reversing the steps of the direct proof.

MISCELLANEOUS EXERCISES

1. How many edges of a tetrahedron may be cut internally by a secant plane?

2. The sum of the areas of any three faces of a tetrahedron is greater than the area of the fourth face

3. Construct a tetrahedron so that its six edges shall pass through six given points.

4. If in a tetrahedron two of the bialtitudes coincide with the respective bimedians, the same is true about the third bialtitude.

5. The perpendiculars AP, BQ erected at A and B to the faces BCD, CDA of the tetrahedron $ABCD$ meet the faces BCD, CDA in the points P, Q. Show that

$$AP : BQ = \text{area } CDA : \text{area } BCD.$$

6. Draw a plane parallel to the base ABC of the tetrahedron $DABC$ meeting the edges DA, DB, DC in the points A', B', C' so that

$$A'B'^2 + B'C'^2 + C'A'^2 = AA'^2 + BB'^2 + CC'^2.$$

7. In a variable tetrahedron the centroid, one vertex, and the sum of the squares of the edges issued from that vertex are constant. Show that the locus of the circumcenter is a plane.

8. In the variable tetrahedron $ABCD$ the vertex A is fixed and the remaining three vertices vary on a fixed sphere so that $BC^2 + CD^2 + DB^2$ is constant. Show that the locus of the centroid of $ABCD$ is a sphere.

9. Let A', B' be the symmetrics of the vertices A, B of the tetrahedron $ABCD$ with respect to the mid-point E of CD, and let C', D' be the symmetrics of C, D with respect to the mid-point F of AB. (a) The tetrahedrons $ABCD$, $A'B'C'D'$ have the same centroid. (b) Express the sum of the squares of the edges of $A'B'C'D'$ in terms of the sum of the squares of the edges of $ABCD$. (c) The ratio of the volumes of the two tetrahedrons is equal to 3.

10. The lines AM, BM, CM joining a point M of the base ABC of the tetrahedron $DABC$, trirectangular at D, to the points A, B, C meet BC, CA, AB in the points A', B', C'. Through A' a line QR is drawn in the plane BCD meeting DB in Q and DC in R so that A' is the mid-point of QR. Through Q in the plane DBA a line QP is drawn meeting DA in P so that the mid-point of QP lies on DC'. Show that the mid-point of PR lies on DB'.

11. Through the vertices of a tetrahedron lines are drawn parallel to the lines joining the centroids of the opposite faces to a fixed point O in space. Show that (a) these parallels will meet in a point I collinear with the point O and the centroid G of the tetrahedron; (b) $GI = 3OG$.

12. Each of the edges AB, AC, AD of the tetrahedron $ABCD$ is produced at both ends to a length equal to the edge. Let (P) denote the plane determined by the points lying beyond the face BCD, and (P') the plane determined by the other three points. (a) The volume of the tetrahedron determined by the plane (P) and its three analogous planes (Q), (R), (S) is equal to 125 times the volume of $ABCD$. (b) The volume of the tetrahedron determined by the plane (P') and its three analogous planes is equal to 343 times the volume of $ABCD$. (c) Generalize the two propositions assuming that the edges were produced to p times their length.

13. Under what conditions is it possible to pass a sphere through the mid-points of five edges of a tetrahedron?

14. If in a skew quadrilateral the opposite sides are equal, the line joining the mid-points of the diagonals is perpendicular to these diagonals. Conversely.

15. A variable plane parallel to the base BCD of the tetrahedron $ABCD$ meets the edges AB, AC, AD in the points B', C', D'. Let B'', C'', D'' be the traces in BCD of the lines through B', C', D' parallel to a given line u. Find the locus of the centroid of the prism $B'C'D'B''C''D''$ (i.e., of the mid-point of the line joining the centroids of the two bases).

16. Construct a sphere which shall cut four given planes along four equal circles of given radius.

17. The points P, Q, R are marked on the edges DA, DB, DC of the tetrahedron $DABC$. Let $U \equiv (BR, \ CQ)$, $V \equiv (CP, \ AR)$, $W \equiv (AQ, \ BP)$; $X \equiv (DU, BC)$, $Y \equiv (DV, CA)$, $Z \equiv (DW, AB)$. Show that the lines AX, BY, CZ meet in a point, say, O; and that the lines AU, BV, CW meet in a point collinear with D and O.

18. Find a plane which shall cut a polyhedral angle of four faces along a parallelogram. When will this parallelogram become a rectangle? a rhombus? a square?

19. Construct a tetrahedron given the base and three of the altitudes of the tetrahedron.

20. Construct a regular tetrahedron so that one pair of its opposite edges shall lie on two skew lines given in position.

21. Construct a regular tetrahedron given its center and so that one of its edges shall lie on a given line.

22. Three vertices of a skew quadrilateral are fixed. Find the locus of the fourth vertex (a) if the diagonals of the parallelogram determined by the midpoints of the sides maintain a fixed ratio; (b) if the area of this parallelogram is fixed; (c) if this parallelogram remains similar to itself.

23. A variable plane ABC cuts the edges of the fixed trihedral angle O–ABC in the points A, B, C. If the differences $OB - OA, OC - OA$ remain constant, what is the locus of the centroid of the triangle ABC?

24. If a plane cuts a tetrahedron along a rhombus, the side of the rhombus is half the harmonic mean between a pair of opposite edges of the tetrahedron.

25. Construct an octahedron such that it shall have two parallel faces equal and similar to each of the faces of a given tetrahedron, and show that its volume is four times that of the tetrahedron.

26. (a) A line through the vertex M of the triangle MAB meets the line AB in S and the parallels through A, B to the respectively opposite sides in D and E. Show that

$$\frac{1}{MS} = \frac{1}{MD} + \frac{1}{ME}.$$

(b) A line through the vertex M of the tetrahedron $MABC$ meets the plane ABC in S and the planes through A, B, C parallel to the respectively opposite faces in the points D, E, F. Show that

$$\frac{1}{MS} = \frac{1}{MD} + \frac{1}{ME} + \frac{1}{MF}.$$

27. The circles having for diameters the sides of a triangle determine on the respective altitudes three pairs of points such that each pair is concyclic with each of the other two pairs, and the three circles thus obtained have for their centers the vertices of the triangle.—If this construction is applied to each of the four faces of an orthocentric tetrahedron, the resulting twenty-four points lie by twelves on four spheres having for centers the four vertices of the tetrahedron.

28. The frustum of a pyramid with a quadrilateral base is such that the intersections of opposite faces lie in the same plane σ; prove that (a) the diagonals of the solid are concurrent, in O; (b) each diagonal of the solid is divided harmonically by O and its point of intersection with σ; (c) the diagonals of each face are divided harmonically by their point of intersection and the plane σ.

29. The edges of the base of a tetrahedron are a, b, c, and each of the lateral edges is equal to d. Show that the volume, V, of the tetrahedron is given by the formula

$$12V = \sqrt{16p(p-a)(p-b)(p-c)d^2 - a^2b^2c^2}$$

where

$$2p = a + b + c.$$

30. A point moves so that the sum of the squares of its distances from the vertices of a regular tetrahedron, edge a, is a constant, k^2. Show that the locus of the point is a sphere concentric with the circumsphere of the tetrahedron, and the square of whose radius is equal to $\frac{1}{8}(2k^2 - 3a^2)$.

31. If M is a point on the edge CD of the tetrahedron $ABCD$, show that

$$ABM^2 \cdot CD^2 = ABC^2 \cdot DM^2 + ABD^2 \cdot CM^2$$
$$- 2ABC \cdot ABD \cdot DM \cdot CM \cdot \cos(CAB, CAD).$$

32. If M is any point in the plane passing through the circumcenter of the tetrahedron $DABC$ and perpendicular to the median passing through A, we have

$$3AM^2 = BM^2 + CM^2 + DM^2.$$

33. Let $X, X'; Y, Y'; Z, Z'; U, U'; V, V'; W, W'$ be pairs of isotomic points marked, respectively, on the edges BC, CA, AB, DA, DB, DC of the given tetrahedron $DABC$, and let $(S_a), (S_a'); (S_b), (S_b'); (S_c), (S_c'); (S_d), (S_d')$ be the spheres passing through the vertices of $DABC$ and through three points marked on the adjacent edges. The parallels to the eight lines AS_a, AS_a'; $BS_b, BS_b'; CS_c, CS_c'; DS_d, DS_d'$ drawn respectively through the points S_a', $S_a; S_b', S_b; S_c', S_c; S_d', S_d$ all pass through the circumcenter of $DABC$.

34. Given the tetrahedron $ABCD$, find a point P such that the planes through P parallel to the faces of $ABCD$ shall cut the respectively opposite trihedral angles along four equivalent triangles. Find the area of one of these triangles.

35. If O, A, B, C, D are any five points in space, prove that the lines drawn from the middle points of BC, CA, AB, respectively parallel to the connectors of D with the middle points of OA, OB, OC meet in one point E such that DE passes through and is bisected by the centroid of the tetrahedron $OABC$.

36. The points A', B', C', D' are marked on the lines joining the point L to the vertices A, B, C, D of the tetrahedron $ABCD$ so that $LA' : LA = \cdots$ $= m$. The planes through the points A', B', C', D' parallel to the respective faces of $ABCD$ form a tetrahedron homothetic to $ABCD$. Find the value of their homothetic ratio; find the locus of the homothetic center of the two tetrahedrons, and the locus of the centroid of the new tetrahedron, assuming that m varies.

37. A variable plane parallel to the base ABC of the tetrahedron $SABC$ cuts the edges SA, SB, SC in the points A', B', C'. Find the locus of the point common to the planes $AB'C', BC'A', CA'B'$.

38. A variable plane parallel to the base ABC of the tetrahedron $SABC$ meets the edges SA, SB, SC in the points A', B', C'; these points are projected orthogonally upon the plane ABC into the points A'', B'', C''. Find the locus of the center of gravity of the prism $A'B'C'A''B''C''$.

39. The plane (A, BC) through the vertex A of the tetrahedron $ABCD$ and perpendicular to the edge BC meets the plane (B, AD) along the line d_1. Let d_2 be the line of intersection of the planes $(B, CD), (C, AB)$; (a) show that d_1 and d_2 are coplanar; (b) if d_3, d_4 denote the lines of intersection of the pairs of planes $(C, AD), (D, BC); (D, AB), (A, CD)$, show that the four lines d_1, d_2, d_3, d_4 form a parallelogram; (c) the plane of this parallelogram passes through the

Monge point of the tetrahedron $ABCD$ and is perpendicular to the bimedian relative to the pair of edges AC, BD.

40. Given five cospherical points, the five lines obtained by joining each point to the Monge point of the tetrahedron determined by the remaining four given points are concurrent.

41. If A', B', C', D' are the orthogonal projections of the vertices A, B, C, D of the given tetrahedron upon a given plane, the perpendiculars from A', B', C', D' upon the planes BCD, CDA, DAB, ABC form a hyperbolic group.

42. The isosceles tetrahedrons $A'BCD$, $B'CDA$, $C'DAB$, $D'ABC$ are constructed on the faces of the given tetrahedron $ABCD$. Show that the four altitudes of these four tetrahedrons passing through the vertices A', B', C', D' form a hyperbolic group.

43. If similar figures be described on the faces of an isosceles tetrahedron, prove that any four corresponding points or planes determine an isosceles tetrahedron.

CHAPTER V

TRANSVERSALS

1. The Skew Quadrilateral

329. Carnot's Theorem. *If a plane cuts the sides AB, BC, CD, DA (Fig. 32) of a skew quadrilateral $ABCD$ in the points P, Q, R, S, respectively, we have, both in magnitude and in sign,*

$$(M) \qquad \frac{AP}{PB} \cdot \frac{BQ}{QC} \cdot \frac{CR}{RD} \cdot \frac{DS}{SA} = 1.$$

If X is the trace of the plane $PQRS$ on the diagonal BD of the quadrilateral we have, by Menelaus' theorem (C. G., p. 122) applied to the triangles ABD, CBD, and the transversals PSX, QRX,

$$\frac{AP}{PB} \cdot \frac{BX}{XD} \cdot \frac{DS}{SA} = -1, \qquad \frac{BQ}{QC} \cdot \frac{CR}{RD} \cdot \frac{DX}{XB} = -1.$$

Multiplying these two equalities we obtain the relation (M).

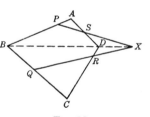

330. Corollary. *If through a point O in space two lines are drawn, one meeting the sides AB, CD of the skew quadrilateral $ABCD$ in the points P, R, and the other line meeting BC, DA in the points Q, S, the four points P, Q, R, S satisfy the relation (M)* (§ 329).

FIG. 32

Indeed, the four points P, Q, R, S are coplanar, by construction.

331. Converse Theorem. *If on the sides AB, BC, CD, DA of a given skew quadrilateral $ABCD$ we mark the points P, Q, R, S, so that the relation (M) is satisfied, the four points are coplanar.*

Through the points P, Q, R pass a plane meeting DA in S'. By the direct theorem (§ 329) we have, both in magnitude and in sign,

$$\frac{AP}{PB} \cdot \frac{BQ}{QC} \cdot \frac{CR}{RD} \cdot \frac{DS'}{S'A} = 1.$$

But since (M) holds, by assumption, we have

$$DS' : S'A = DS : SA,$$

111

hence S and S' are identical, which proves the proposition.

332. Theorem.　*The four planes determined by a given point in space and the four sides of a given skew quadrilateral meet the respective opposite sides in four coplanar points.*

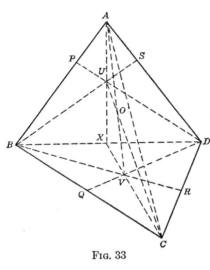

Fig. 33

Let P, Q, R, S be the traces on the sides AB, BC, CD, DA (Fig. 33) of the planes passing through the sides CD, DA, AB, BC and the given point O. Let X be the trace of the diagonal BD on the plane ACO, and U, V the traces of the lines CO, AO in the planes ABD, CBD, respectively. Since the line AOV lies in the plane $ABOR$, the points B, V, R are collinear. The points C, V, X; D, V, Q are collinear, for similar reasons, hence we have, by Ceva's theorem (C. G., p. 127), both in magnitude and in sign,

$$\frac{BQ}{QC} \cdot \frac{CR}{RD} \cdot \frac{DX}{XB} = 1.$$

Similarly, in the plane ABD we have

$$\frac{AP}{PB} \cdot \frac{BX}{XD} \cdot \frac{DS}{SA} = 1.$$

Multiplying these two relations we have

$$\frac{AP}{PB} \cdot \frac{BQ}{QC} \cdot \frac{CR}{RD} \cdot \frac{DA}{SA} = 1,$$

hence by the converse theorem (§ 331) the points P, Q, R, S are coplanar.

OTHERWISE.　The plane $ABOR$ contains the point P, and the plane $CDOP$ contains R, hence P, O, R are collinear. Similarly Q, S, O are collinear, hence P, Q, R, S lie in the same plane, which plane also contains O.

333. Converse Theorem. *If on the four sides of a skew quadrilateral are marked four coplanar points, the four planes determined by these four points and the respective opposite sides of the quadrilateral have a point in common.*

Since the points P, Q, R, S on the sides AB, BC, CD, DA of the skew quadrilateral $ABCD$ are coplanar, by assumption, we have, both in magnitude and in sign (§ 329),

$$\frac{AP}{PB} \cdot \frac{BQ}{QC} \cdot \frac{CR}{RD} \cdot \frac{DS}{SA} = 1.$$

Now let O be the point common to the three planes PCD, QDA, RAB, and let S' be the trace of the plane OBC on the side DA. By the direct proposition (§ 332) we have

$$\frac{AP}{PB} \cdot \frac{BQ}{QC} \cdot \frac{CR}{RD} \cdot \frac{DS'}{S'A} = 1,$$

hence

$$DS : SA = DS' : S'A$$

and S' is identical with S, which proves the proposition.

OTHERWISE. Since the points P, Q, R, S are coplanar, the lines PQ, RS intersect, say, in O. Now the plane ABR contains P, hence also O. Similarly BCS, CDP, DAQ pass through O.

334. Theorem. *The symmetrics, with respect to the midpoints of the corresponding sides, of the four points determined by a plane on the four sides of a skew quadrilateral are coplanar.*

If the four points P, Q, R, S (Fig. 34) are coplanar, we have,

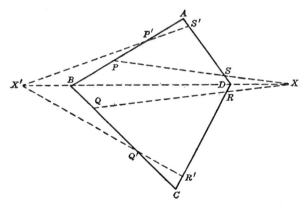

FIG. 34

by Carnot's theorem (§ 329),

$$\frac{AP}{PB} \cdot \frac{BQ}{QC} \cdot \frac{CR}{RD} \cdot \frac{DS}{SA} = 1.$$

Now if P', Q', R', S' are the symmetrics of P, Q, R, S with respect to the mid-points of the sides AB, BC, CD, DA, we have

$$AP : PB = BP' : P'A, \text{etc.},$$

hence

$$\frac{BP'}{P'A} \cdot \frac{CQ'}{Q'B} \cdot \frac{DR'}{R'C} \cdot \frac{AS'}{S'D} = 1,$$

hence the four points are coplanar (§ 331).

335. Definition. Two planes like $PQRS$, $P'Q'R'S'$ (§ 334) are called, by analogy with the case of the plane (C. G., p. 126), *reciprocal transversal planes* with respect to the quadrilateral.

336. Theorem. *Two reciprocal transversal planes of a skew quadrilateral determine on a diagonal of this quadrilateral two points symmetrical with respect to the mid-point of the diagonal considered.*

With the same notations as in the preceding theorem (§ 334), let X, X' be the traces of the lines PS, $P'S'$ on the diagonal BD. The points X, X' are also the traces of the two reciprocal transversal planes $PQRS$, $P'Q'R'S'$ on BD. Applying Menelaus' theorem to the triangle ABD and the two transversals PSX, $P'S'X'$, we have, both in magnitude and in sign,

$$\frac{AP}{PB} \cdot \frac{BX}{XD} \cdot \frac{DS}{SA} = -1, \qquad \frac{AP'}{P'B} \cdot \frac{BX'}{X'D} \cdot \frac{DS'}{S'A} = -1.$$

But we have, by assumption,

$$AP = -BP', \qquad PB = AP', \qquad DS = -AS', \qquad SA = DS',$$

hence

$$BX : XD = X'D : BX',$$

and the points X, X' are thus symmetrical with respect to the mid-point of BD.

337. Corollary. *If one of two reciprocal transversal planes of a skew quadrilateral passes through the mid-point of a diagonal, the other plane also passes through this mid-point.*

Exercise. (a) On the sides AB, BC, CD, DA of a skew quadrilateral $ABCD$ are marked the coplanar points P, Q, R, S; let P', Q', R', S' be the harmonic conjugates of these points with respect to the pairs of points A, B;

$B, C; C, D; D, A$. Show that the points P', Q', R', S' are coplanar. (b) The line of intersection of the two planes $PQRS$, $P'Q'R'S'$ meets the diagonals AC, BD of $ABCD$. (c) The line joining the point $O \equiv (PR, QS)$ to the point $O' \equiv (P'R', Q'S')$ also meets the diagonals AC, BD.

2. The Tetrahedron

338. Definitions. The segment intercepted by a tetrahedron on a line passing through a vertex may be called, by analogy with the case of the plane, a *cevian* of the tetrahedron.

The feet of four cevians concurrent in a point M determine a tetrahedron which may be referred to as the *cevian tetrahedron* of the point M with respect to the given tetrahedron.

339. Theorem. *If P, Q, R, S (Fig. 35) are the feet of four cevians having the point M in common, we have*

$$\frac{MP}{AP} + \frac{MQ}{BQ} + \frac{MR}{CR} + \frac{MS}{DS} = 1.$$

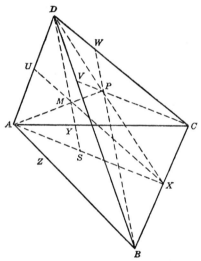

We have

$$\frac{MP}{AP} = \frac{\text{vol. } MBCD}{\text{vol. } ABCD}$$

and similarly for the other three ratios. Adding the four equalities thus obtained, we observe that the sum of the four numerators on the right hand side is equal to the volume of $ABCD$, hence the proposition.

340. Corollary. *We have*

Fig. 35

$$\frac{AM}{AP} + \frac{BM}{BQ} + \frac{CM}{CR} + \frac{DM}{DS} = 3.$$

For

$$1 = \frac{AP}{AP} = \frac{AM}{AP} + \frac{MP}{AP},$$

hence

$$\frac{AM}{AP} = 1 - \frac{MP}{AP},$$

and similarly for the other three ratios. Adding these four equalities we obtain the announced result.

341. Remark. These two propositions (§§ 339, 340) are valid whether the point M lies within or without the tetrahedron, provided due respect is paid to the signs of the ratios, i.e., when the point M lies outside, say, the segment AP, the corresponding ratio $AM : MP$ is to be taken negatively.

The reader may verify this statement by considering the different positions the point M may occupy with respect to the tetrahedron.

342. The lines AS, DP (§ 339) lie in the same plane DAM and therefore meet the edge BC in the same point X. Let Y, Z, U, V, W (Fig. 35) be the analogous points on the edges CA, AB, DA, DB, DC.

THEOREM. *We have*

$$\frac{DM}{MS} = \frac{DU}{UA} + \frac{DV}{VB} + \frac{DW}{WC}$$

and three analogous relations corresponding to the vertices A, B, C.
In the two triangles DAX, DBC, we have (C. G., p. 131)

$$\frac{DM}{MS} = \frac{DU}{UA} + \frac{DP}{PX}, \qquad \frac{DP}{PX} = \frac{DV}{VB} + \frac{DW}{WC}.$$

Eliminating the ratio $DP : PX$ we obtain the announced relation.

EXERCISE. Apply this proposition to (a) the centroid; (b) the incenter; (c) the excenters.

343. Observation. If four parallel lines are drawn through the four vertices of a tetrahedron, one of the cevians determined by the tetrahedron on these four lines lies within the tetrahedron, while the remaining three fall outside the tetrahedron.

344. Theorem. *Given four parallel cevians of a tetrahedron, the reciprocal of the one falling within the tetrahedron is equal to the sum of the reciprocals of the remaining three.*

Of the four parallel cevians considered, let DS be the one lying within the tetrahedron $ABCD$. If AS meets BC in L, the line DL passes through the trace P, in the plane BCD, of the cevian AP through A. In the triangle LPA we have

$$DS : AP = SL : AL.$$

If M, N are the traces of the lines BS, CS on CA, AB, respectively, the lines DM, DN will meet the cevians BQ, CR in the points Q, R, and we have

$$DS : BQ = SM : BM, \qquad DS : CR = SN : CN,$$

hence, adding,

$$DS \left(\frac{1}{AP} + \frac{1}{BQ} + \frac{1}{CR} \right) = \frac{SL}{AL} + \frac{SM}{BM} + \frac{SN}{CN}.$$

Now the right hand side of this equality is equal to 1 (C. G., p. 131), hence the proposition.

REMARK. If the four cevians are considered as directed lines, the three cevians falling outside the tetrahedron are directed in the same sense, counting from the respective vertices of the tetrahedron, while the fourth cevian has the sense opposite to the one on the first three. Now if both magnitude and the sense of direction are taken into consideration, the above proposition may be stated as follows: *The algebraic sum of the reciprocals of four parallel cevians of a tetrahedron is equal to zero.*

345. Theorem. *The volume of the tetrahedron determined by the feet of four parallel cevians of a given tetrahedron is equal to three times the volume of the given tetrahedron.*

Let DD' (Fig. 36) be the cevian lying within the tetrahedron $ABCD$. The point D' thus lies within the triangle ABC. Let $E \equiv (AD', BC)$, $F \equiv (BD', AC)$, $G \equiv (CD', BA)$. If A', B', C' are the traces of the parallel cevians AA', BB', CC' in the planes BCD, CDA, DAB, respec-

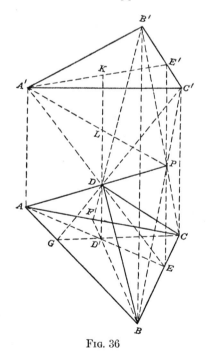

FIG. 36

tively, we have

$$A' \equiv (AA', DE), \qquad B' \equiv (BB', DF), \qquad C' \equiv (CC', DG).$$

The plane $A'AE$ cuts the plane $BCC'B'$ along a line passing through E and parallel to AA', hence also to BB' and CC'. Let E' be the point of intersection of this line with $B'C'$. The line AD lies in the plane $A'AEE'$, hence AD meets EE', say, in P. But, by construction, AD is also coplanar with the lines BC', $B'C$, and since AD does not lie in the plane $BCC'B'$, the lines BC', $B'C$ pass through P, i.e., the point P is the intersection of the diagonals of the trapezoid $BCC'B'$, hence the parallel EE' through P to the bases is bisected at P.

Let K, L be the traces of DD' on the lines $A'E'$, $A'P$. The diagonals AP, $A'E$ of the trapezoid $AA'PE$ meet in D, hence D is the mid-point of the parallel $D'L$ through D to the bases AA', EP, and therefore $D'D = DL$.

The line $A'P$ is the median of the triangle $EA'E'$, hence $A'P$ bisects the parallel DK to the base EE', and therefore $DL = LK$. Thus DD' is equal to one third of $D'K$.

If a plane is passed through D parallel to ABC, we obtain a prism the volume of which is equal to the area of the right section (R) multiplied by DD', hence

$$\text{vol. } ABCD = \tfrac{1}{3}DD'\cdot(R).$$

If a plane is passed through D' parallel to $A'B'C'$, we have,

$$\text{vol. } A'B'C'D' = \tfrac{1}{3}\cdot D'K\cdot(R)$$

But $DD' = \tfrac{1}{3}D'K$, hence the proposition.

EXERCISE. Show that if A'' is the trace of AA' in the plane $B'C'D'$, we have $AA' : AA'' = 1 : 2$. HINT. $A'' \equiv (AA', D'E')$.

346. Theorem. *Given a tetrahedron, if through a point in space the three lines are drawn meeting the three pairs of opposite edges, the six points thus marked on the edges are such that, in each face of the tetrahedron, the three lines joining these points to the opposite vertices are concurrent.*

Let $ABCD$ (Fig. 37) be the given tetrahedron, OPP', OQQ', ORR' the lines drawn through the given point O so that P, Q, R lie on the edges BC, CA, AB, and P', Q', R' on the respectively opposite edges DA, DB, DC.

The line DO lies in the plane $DAPP'$, hence the trace D' of DO in the plane ABC lies on the line of intersection AP of the two planes $DAPP'$, ABC. Similarly for the points B, D', Q; C, D', R.

The traces A', B', C' of the lines AO, BO, CO in the planes BCD, CDA, DAB may be treated in an analogous way, hence the proposition.

347. Remark. We have also proved incidentally that the four points thus obtained in the four faces are the traces in these faces of the lines joining the respectively opposite vertices to the given fixed point.

348. Converse Theorem. *If on the edges of a given tetrahedron six points are marked so that, in three of the faces of the tetrahedron, the lines joining these points to the opposite vertices of the respective face are concurrent, (a) the same holds for the fourth face; (b) the three lines joining the points situated on the three pairs of opposite edges of the tetrahedron are concurrent.*

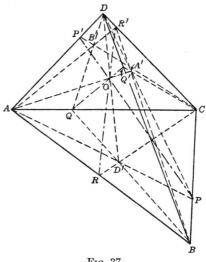

FIG. 37

Using the same notation as in the direct theorem, we assume that the lines are concurrent in the faces DAB, DBC, DCA (Fig. 37).

The lines AA', BB' lie in the plane ABR', hence they meet in a point, say, O. Again the lines BB', CC' lie in the plane BCP', and the lines CC', AA' lie in the plane ACQ'. Thus each of the lines AA', BB', CC' meets the other two. This may happen only in two ways: (a) either the three lines are coplanar, or (b) these lines are concurrent. Now the plane $AA'BB' \equiv ABR'$ meets the line DC in the point R' and does not contain the point C, hence the line CC' does not lie in the plane $AA'BB'$, and therefore CC' passes through O.

The plane DAP contains the line AOA', hence the trace D' of DO in ABC is collinear with the points A and P. Similarly for the points B, D', Q; C, D', R, which proves the first part of the theorem.

The planes ADP, BCP' have the points P, P' in common, hence PP' is their line of intersection. But these two planes have also the point O in common, hence PP' passes through O. Similarly for QQ', RR', which proves the second part of the proposition.

349. Remark I. We have also proved that our assumptions imply that the lines AA', BB', CC', DD' joining the vertices of the tetrahedron to the common points of the three concurrent lines in the faces respectively opposite the vertices considered are also concurrent, and that their common point coincides with the common point of the lines joining the points on the pairs of opposite edges of the tetrahedron.

350. Remark II. The theorems concerning the medians and the bimedians of the tetrahedron (Chap. IV) are special cases of the last two propositions (§§ 346, 348).

351. Remark III. The condition given in the converse theorem (§ 348) may be expressed as follows, by the use of Ceva's theorem,

$$\frac{AP'}{P'D} \cdot \frac{DQ'}{Q'B} \cdot \frac{BR}{RA} = 1,$$

$$\frac{BQ'}{Q'D} \cdot \frac{DR'}{R'C} \cdot \frac{CP}{PB} = 1,$$

$$\frac{CR'}{R'D} \cdot \frac{DP'}{P'A} \cdot \frac{AQ}{QC} = 1.$$

These conditions are thus necessary and sufficient for the lines PP', QQ', RR' to be concurrent.

Multiplying these three equalities we obtain

$$\frac{AQ}{QC} \cdot \frac{CP}{PB} \cdot \frac{BR}{RA} = 1,$$

which, by the converse of Ceva's theorem, shows that the lines AP, BQ, CR are concurrent, i.e., we have here another proof of the first part of the converse theorem (§ 348).

352. Theorem. *If six points marked on the six edges of a tetrahedron are coplanar, the three points situated in any of the faces of the tetrahedron are collinear.*

CONVERSELY. *If the six points marked on the edges of a tetrahedron are such that the triads of points situated in three of the faces of the tetrahedron are collinear, the six points are coplanar.*

Let P, P'; Q, Q'; R, R' (Fig. 38) be the points marked on the edges BC, DA; CA, DB; AB, DC of the tetrahedron $ABCD$. If these six points are coplanar, the points P, Q, R lie on the line of intersection of this plane with the plane ABC, and similarly for the other faces of $ABCD$, which proves the direct theorem.

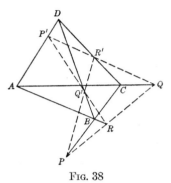

FIG. 38

Suppose, conversely, that the triads of points P', Q', R; P, Q', R'; P', Q, R' are collinear. The plane determined by the points P', Q', R' contains also the points P, Q, R, hence the six points are coplanar.

REMARK. Using Menelaus' theorem, the hypothesis of the converse theorem may be expressed by the following equalities

$$\frac{AQ}{QC} \cdot \frac{CR'}{R'D} \cdot \frac{DP'}{P'A} = -1,$$

$$\frac{BR}{RA} \cdot \frac{AP'}{P'D} \cdot \frac{DQ'}{Q'B} = -1,$$

$$\frac{CP}{PB} \cdot \frac{BQ'}{Q'D} \cdot \frac{DR'}{R'C} = -1.$$

Multiplying these three equalities we get

$$\frac{AQ}{QC} \cdot \frac{CP}{PB} \cdot \frac{BR}{RA} = -1,$$

which shows that P, Q, R are collinear.

353. Theorem. *If six coplanar points are marked on the six edges of a tetrahedron, the symmetrics of these points with regard to the mid-points of the respective edges are coplanar.*

This is a different way of stating the proposition proved about the skew quadrilateral (§ 336).

354. Definition. Two such planes may be referred to as *reciprocal transversal planes* with respect to the tetrahedron.

EXERCISES

1. The sum of the reciprocals of the four cevians of a tetrahedron passing through the circumcenter of the tetrahedron is equal to three times the reciprocal of the circumradius of the tetrahedron.

2. The four lines joining the vertices of a tetrahedron to the incenters of the opposite faces form a hyperbolic group. The supplementary hyperbolic group consists of the centroidal lines of the four trihedral angles of the tetrahedron. State similar propositions involving the excenters.

3. The external bisectors of the angles of a face of a tetrahedron meet the sides of this triangle in three collinear points (C. G., p. 123). Show that the four lines thus obtained in the four faces of the tetrahedron form a hyperbolic group. State similar propositions involving the internal bisectors, or both the internal and external bisectors.

4. A plane meets the edges DA, DB, DC, BC, CA, AB of the tetrahedron $DABC$ in the points U, V, W, X, Y, Z. The lines AV, BU meet in E, and the lines AX, BY meet in F. Show that the points E, F, W, are collinear. Find other analogous triads of collinear points.

CHAPTER VI

THE OBLIQUE CONE WITH A CIRCULAR BASE

355. Problem. *Given a fixed line s through the vertex V of an oblique cone with a circular base and a variable line m meeting the cone in X, Y, and s in P, find the locus of the harmonic conjugate Q of P with respect to X, Y.* (Fig. 39.)

The traces X', Y', Q', R of the four coplanar lines VX, VY, VQ, VP in the plane of the base of the cone are collinear, hence these four points are harmonic (C. G., p. 140). Now the lines VX, VY are elements of the cone, hence X', Y' lie on the circle (O) of the base, and therefore the point Q' lies on the polar p of R with respect to the circle (O) (C. G., p. 148). Thus Q lies in the plane V–p.

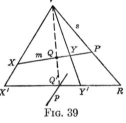

Fig. 39

As the line m varies, constantly meeting s, the point R, and therefore also the line p, remain fixed, hence the locus of Q is a fixed plane V–p.

356. Remark I. The mid-point M of the segment EF which the cone (V) intercepts on a line parallel to s (§ 355) also lies in the plane V–p, for the traces E', F', M' of the lines VE, VF, VM on the plane of the base of the cone lie on the line of intersection of the plane of the base with the plane s–EF, hence E', F', M', R are collinear and therefore harmonic (C. G., p. 139) and M' lies on the polar of R with respect to (O). Thus: *The locus of the mid-point of the segment which an oblique circular cone intercepts on a line having a fixed direction is a plane passing through the vertex of the cone.*

357. Remark II. In the solution of the preceding problem (§ 355) it was assumed that the given line s meets the plane of the base in R. The result however remains valid if s is parallel to this plane.

Indeed, in such a case the line $X'Q'Y'$ will be parallel to s, and Q' will be the mid-point of $X'Y'$ (C. G., p. 139), hence Q' lies on the diameter of (O) which is perpendicular to $X'Y'$ and therefore to s. Thus the point Q lies in the plane determined by this diameter and the vertex V of the cone.

358. Definition. The plane V–p (§ 355) is called the *polar plane* of the ray s with respect to the cone, and s the *polar ray* of the plane V–p with respect to the cone.

It follows from the preceding propositions (§§ 355–357) that *every ray passing through the vertex of the cone has a polar plane.*

If the ray s lies outside the cone, its polar plane is determined by two elements of the cone along which the two tangent planes through s to the cone touch the cone.

The polar plane of an element of the cone is the tangent plane to the cone along the element considered.

359. Theorem. *If the polar plane of a passes through b, the polar plane of b passes through a.*

360. Theorem. *If a ray passing through the vertex of the cone describes a plane, its polar plane turns about a fixed line.*

361. Definitions. (a) If the ray b lies in the polar plane of a, the two rays a, b are said to be *conjugate* with respect to the cone.

(b) If the plane α passes through the polar ray of the plane β, the two planes are said to be *conjugate* with respect to the cone.

EXERCISE. The reader may formulate and prove propositions regarding polar rays and polar planes with respect to a cone analogous to those which were proved regarding poles and polars with respect to a circle.

362. Definitions. (a) In an oblique circular cone the diameter of the base which passes through the foot of the altitude of the cone is the *principal diameter* of the base.

(b) The two elements of the cone which pass through the ends of the principal diameter of the base are the *principal elements* of the cone.

(c) The plane determined by the principal elements of the cone is called the *principal plane* of the cone.

(d) The line joining the vertex of the cone to the center of the base is the *axis* of the cone.

(e) The principal elements and the principal diameter of the cone form the *principal triangle* of the cone.

363. Theorem. *The axis of an oblique circular cone lies in the principal plane of the cone.*

Indeed, the axis and the principal plane have in common the center of the base and the vertex of the cone.

364. Theorem. *The principal plane of an oblique circular cone is perpendicular to the base of the cone.*

Indeed, the principal plane contains the altitude of the cone.

365. Problem. *Find a plane which is perpendicular to its polar ray with respect to an oblique circular cone.*

Let t (Fig. 40) be a ray perpendicular to its polar plane τ with respect to the oblique circular cone (V), and let C, H be the traces of t and of the altitude VH in the plane of the base β of

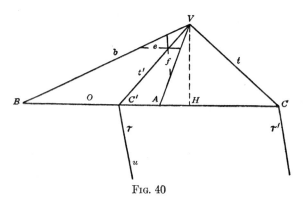

FIG. 40

(V). The plane t–VH is perpendicular to both τ and β, hence this plane is perpendicular to the line of intersection u of τ and β, i.e., u is perpendicular to CH. Now u is the polar of C with respect to the circle of the base (O) (§ 355), hence CH passes through the center O of (O), and therefore the plane t–VH is the principal plane of the cone (§ 364).

Furthermore, if C' is the trace of u on CH, the lines t, $VC' \equiv t'$ are harmonically separated by the principal elements $a \equiv VA$, $b \equiv VB$, and t is perpendicular to t', hence t, t' are the bisectors of the angles formed by a, b. Thus: *The two planes τ, τ' perpendicular to the principal plane and passing through the bisectors of the angles formed by the principal elements of the cone satisfy the conditions of the problem.*

We assumed that t meets β in C. If t is parallel to β its polar plane τ passes through the axis VO of the cone [§ 362(d)], and if t is to be perpendicular to τ, this plane must be perpendicular to the plane of the base of the cone (§ 364), i.e., must coincide with the principal plane VOH.

366. Definition. A plane perpendicular to its polar ray with respect to a given oblique circular cone is called a *plane of symmetry* of the cone. The polar ray of a plane of symmetry is called an *axis of symmetry* of the cone. It follows from the preceding paragraph (§ 365) that *an oblique cone with a circular base has three planes of symmetry and three axes of symmetry.*

The planes of symmetry are the principal plane of the cone and the two planes perpendicular to the principal plane and passing through the bisectors of the angles formed by the two principal elements of the cone.

The axes of symmetry are the lines of intersection of the three planes of symmetry.

The planes of symmetry of a cone form a trirectangular trihedral angle, conjugate with respect to the cone.

367. Remark I. The names " plane of symmetry " and "axis of symmetry" are justified by the following

THEOREM. *The segment intercepted by an oblique circular cone on a line perpendicular to a plane of symmetry is bisected by the plane of symmetry considered.*

The segment intercepted by an oblique circular cone on a line perpendicular to an axis of symmetry and meeting this axis is bisected by the axis considered. The proof is left to the reader.

368. Remark II. If a point P is taken on the surface of the cone, its symmetric with respect to the principal plane will lie on the same nappe of the cone as P.

Of the two symmetrics of P with respect to the other two planes of symmetry one will lie on the same nappe with P, while the other will lie on the opposite nappe.

369. Definition. A plane perpendicular to the principal plane of an oblique circular cone and cutting this plane along a line antiparallel (C. G., p. 83) to the principal diameter with respect to the principal elements of the cone is said to be *antiparallel to the base* of the cone.

All antiparallel planes are parallel to each other, or in other words, an antiparallel plane has a fixed orientation.

370. Theorem. *Two planes, one parallel and the other antiparallel to the base of an oblique circular cone, drawn through the*

same point of a bisector of the angle formed by the principal elements of the cone, are symmetrical with respect to the plane of symmetry of the cone passing through the bisector considered and distinct from the principal plane.

Let e, f be the traces on the principal plane VOH (Fig. 40) of the two planes ϵ, φ, one parallel and the other antiparallel to the base of the cone (V), drawn through the point M of the, say, internal bisector of the angle AVB formed by the principal elements VA, VB of (V).

The lines e, f are respectively parallel and antiparallel to the principal diameter AB, hence they are antiparallel to each other with respect to VA, VB, and since e, f intersect on the bisector $VM \equiv t'$ of the angle AVB, they are symmetrical with respect to t'. Now both ϵ and φ are perpendicular to the principal plane OVH, and since the plane of symmetry τ passing through t' is also perpendicular to OVH (§ 365), the proposition is proved. Similarly for any point of the external bisector.

371. Theorem. *A plane antiparallel to the base of an oblique circular cone cuts the cone along a circle.*

Let C, D be the points of intersection of the principal elements VA, VB of an oblique circular cone (V) with a plane antiparallel to the base of the cone. Through any point M of the curve of intersection of (V) with the antiparallel plane CMD pass a plane $MA'B'P$ parallel to the base cutting VA, VB, CD in A', B', P. This plane cuts (V) along a circle having $A'B'$ for diameter. The two planes $A'MB'$, CMD are both perpendicular to the plane VAB, therefore their line of intersection MP is perpendicular to this plane, hence MP is perpendicular to both $A'B'$ and CD.

Now in the circle $A'MB'$ we have

$$MP^2 = PA' \cdot PB'.$$

On the other hand CD being antiparallel to AB, the two triangles $A'PC$, $B'PD$ are similar and we have

$$PC \cdot PD = PA' \cdot PB',$$

hence

$$MP^2 = PC \cdot PD,$$

and therefore the point M belongs to the circle having CD for diameter. Since M is any point common to the cone and the plane CMD, the proposition is proved.

OTHERWISE. Through the trace of the antiparallel plane φ on, say, the internal bisector t' of the angle VAB draw a plane ϵ parallel to the base of the cone. The symmetric of the circle common to ϵ and (V) with respect to the plane of symmetry τ passing through t' (and different from the principal plane) also lies on (V) (§ 370). But this circle must lie in the symmetric of ϵ with respect to τ, i.e., in the plane φ, hence the proposition.

372. Definition. A plane cutting an oblique circular plane along a circle is called a *cyclic plane* of the cone.

An oblique circular cone has two systems of parallel planes which are cyclic with respect to the cone: the planes parallel to the base and the planes antiparallel to the base.

We may express the same thing by saying that *an oblique circular cone has cyclic planes of two different orientations.*

We shall prove that the cone has no more than two such systems of planes.

373. Lemma. *If a circle is drawn on an oblique circular cone, the plane of the circle is perpendicular to the principal plane of the cone.*

Let the circle (O) (Fig. 41) be the base and the point V the

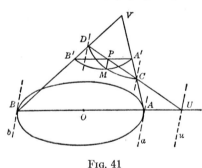

FIG. 41

vertex of the oblique circular cone (V), and let (O') be a circle on (V). If the plane of (O') is parallel to the plane of the base, the proposition is proved (§ 364).

If the two planes are not parallel, let u be their line of intersection. From the center O of (O) drop the perpendicular OU upon u and draw the tangents a, b to (O) at the points of intersection A, B of (O) with OU, which tangents are obviously parallel to u.

The line VA meets the plane of (O') in a point C of (O'), and the tangent plane $VA-a$ to (V) meets the plane of (O') along a line c which is tangent to (O') at C, for c cannot meet (O') in any other point besides C. Furthermore, since the plane $VC-a$ passes through the line a parallel to the line u, the lines u, c are parallel.

Similarly the tangent plane $VB-b$ meets the plane of (O') along the tangent d to (O') at the trace D of VB on (O').

The line of intersection CD of the plane of (O') with the plane VAB passes through the point U, and since the tangents to (O') at C, D are parallel, the line CD is a diameter of (O') and is perpendicular to c, d, and therefore also to u.

The line u is thus perpendicular to both AB and CD, hence to the plane VAB, and since the planes of both (O) and (O') contain the line u, both these planes are perpendicular to VAB. Now the plane VAB contains the principal axis VO and is perpendicular to the plane of the base of the cone, hence VAB is the principal plane of (V), and the proposition is proved.

374. Remark. From the above proof (§ 373) it follows that *if a circle is drawn on an oblique circular cone, the center of the circle lies in the principal plane of the cone.*

375. Theorem. *A plane cutting an oblique circular cone along a circle is either parallel or antiparallel to the base.*

Let a plane λ cut the oblique cone (V) (Fig. 41) with the circular base (O) along a circle (O'). If λ is parallel to the base (O), the proposition is proved.

If λ is not parallel to the base of (V), draw a plane μ parallel to the base through any point M of (O') cutting the principal elements VA, VB of (V) in A', B', and let C, D be the traces of (O') on the same elements. The lines $A'B'$, CD are diameters of the respective circles (§ 374), and the planes λ, μ are both perpendicular to the principal plane VAB, hence their line of intersection is perpendicular to the plane VAB and joins M to the point P common to $A'B'$ and CD. We thus have

$$PA' \cdot PB' = MP^2 = PC \cdot PD.$$

The triangles PCA', PDB' are thus similar, and from the equality of their angles it follows that CD is antiparallel to AB with respect to VA, VB, which proves the proposition.

376. Corollary. *The centers of the anti-parallel circular sections lie on the symmedian of the principal triangle of the cone issued from the vertex of the cone* (C. G., p. 223).

377. Consequence. *The centers of all the circular sections of an oblique circular cone lie on the median and the symmedian of the principal triangle issued from the vertex of the cone.*

378. Theorem. *Any two circular sections of a cone one of which is parallel and the other antiparallel to the base lie on the same sphere.*

The principal plane VAB of the cone cuts the two sections along two diameters $A'B'$, CD, antiparallel to each other with respect to the principal elements of the cone. Hence the four points A', B', C, D are concyclic. Now the two circular sections have their planes perpendicular to VAB (§ 373), hence the two circular sections lie on the sphere having $A'B'CD$ for its great circle.

379. Converse Theorem. *If two circles lie on a sphere, they also lie on an oblique circular cone.*

Through the center M of the given sphere (M) (Fig. 42) and through the centers O', P of the two given circles $(A'B')$, (CD)

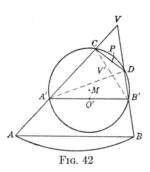

Fig. 42

pass a plane cutting the circles along the diameters $A'B'$, CD. The perpendicular VH from the point $V \equiv (A'C, B'D)$ to the line $A'B'$ is parallel to MO', hence VH is perpendicular to the plane of $(A'B')$. Thus $VA'B'$ is the principal plane of the cone having $(A'B')$ for base and V for vertex.

Now the lines $A'B'$, CD are chords of the circle of intersection of (M) with $VA'B'$, hence they are antiparallel with respect to the angle $A'VB'$, therefore the plane through CD perpendicular to $VA'B'$ will cut the cone (V) along a circle having CD for diameter, i.e., this intersection will coincide with the given circle (CD), which proves the proposition.

N. B. The two circles $(A'B')$, (CD) also lie on the cone having the point $V' \equiv (A'D, B'C)$ for vertex.

380. Remark I. In the above proof (§ 379) it was assumed that the planes of the two given circles are not parallel. The proposition remains valid, if these planes are parallel. The proof is very simple.

Remark II. In some cases instead of a cone (§ 379) we may get a cylinder.

381. Theorem. *If a cone and a sphere have a circle in common, they have a second circle in common.*

Let $(A'B')$ (Fig. 42) be the circle common to the cone (V) and to the sphere (M). The line MO' joining the centers M, O' of

(M), $(A'B')$ and the altitude VH from V to the plane of $(A'B')$ are both perpendicular to the same plane, hence they are parallel, and since VH lies in the plane $VA'B'$, the point M also lies in the principal plane $VA'B'$. Thus the plane $VA'B'$ cuts (M) along a great circle $A'B'CD$ meeting VA', VB' again in C, D, and the plane perpendicular to $VA'B'$ through CD cuts (M) along a circle (CD) having CD for diameter. But A', B', C, D being concyclic, CD is antiparallel to $A'B'$ with respect to VA', VB', and the plane perpendicular to $VA'B'$ through CD cuts (V) along a circle having CD for diameter, i.e., the two circles are identical.

382. Problem. *Determine the locus generated by a variable line equidistant from two fixed points in space and passing through a third fixed point.*

Let SCD be one position of the variable line passing through the fixed point S, and let AC, BD be the two perpendiculars dropped upon SCD from the two given points A, B.

From the congruent right triangles ACD, BCD we have $AD = BC$, hence the triangles CAB, DAB are congruent, and if P is the mid-point of AB, the medians CP, DP of these triangles are equal. Thus the triangle PCD is isosceles, and the line PQ joining P to the mid-point Q of CD is perpendicular to CD at Q, and therefore Q lies on the sphere (PS) having for diameter the line PS joining P to the fixed point S of SCD.

Again from the congruent right triangles ACQ, BDQ we have $AQ = BQ$, hence Q lies in the mediator of the segment AB.

Thus Q lies on the circle of intersection of the fixed sphere (PS) with a fixed plane, and the line SCD joins S to a point Q of this circle, hence the required locus is a cone of the second degree.

383. The Oblique Circular Cylinder. The theory of the planes of symmetry, of polar rays and planes of circular sections relative to the oblique circular cone may be extended to the oblique circular cylinder. The task of formulating these propositions and of proving them is left to the reader. Both the propositions and the proofs differ but slightly, if at all, from the propositions regarding the cone.

EXERCISES

1. Given a circle (C) and a point L inside of (C), find the locus of the point M such that it shall be possible to draw a plane through L cutting the cone M–(C) along a circle having L for its center.

2. The line of centers of the antiparallel sections of an oblique cone with a circular base passes through the vertex of the cone circumscribed, along the base of the cone, to the sphere determined by this base and by the vertex of the cone.

3. The circle is constructed having for diameter the limiting points of two given circles, in the plane perpendicular to these circles. Show that the two cones having for their bases the two coplanar circles and for their common vertex a point of the third circle are such that a plane cutting one of them along a circle also cuts the second along a circle.

4. (a) If two rectangular planes turn about two fixed intersecting lines, their line of intersection generates a cone of the second degree passing through the two fixed lines. A plane perpendicular to either of these two lines will cut the cone along a circle.   (b) The ratio of the distances of any point on the cone to two lines harmonically separated by the two fixed lines and lying in their plane is constant.

5. Through any point A of the circular base (C) of a cone (S) the element SA is drawn, and through the vertex S of (S) a plane is drawn perpendicular to SA meeting (C) in P, Q. The foot of the perpendicular from A upon PQ lies on a fixed circle.

6. (a) If a cone with a circular base has a triad of mutually rectangular elements, the power of the foot of the altitude of the cone with respect to the circle of the base is equal to twice the square of the altitude, with the sign changed.   (b) If the latter condition holds, every element of the cone belongs to a triad of trirectangular elements.

7. If a cone with a circular base has one triad of mutually rectangular elements (and therefore an infinite number of such triads), the feet of the altitudes of the triangles determined by these triads in the plane of the base of the cone lie on a fixed circle.

8. (a) If a cone with a circular base has a triad of mutually orthogonal elements, the square of the chord of the base which is perpendicular to the principal diameter and passes through the foot of the altitude is equal to eight times the square of the altitude of the cone.   (b) Given the circle of the base and the foot of the altitude of a cone (S), construct the vertex S of the cone so that (S) shall have a triad of rectangular elements.

CHAPTER VII

SPHERES

1. Preliminaries

384. Theorem. (a) *The tangents drawn to a sphere from a point outside lie on a cone of revolution.*

(b) *These tangents are all of equal length.*

(c) *Their points of contact lie on a small circle of the sphere.*

(d) *The tangent planes to the cone are also tangent to the sphere.*

The figure may be considered as generated by the revolution of the semi-circle *ETF* and the tangent *PT* to it around the diameter *EF* passing through *P*. The semi-circle *ETF* will generate the sphere *(O)*, the line of fixed length *PT* will generate a cone *(P)* tangent to this sphere along the circle generated by the point *T*.

385. Definition. The cone *(P)* (§ 384) is said to be " circumscribed" to the sphere.

386. Converse Theorem. *Along any small circle of a sphere a cone of revolution may be circumscribed to the sphere.*

The vertex of the cone is determined by the tangent plane to the sphere at any point on the given circle and the diameter of the sphere perpendicular to the plane of the circle.

387. Theorem. (a) *All the tangents to a given sphere having a fixed direction form a cylinder of revolution.*

(b) *The tangent planes to this cylinder are also tangent to the sphere and are the only tangent planes to the sphere parallel to the given direction.*

(c) *The line of contact of the cylinder and the given sphere is a great circle of the sphere the plane of which is perpendicular to the direction of the tangents.*

The proof of this proposition is quite similar to the corresponding proposition relative to the cone (§ 384).

388. Definition. The *angle between a plane and a sphere* is the angle determined by the plane and the tangent plane to the sphere at any point common to the plane and the sphere.

The reader may show that this angle does not depend upon the choice of the point on the circle of intersection of the plane and the sphere.

389. Theorem. *If p is the distance of a plane from the center of a sphere, radius R (p < R), the angle m between the plane and the sphere satisfies the relation*

$$p = R \cos m.$$

The proof is left to the reader.

390. Corollary. *The planes which make a given angle with a given sphere are tangent to a fixed sphere concentric with the given sphere.*

391. Definition. The *angle between two spheres* is the angle formed by the tangent planes to the spheres at a point common to the two spheres.

392. Theorem. *If R, R' are the radii of two spheres and d the length of their line of centers, the angle m between the two spheres satisfies the relation*

$$\cos m = (R^2 + R'^2 - d^2)/2RR'.$$

EXERCISES

1. Draw a sphere touching two given skew lines at two given points.

2. A sphere has a fixed center and a variable radius. Find the locus of the circle of contact of this sphere with the circumscribed cone having a fixed point for its vertex.

3. The locus of the foot of the perpendicular dropped from a point on the axis of a cone of revolution upon a variable plane tangent to the cone is a circle lying on the cone; the plane of this circle is perpendicular to the axis of the cone.

4. A segment fixed both in length and in direction moves so that its extremities remain on two fixed spheres. What is the locus described by each end on the corresponding sphere?

5. Through two given points on a sphere to draw a circle so that its points of intersection with a given circle on this sphere shall be a given distance apart.

6. Through a given line to draw a plane so that the circle of intersection of the plane with a given sphere shall pass through the center of the circle of intersection of the same plane with a second given sphere.

7. If a line CD meets a given sphere (O) in two points C, D, and the line AC joining a given point A (not on the sphere) to C is perpendicular to CD, the line BD joining D to the symmetric B of A with respect to the center O of (O) is also perpendicular to CD.

8. If a perpendicular is erected to a chord of a sphere at each of its ends, the line passing through the center of the sphere and meeting the two perpendiculars is bisected by the center of the sphere.

9. Two skew lines revolve about two fixed points in such a way that the mid-point of their common perpendicular remains fixed. Show that the feet of this common perpendicular describe two circles.

10. Given two orthogonal skew lines x, y having AB for their common perpendicular. The points X, Y move on x, y, respectively, so that $AX = BY$. (a) Prove that the sphere having XY for diameter passes through A, B. (b) Find the locus of the center of this sphere. (c) Prove that the tangent plane to this sphere at A passes through a second fixed point. (d) Show that the line XY is always parallel to a fixed plane.

11. A variable sphere is tangent to a fixed plane at a fixed point. Find the locus of the point of contact of this sphere with the planes having a given orientation.

12. Pass a sphere through two given circles situated in two parallel planes.

13. If two circles situated in two intersecting planes are cospherical, their line of centers is perpendicular to the line of intersection of the two planes. Is the converse true?

14. M is a variable point on a fixed circle, and A is a fixed point, not in the plane of this circle. Show that the plane which is perpendicular to the line AM at M passes through a fixed point.

2. Inverse Points

393. Definition. Two points which divide harmonically a diameter of a sphere are said to be *inverse points* with respect to the sphere.

394. Corollary. Two inverse points with respect to a sphere are also inverse points with respect to any great circle of the sphere which contains the diameter considered.

CONVERSELY. If two points are inverse with respect to a circle, they are inverse points with respect to the sphere having this circle for a great circle.

395. Theorem. *The product of the distances of two inverse points from the center of the sphere considered is equal to the square of the radius of the sphere.*

Indeed, if A, B divide the diameter EF harmonically, and O is the center of the sphere, we have (C. G., p. 135)

$$OE^2 = OA \cdot OB.$$

396. Remark I. Of two points inverse with respect to a sphere one lies inside and the other outside the sphere.

397. Remark II. If one of two inverse points lies on the sphere, the other coincides with it, i.e., a point on the sphere is its own inverse point.

398. Remark III. Two inverse points with respect to a sphere lie on the same side of the center of the sphere.

399. Remark IV. *Two given points and their inverses with respect to a sphere are concyclic, or collinear.*

400. Theorem. *If the product of the distances of two points from the center of a sphere is equal to the square of the radius of the sphere, and if the two points are collinear with the center of the sphere and lie on the same side of this center, the two points are inverse with respect to the sphere.*

For if $OE^2 = OA \cdot OB$ (§ 395), the points E, F are separated harmonically by A, B (C. G., p. 136), hence the points A, B are inverse with respect to the sphere (§ 394).

401. Theorem. *The ratio of the distances of a variable point of a sphere from two given inverse points is constant.*

Let A, B be two inverse points lying on the diameter EF. If M is a point on the sphere, the proposition is true for all the points on the great circle MEF (C. G., p. 143). As this circle revolves about EF it generates the given sphere; now this rotation does not alter the distances of any given point of this circle from the points A, B, hence the ratio $MA : MB$ remains unchanged by this rotation, which proves the proposition.

EXERCISES

1. Through a given point to draw a sphere so that a given pair of points shall be inverse with respect to this sphere.

2. If A, B, C, D, $\cdots$, are points on a sphere, and U, V, are two points inverse with respect to this sphere, we have

$$UA : UB : UC : UD : \cdots = VA : VB : VC : VD : \cdots.$$

3. Orthogonal Spheres

402. Definition. Two spheres are said to be **orthogonal,** if the square of their line of centers is equal to the sum of the squares of their radii.

403. Corollary. *The two radii of two orthogonal spheres which pass through a point common to the two spheres are perpendicular to each other.*

CONVERSELY. *If the radii passing through a point common to two spheres are rectangular, the spheres are orthogonal.*

404. Theorem. *The tangent planes to two orthogonal spheres at a point common to these spheres are rectangular.*

Let M be a point common to two rectangular spheres (A), (B). The tangent planes to (A), (B) at M are perpendicular to the radii AM, BM. Now the spheres being orthogonal, the radii are perpendicular to each other (§ 403), hence the same is true about the tangent planes.

405. Remark I. *The tangent plane to one of two orthogonal spheres at a point common to these spheres passes through the center of the second sphere.*

406. Remark II. *If two spheres are orthogonal, the radius of one sphere passing through a point common to the two spheres, is tangent to the other sphere.*

407. Converse Proposition. *If the tangent planes to two spheres at a point common to these spheres are rectangular, the spheres are orthogonal.*

Indeed, the radii of the two spheres drawn to the point considered are perpendicular.

REMARK. This property is often taken as the definition of orthogonal spheres.

408. Corollary. *Given two intersecting spheres, if the radius of one sphere passing through a point common to the two spheres is tangent to the other sphere, the two spheres are orthogonal.*

409. Theorem. *If two spheres are orthogonal, the sphere described on their line of centers as a diameter passes through the circle common to the two given spheres.*

Indeed, the line of centers subtends a right angle at any point common to the two given spheres (§ 403).

410. Converse Theorem. *If the sphere having for diameter the line of centers of two intersecting spheres passes through the circle common to the two spheres, the given spheres are orthogonal.*

Indeed, in such a case the radii of the two given spheres drawn to a point common to these spheres will be rectangular, hence the spheres will be orthogonal (§ 403).

411. Problem. *With a given point as center to draw a sphere orthogonal to a given sphere.*

Construct the sphere (AB) having for diameter the line AB joining the given point B to the center A of the given sphere (A). The sphere having B for center and passing through the circle common to (A) and (AB) is the required sphere (§ 410).

412. Theorem. *If two spheres are orthogonal, any two points of one of them collinear with the center of the second sphere are inverse points with respect to the second sphere.*

Let (A), (B) be two orthogonal spheres; E, F two points of (B) collinear with the center A of (A), and let C, D be the ends of the diameter AEF of (A).

If M is a point common to (A) and (B), we have (§ 406) $AM^2 = AE \cdot AF$. But $AM = AC = AD$, hence (C. G., p. 136) (CD, EF) is harmonic, which proves the proposition (§ 393).

413. Converse Theorem. *If two points of one sphere are inverse points with respect to a second sphere, the two spheres are orthogonal.*

By hypothesis, the points E, F of (B) (§ 412) are collinear with A and are harmonic with respect to C, D, hence

$$AC^2 = AE \cdot AF,$$

and therefore

$$AM^2 = AE \cdot AF.$$

Thus AM is tangent to (B), hence the spheres are orthogonal (§ 408).

414. Problem. *Through three given points to pass a sphere orthogonal to a given sphere.*

The three given points A, B, C and the inverse A' of one of them, say A, with respect to the given sphere (O) determine the required sphere (S).

The problem has, in general, only one solution, for the inverses B', C' of B, C with respect to (O) will also lie on (S) (§ 413).

415. Corollary. *Three pairs of inverse points with respect to a given sphere* (no three of these points being collinear) *are cospherical.*

Exercise. Discuss the special cases of this problem (§ 414).

416. Definition. A circle and a sphere are said to be **orthogonal** to each other, if the plane of the circle passes through the center of the sphere, and the circle is orthogonal to the circle of the sphere lying in its plane.

417. Theorem. *If a circle is orthogonal to a sphere, the tangent to the circle at a point common to the circle and the sphere is perpendicular to the plane tangent to the sphere at the point considered.*

The given circle (A) is orthogonal to the great circle (B) of the given sphere (O) (§ 410), hence the tangent to (A) at a point common to (A) and (B) passes through the center O of (B) (C. G., p. 144), i.e., this tangent is the radius OM of (O). Now the tangent plane to (O) at M is perpendicular to the radius OM, hence the proposition.

This property is sometimes taken as the definition of the orthogonality of a circle and a sphere.

418. Theorem. *If a circle is orthogonal to a sphere, any sphere passing through the circle is orthogonal to the sphere.*

A diameter of (B) (§ 417) will cut (A) in two inverse points with respect to (B) and therefore with respect to (O) (§ 394). Any sphere through (A) will pass through these inverse points, and therefore will be orthogonal to (O) (§ 413).

419. Definition. If one of two given coplanar orthogonal circles is turned about their common line of centers by an angle of 90 degrees so that its plane becomes perpendicular to the given plane, the two circles form an *orthogonal link.*

420. Consequence. The line of centers of two circles of an orthogonal link contains a point which has equal powers with respect to the two circles, namely the trace on this line of the radical axis of the two circles in their coplanar position.

This point is the only one having equal powers with respect to the two circles.

421. Theorem. *Any sphere passing through one of the circles of an orthogonal link is orthogonal to the other circle of the link.*

It is obvious that a sphere passing through one of the two circles of an orthogonal link has its center in the plane of the other circle of the link. Furthermore, any sphere passing through one circle of the link and the sphere having the other circle for a great circle, are orthogonal, for one of them passes through two inverse points with respect to the other, on the line of centers of the circles of the link.

EXERCISES

1. Determine the vertices of the two cones circumscribed to two orthogonal spheres along the circle common to the two spheres.

2. Through a given circle to pass a sphere orthogonal to a given sphere.

3. Through two given points to draw a sphere orthogonal to a given circle.

4. Find the locus of the centers of the spheres passing through two given points and orthogonal to a given sphere.

5. Find the locus of the centers of the circles passing through a given point and orthogonal to a given sphere.

6. Draw a circle forming an orthogonal link with each of two given coplanar circles.

7. All the planes which cut two circles of an orthogonal link in four concyclic points have a fixed point in common.

8. The circle common to the three spheres having for great circles the Appollonian circles of a triangle forms an orthogonal link with the circumcircle of the triangle.

9. Given two circles (A), (B) forming an orthogonal link, if P, Q are any two points on (A), and R, S any two points on (B), we have

$$PR \cdot QS = PS \cdot QR.$$

4. Poles and Polar Planes with Respect to a Sphere

422. Theorem. *The locus of the harmonic conjugate of a fixed point with respect to a variable pair of points of a given sphere which are collinear with the fixed point is a plane.*

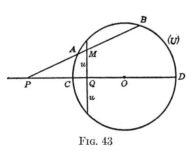

FIG. 43

Let A, B be any pair of points on a given sphere (O) (Fig. 43) collinear with the fixed point P, and M the harmonic conjugate of P with respect to A, B.

The plane determined by the line PAB and the center O of (O) cuts the sphere along a great circle (U), and in this plane the locus of M, as the points A, B vary, is a straight line, namely the polar u of P with respect to (U) (C. G., p. 148).

The polar u meets the diameter PO of (U) in the inverse Q of P with respect to (U) and is perpendicular to the diameter PO, hence M lies in the plane π perpendicular to PO at Q.

Conversely, any point M of the plane π such that MP cuts (O) belongs to the locus. The plane PMO cuts (O) along a great circle (U) and the plane π along the line QM which is perpendicular to PO at Q, hence QM is the polar of P with respect to (U), and therefore M is the harmonic conjugate of P with respect to the two points of intersection A, B of PM with the circle (U), and since A, B are also points on (O), the proposition is proved.

OTHERWISE. Revolve the circle (U) and the line u about the line PO. The circle will generate the sphere (O) and the line will generate a plane, the locus of the point M.

423. Definition. The plane π (§ 422) is called the *polar plane* of the point P with respect to the sphere (O), and the point P is said to be the *pole* of the plane π with respect to (O).

424. Theorem. *The polar plane of a point with respect to a sphere is the plane which passes through the inverse of the given point with respect to the given sphere and is perpendicular to the diameter on which these two points are situated.*

This follows immediately from the proof of the preceding proposition (§ 422).

425. Remark I. This property (§ 424) is sometimes taken as the definition of the polar plane of a point with respect to a sphere.

426. Remark II. *The polar plane of a point with respect to a sphere contains the polar of the point with respect to the circle of intersection of the sphere with any plane passing through the point considered.*

427. Theorem. *The pole of a given plane with respect to a sphere is the inverse, with respect to the sphere, of the foot of the perpendicular dropped upon the given plane from the center of the sphere.*

This follows immediately from the proof above (§ 422).

428. Remark I. If the point lies inside the sphere, its polar plane does not cut the sphere; if the point lies outside the sphere, its polar plane cuts the sphere.

429. Remark II. Every plane has a pole, except the planes passing through the center of the sphere.

Every point has a polar plane, except the center of the sphere.

430. Remark III. The polar plane of a point on the sphere is the tangent plane to the sphere at that point, for a point on the sphere is its own inverse (§ 397).

431. Remark IV.   In the converse of the proof of the proposition § 422 we assumed that the line PM meets the sphere in two points.   This is always the case when P lies inside the sphere (O).   When the point P lies outside the sphere, the line PM will meet the sphere only if the point M is taken inside the circle of intersection of the plane with the sphere.

432. Remark V.   Suppose P lies outside of (O) (§ 422), and let PT be a tangent to (O).   The plane PTO cuts (O) along a great circle (U).   The point of contact T of PT with (O) lies on (U) and is a point common to (U) and the polar u of P with respect to (U) (C. G., p. 150).   Now u lies in the polar plane of P, hence T lies on the circle of intersection of (O) with the polar plane π of P with respect to (O).   We find thus another proof of the proposition of § 384, and in addition a new relation between the vertex of the cone and the plane of the base of the cone.

433. Theorem.   *If the polar plane of the point A passes through the point B, the polar plane of the point B passes through A.*

If the line AB meets the given sphere in two points M, N, the proposition is almost obvious.   Indeed, if the polar plane α of A passes through B, the point B is the harmonic conjugate of A with respect to M, N, hence A is the harmonic conjugate of B with respect to M, N, and the polar plane β of B will pass through A.

We shall now give a proof which is valid whether the line AB cuts the sphere or not.

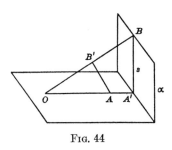

FIG. 44

Since B (Fig. 44) lies in α, the foot A' of the perpendicular BA' from B upon the diameter OA is the inverse of A with respect to the sphere (O), and we have

$$OA \cdot OA' = R^2,$$

where R is the radius of (O).

Now let B' be the foot of the perpendicular AB' from A upon the diameter OB.   The points A', B' lie on the circle having AB for diameter, hence

$$OA \cdot OA' = OB \cdot OB'$$

and therefore

$$OB \cdot OB' = R^2,$$

i.e., B' is the inverse of B with respect to (O); but the plane β is perpendicular to OBB' at B', and $B'A$ is perpendicular to OBB' at B', by construction, hence $B'A$ lies in β, which proves the proposition.

OTHERWISE. The plane ABO meets the sphere (O) along a great circle (S) and the polar plane α of A along the polar s of A with respect to (S), hence B lies on s, and therefore A lies on the polar t of B with respect to (S). But t lies in the polar plane β of B with respect to (O), hence the proposition.

434. Definition. Two points such that the polar plane of one passes through the other are called *conjugate* points with respect to the sphere.

A given point has an infinite number of conjugate points, namely all the points of its polar plane.

435. Remark. From the preceding theorem (§ 433) it follows that two points inverse with respect to a sphere are also conjugate with respect to this sphere.

Two conjugate points with respect to a sphere are inverse with respect to the sphere only if they are collinear with the center of the sphere.

436. Theorem. *If a plane α passes through the pole of another plane β, the plane β passes through the pole of α.*

Indeed, if α passes through the pole B of β, that means that the polar plane α of A passes through B, hence the polar plane β of B passes through A (§ 433).

437. Definition. Two planes such that one passes through the pole of the other are called *conjugate planes* with respect to the sphere.

A given plane has an infinite number of conjugate planes, namely all the planes which pass through the pole of the given plane.

438. Theorem. (a) *The polar planes of all the points of a given plane pass through a fixed point, the pole of the given plane.*

(b) *The poles of all the planes which pass through a given point lie in a plane, the polar plane of the given point.*

The proof is left to the reader.

439. Theorem. *The polar planes of all the points on a straight line pass through another straight line, and the polar planes of the points on the second straight line pass through the first line.*

Let A, B be any two points on the given line p, and let q be the line of intersection of the polar planes α, β of A, B. Any point A' of q is conjugate to both A and B, hence the polar plane α' of A' will contain both A and B, and A' is conjugate to every point of p. Similarly any point of p is conjugate to every point of q, hence the proposition.

440. Definition. Two lines such that the polar plane of any point of one passes through the other are called *conjugate lines* or *reciprocal lines,* or *polar lines* with respect to the sphere.

441. Corollary. *The poles of all the planes passing through a given line lie on another line, the conjugate of the given line.*

442. Theorem. *A plane passing through one of two conjugate lines cuts the other line in the pole of the first line with respect to the circle along which the sphere is cut by the plane considered.*

Let the plane μ passing through the given line p cut the conjugate q of p with respect to a given sphere (O) in the point A, and (O) along a circle (U). The polar of A with respect to (U) lies in the plane μ and in the polar plane α of A with respect to (O) (§ 426), and since α must pass through p (§ 439), the proposition is proved.

443. Theorem. *Two polar lines are perpendicular to each other, and the feet of the common perpendicular to the two lines are a pair of inverse points with respect to the sphere.*

Through the given line p (Fig. 45) and the center O of the given sphere (O) pass a plane λ cutting the conjugate q of p in A, and

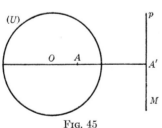

the sphere along a great circle (U). The point A is the pole of p with respect to (U) (§ 442), hence OA is perpendicular to p and the foot A', on p, of this perpendicular is the inverse of A with respect to (U), and therefore also with respect to (O) (§ 394).

FIG. 45

On the other hand the polar plane μ of any point M of p passes through A (§ 439) and is perpendicular to the line MO (§ 424), and therefore also to the plane λ, hence μ passes through the perpendicular to λ at A. Now this perpendicular lies in the polar plane of any point M of p, hence it coincides with q, and the proposition is proved.

444. Problem. *Construct the conjugate of a given line with respect to a given sphere.*

From the center O of the given sphere (O) drop the perpendicular OA upon the given line p and construct the inverse A' of A with respect to (O). The perpendicular q at A' to the plane O–p is the required line.

This solution is based on the preceding theorem (§ 443).

445. Remark I. If the point A lies on the sphere (O), the line p is tangent to the sphere at A (§ 397). Now the polar plane of A is the tangent plane to (O) at A, and this plane must pass through q, hence q lies in the tangent plane to (O) at A, and is perpendicular to p at this point.

446. Remark II. The points A, A' (§ 444) being inverse with respect to (O), one of these points lies inside and the other outside of (O) (§ 396), and since the conjugate lines p, q are perpendicular to OAA', therefore

Of two conjugate lines one meets the sphere in real points and the other does not.

447. Remark III. A given line has one and only one conjugate line with respect to a sphere, except the lines passing through the center, which lines have no conjugates.

It may be said that these lines also have conjugates, but that these conjugates are infinitely distant. This is the point of view adopted in PROJECTIVE GEOMETRY.

448. Theorem. *Through a line not meeting a given sphere two tangent planes may be drawn to the sphere.*

Indeed, these planes are the tangent planes to the sphere at the point of intersection of the sphere with the conjugate of the given line (§ 446).

449. Theorem. *If the line of intersection of two conjugate planes does not cut the sphere, the two planes are harmonically separated by the two tangent planes which may be drawn from this line to the sphere.*

Let p be the line of intersection of the two given planes α, β. If E, F are the points of contact of the two tangent planes through p to the sphere (§ 448), the line EF is the conjugate of p.

The planes α, β being conjugate, their poles A, B are conjugate points, and since α, β pass through p, their poles must lie on EF, hence A, B are the traces of the planes β, α on EF. Now since A, B are conjugate points, they are therefore harmonically separated by E, F (§ 443), hence the proposition (§ 34).

450. Theorem. *If a cone cuts a sphere along two circles* (§ 381), *the planes of these circles intersect in the polar plane of the vertex of the cone with respect to the sphere.*

Let (C), (C') be the two circles common to the sphere (O) (Fig. 46) and the cone (S). If P, P' are two points on (C), (C'),

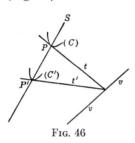

FIG. 46

respectively, and collinear with the vertex S of (S), the tangents t, t' to (C), (C') at P, P' are the intersections of the planes of (C), (C') with the tangent planes (U), (U') to (O) at P, P', hence t, t' meet on the line of intersection v of the planes (U), (U'). But v is the conjugate line of SPP' with respect to the sphere (§ 441), hence the polar plane σ of S with respect to (O) passes through v, i.e., the point tt' common to the planes of (C), (C') lies in σ. The proof is completed by considering another position of the line SPP'.

451. Corollary. *Two circles belonging to the same sphere determine two cones* (§ 379). *The line joining the vertices of the two cones is the conjugate, with respect to the sphere, of the line of intersection of the planes of the two circles.*

452. Definition. A tetrahedron the faces of which are the polar planes of the respective opposite vertices is said to be *conjugate,* or *self-polar* or *polar* with respect to the sphere.

453. Problem. *Construct a tetrahedron conjugate with respect to a given sphere.*

Take a point A arbitrarily in space, and in its polar plane α take arbitrarily a point B. The polar plane β of B passes through A (§ 433) and cuts α along a line m. On m take arbitrarily a point C. The polar plane γ of C passes through both A and B (§ 433) and cuts m in D.

By construction, the faces BCD, CDA, DAB are the polar planes of A, B, C, and since D lies in each of these planes, its polar plane δ coincides with ABC, hence $ABCD$ is a tetrahedron conjugate with respect to the sphere.

454. Remark. From the way the points A, B, C, D were chosen it follows that there exists in space an infinite number of tetrahedrons conjugate with respect to a given sphere.

455. Theorem. *A tetrahedron conjugate with respect to a sphere is orthocentric* (§ 212).

Indeed, if the vertices of a tetrahedron are the poles of the opposite faces, the perpendiculars dropped from these points upon their polar planes must pass through the center of the sphere (§ 422).

456. Corollary. *If a tetrahedron is conjugate with respect to a sphere, its orthocenter coincides with the center of the sphere.*

457. Theorem. *Every orthocentric tetrahedron is conjugate with respect to a sphere the center of which coincides with the orthocenter of the tetrahedron.*

This is the converse of the proposition of § 455. The sphere is real, if the orthocenter of the tetrahedron lies outside this solid. A proof will be given later (§ 795).

458. Theorem. *The polar planes, with respect to a given sphere, of the vertices of a tetrahedron form a tetrahedron whose vertices are the poles of the faces of the given tetrahedron.*

The proof is left to the reader.

459. Definition. Two tetrahedrons such that each face of one has for its pole, with respect to a given sphere, a vertex of the other are said to be *polar* or *polar reciprocal* with respect to the sphere.

If two tetrahedrons are polar with respect to a sphere, the perpendiculars dropped from the vertices of one tetrahedron upon the corresponding faces of the other pass through the center of the given sphere.

460. Theorem. *If the perpendiculars dropped from the vertices of a tetrahedron upon the respective faces of another tetrahedron are concurrent, the same is true about the perpendiculars dropped from the vertices of the second upon the corresponding faces of the first tetrahedron.*

Let O (Fig. 47) be the point common to the perpendiculars dropped from the vertices of the tetrahedron $ABCD$ upon the corresponding faces of the tetrahedron $A'B'C'D'$. Imagine a sphere (O) having O for center, and let $A''B''C''D''$ be the polar reciprocal tetrahedron of $ABCD$ with respect to (O). The faces of $A''B''C''D''$ are perpendicular to the lines OA, OB, OC, OD,

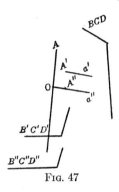

Fig. 47

respectively, hence the respective faces of the two tetrahedrons $A'B'C'D'$, $A''B''C''D''$ are parallel, i.e., these two tetrahedrons are homothetic (§ 58).

The perpendiculars a', a'' dropped from A' and A'' upon the face BCD are parallel and pass through a pair of corresponding points in the homothetic figures considered, hence the two lines are homothetic. We have analogous pairs of lines b', b''; c', c''; d', d''. Now the lines a'', b'', c'', d'' pass through the center of (O), hence the lines a', b', c', d' pass through the point O' which corresponds to O in the two homothetic figures considered.

461. Definition. Two such tetrahedrons (§ 460) are said to be mutually "orthological."

EXERCISES

1. If through a point M of a sphere (A) the line is drawn meeting two given lines conjugate with respect to (A), in the points P, Q, the harmonic conjugate of M with respect to P, Q lies on (A).

2. Find a necessary and sufficient condition for the polar planes of two points with respect to a given sphere to be parallel.

3. Construct a sphere passing through a given point so that the polar plane, with respect to this sphere, of another given point shall coincide with a given plane.

4. If a diameter of one of two orthogonal spheres cuts the other sphere, the ends of this diameter are conjugate points with respect to the second sphere.

5. Find the locus of the pole of a given line with respect to the circle of intersection of a given sphere with a variable plane passing through the given line.

6. Given a sphere and two points in space, the distances of these points from the center of the sphere are directly proportional to the respective distances of each of these points from the polar plane of the other point.

7. The circle of intersection of a given sphere with a plane (P) is taken for the base of a cone the vertex of which is a given point S. This cone cuts the sphere along a second circle (§ 381). Show that if the plane (P) varies so as to pass constantly through a fixed point, the plane of the second circle considered will also pass through a fixed point.

8. If two points lie on two reciprocal lines with respect to a sphere, these points are harmonically separated by the two points which the sphere determines on the line joining the given points.

9. If a line t meeting two polar lines p, q of a sphere (O) is tangent to (O), then t passes through a point common to (O) and one of the lines p, q.

10. (a) The conjugates, with respect to a given sphere, of two coplanar lines are coplanar. (b) The conjugates, with respect to a given sphere, of all the lines meeting a given line are met by a fixed line.

11. The conjugates, with respect to a given sphere, of four given lines belonging to a hyperbolic group also form a hyperbolic group.

12. Through a given line in space to draw a plane so that the algebraic sum of its distances from the vertices of a given tetrahedron shall have a given value.

5. The Imaginary Sphere

462. Two inverse points A, B with respect to a sphere of radius R may be defined as two points collinear with the center O of the sphere and such that

$$(1) \qquad OA \cdot OB = R^2,$$

the points A, B being situated on the same side of the center O (§ 398). A point on the sphere is its own inverse point (§ 397).

Suppose now that we replace in the above relation (1) the point B by its symmetric A' with respect to O. The product $OA \cdot OA'$ will remain numerically equal to R^2. It is however easy to distinguish between the points A' and B by saying that since the points A and A' lie on opposite sides of O, the product $OA \cdot OA'$ is negative, and we have thus

$$(2) \qquad OA \cdot OA' = -R^2.$$

By analogy with the formula (1), the formula (2) may be said to define the relation between two inverse points with respect to the sphere having for center O and for the square of its radius the negative quantity $-R^2$.

A sphere thus defined has no real points, for if a point is to lie on this sphere, its distance from the center O would have to be equal to $\sqrt{-R^2}$, which distance is imaginary. In other words there are no points which are their own inverses with respect to such a sphere. To distinguish this sort of a sphere from the case when R^2 is positive, we agree to call this new sphere an "imaginary" sphere. We thus have the

DEFINITION. *A sphere whose center is a real point and the square of whose radius is negative is called an **imaginary** sphere.*

Since such a sphere has no real points, we cannot speak of the tangent plane to such a sphere, or of the points of intersection of

the sphere with a straight line, etc. However the introduction of
the concept of the imaginary sphere will be justified in what follows, in many different connections. A first instance is furnished
by the theory of poles and polar planes.

463. We may define the polar plane of a point A with respect
to a real sphere (O) as the plane perpendicular to the line joining
A to the center O of the sphere at the inverse A' of A with respect
to (O) (§ 425). This definition remains applicable to an imaginary sphere, and it is readily seen that the proof of the basic
theorem (§ 433) also holds in this case. The entire theory of
poles and polar planes is thus retained intact with regard to an
imaginary sphere. In some ways this theory is more symmetrical
with respect to an imaginary sphere than with respect to a real
sphere. With respect to a real sphere, for instance, we have to
distinguish between two conjugate lines one meeting the sphere in
real points, while the other does not (§ 446). No such distinctions
are necessary with respect to an imaginary sphere.

It is clear that the use of the concept of an imaginary sphere is
not an unavoidable necessity. If we say that the plane α is the
polar plane of the point A with respect to the imaginary sphere
(O) of center O the square of its radius being $- R^2$, we mean to
say that α is the symmetric, with respect to the point O, of the
polar plane α' of A with respect to the sphere (O) having for
center the same point O and for the square of its radius the
quantity $+ R^2$. Nevertheless the use of the imaginary sphere
gives us the advantage of replacing two operations by the mental
image of one.

Similar considerations may be advanced to justify the use of
the concept of *imaginary circle*.

464. The consideration of inverse points with respect to an
imaginary sphere, or of poles and polar planes with respect to such
a sphere, involves only real operations, for in these connections
the square of the radius, which is real, comes into play. We shall
limit the use of the imaginary sphere to operations when the
square of the radius is involved. Where the radius itself is to be
considered, as for instance, when we have to use a point on the
sphere, we shall only consider real spheres. However, in more
advanced works the points on an imaginary sphere are utilized to
great advantage. Furthermore, there are more general cate-

gories of imaginary spheres than the imaginary spheres defined above (§ 462). But such geometric elements are beyond the scope of this book.

465. Orthogonal Spheres. Whether the sphere is real or imaginary, its center is a real point. Consequently the line of centers of two spheres is always a real length. The sum of the squares of the radii of two orthogonal spheres is equal to the square of the line of centers (§ 402). Hence two imaginary spheres cannot be orthogonal, for the sum of the squares of their radii is negative. But this condition of orthogonality of two spheres may be satisfied, if one of the spheres is real and the other imaginary. Thus a real sphere and an imaginary sphere may be orthogonal to each other.

6. Centers, Axes, and Planes of Similitude

466. Homothetic Spheres. Given a sphere, a homothetic center and a homothetic ratio, we constructed a sphere homothetic to the given sphere (§ 54); it was found that the homothetic center divides the line of centers of the two spheres in the ratio of the radii (§ 55).

Let us now consider the converse problem. Given two spheres (A), (B), to find a point S such that the sphere (B) shall be the homothetic of (A) with respect to S. If such a point is to be found, it must divide the line of centers AB of the given spheres in the ratio $a : b$ of the radii a, b of the two spheres, which ratio must be taken for the homothetic ratio. There are two and only two points which divide AB in the ratio $a : b$, namely S which divides AB externally and S' which divides AB internally in the ratio $a : b$. If we take one of these points, say S, as homothetic center and $a : b$ as homothetic ratio, it is readily shown that the homothetic of (A) coincides with the sphere (B). We have thus arrived at the

THEOREM. *Two spheres are homothetic in two and only two ways.*

467. Remark I. To obtain the centers of similitude of two spheres we divide the line of centers of the spheres in the ratio of the radii, internally and externally. Hence: *The centers of similitude of two spheres are separated harmonically by the centers of the two spheres.*

468. Remark II. If two spheres are equal, they have only an internal center of similitude.

If two spheres are tangent to each other, the point of contact is a center of similitude of the two spheres.

If the two spheres are concentric their common center is their only center of similitude.

469. Remark III. The centers of similitude of two spheres are also the centers of similitude of any two of their great circles which lie in the same plane, i.e., of two circles along which the two spheres are cut by any plane passing through their line of centers.

The proposition § 466 may thus be arrived at by revolving two circles about their line of centers.

470. Remark IV. A plane passing through a center of similitude of two spheres cuts the two spheres along two circles, one of the centers of similitude of which coincides with the center of similitude considered (of the two spheres).

What is the relation of the second center of similitude of the two circles to the second center of similitude of the two spheres?

471. Theorem. *A tangent plane common to two spheres passes through a center of similitude of the two spheres.*

This follows from the fact that the radii AP, BQ drawn to the points of contact P, Q of the tangent plane with the spheres (A), (B) are both perpendicular to this plane and therefore parallel to each other.

472. Conversely. *A tangent plane to one of two given spheres which passes through a center of similitude of the two spheres is also tangent to the second sphere.*

473. Remark. A common tangent plane of two spheres passes through the external center of similitude of the two spheres, if the tangent plane is external, i.e., if the two spheres are situated on the same side of this plane.

If the common tangent plane is internal, i.e., if the two spheres lie on opposite sides of this plane, the plane will pass through the internal center of similitude of the two spheres.

Corollary. *The cone circumscribed about one of two given spheres (§ 385) and having for its vertex a center of similitude of the two spheres is also circumscribed about the other given sphere.*

Thus two spheres external to each other have two common circumscribed cones. Two intersecting spheres have one common circumscribed cone. If one of the two spheres lies inside the other, they have no circumscribed cone in common.

474. Definitions. *Homologous* and *antihomologous* points on two spheres are defined in the same way as in the case of two circles. Also "homologous" and "antihomologous" chords (C. G., p. 158). The plane determined by three points of one sphere and the plane determined by the three points of the second sphere antihomologous to the first three points are said to be *two antihomologous planes* of the two spheres.

475. Theorem. *The product of the distances of a center of similitude of two spheres from two antihomologous points is constant.*

Consider the circles of intersection of the two spheres with the plane determined by the line of centers and the line joining the two antihomologous points to the corresponding center of similitude. The proof is thus reduced to the proof of the corresponding theorem in the plane (C. G., p. 158).

476. Corollary. Two pairs of antihomologous points are concyclic, or collinear.

477. Theorem. *If a sphere touches two given spheres, the points of contact are antihomologous points on the given spheres.*

Consider the three great circles of intersection of the three spheres with the plane determined by their centers, and the proposition reduces to the corresponding proposition in the plane (C. G., p. 159).

478. Definition. The sphere having for diameter the segment determined by the centers of similitude of two given spheres is called the *sphere of similitude* of these two spheres.

479. Theorem. *The ratio of the distances of any point on the sphere of similitude of two given spheres from the centers of these spheres is equal to the ratio of the radii of the two given spheres.*

The proof is analogous to the proof in the plane (C. G., p. 160).

480. Corollary. *The circle common to two intersecting spheres lies also on their sphere of similitude.*

481. Theorem. (a) *The three external centers of similitude of three spheres taken in pairs are collinear.*

(b) *Each of these external centers of similitude is collinear with two internal centers of similitude of these spheres taken in pairs.*

The ends of three similarly directed parallel radii of the three spheres lie in the same plane with the external centers of similitude of the three spheres taken in pairs, hence these centers of similitude lie on the line of intersection of the plane considered with the plane of the centers of the three spheres.

If the sense of one of the three parallel radii considered is different from the sense of the other two we obtain the second part of the proposition.

OTHERWISE. The centers of similitude of the three given spheres taken in pairs are also the centers of similitude of the three great circles of these spheres along which the spheres are cut by the plane determined by their centers, and the proposition follows from the case in the plane (C. G., p. 160).

482. Definition. The four lines which contain the six centers of similitude of the three spheres taken two-by-two are called the *axes of similitude* of these spheres.

483. Remark. If Z, X, Y are the external centers of similitude of the pairs of spheres (A), (B); (B), (C); (C), (A), and if Z', X', Y', are the corresponding internal centers of similitude, these six points are distributed on the four axes of similitude in the following way:

$$XYZ, \quad YZ'X', \quad ZX'Y', \quad XY'Z'.$$

484. Theorem. *A tangent plane common to three spheres passes through an axis of similitude of the three spheres.*

Indeed, this plane must pass through a center of similitude of the first and the second sphere (§ 471), and again through a center of similitude of the first and the third sphere (§ 471).

485. Conversely. *A plane passing through an axis of similitude of three spheres and tangent to one of these spheres is also tangent to the remaining two spheres* (§ 472).

486. Corollary. *Three spheres may have eight tangent planes in common.*

For through the four axes of similitude (§ 482) four pairs of tangent planes may be drawn to one of these spheres (§ 448), and therefore to all the three spheres (§ 485).

487. Remark. These eight tangent planes will exist, if neither of the four axes of similitude has any points in common with either of the three given spheres. If this is not the case, the number of common tangent planes will diminish by two or more. It may happen that the three spheres have no common tangent planes, as, for instance, in the case when one of the three spheres lies entirely inside another of these spheres.

488. Problem. *To each of three given spheres to draw a tangent plane so that these three planes shall be parallel and that their distances from a given fixed point shall be proportional to three given segments (quantities).*

FIRST SOLUTION. Let (A), (B), (C) be the three given spheres, M the given point, and p, q, r the three given segments.

With M as homothetic center and $p : q$, $p : r$, as homothetic ratios construct the homothetics (B'), (C') of (B), (C) (§ 54). Now construct a plane tangent to the three spheres (A), (B'), (C') (§ 485) say, at P, Q', R', respectively.

The plane $PQ'R'$ together with the planes tangent to (B), (C) at the homothetics Q, R of Q', R' constitute a solution of the problem.

The plane $PQ'R'$ may have eight different positions (§ 486), and in the above construction either of the two homothetic ratios may be taken either positively or negatively. Thus the problem may have, in all, thirty-two solutions.

SECOND SOLUTION. Let α, β, γ be the required three planes (Fig. 48). The parallel tangent planes α, β are homothetic with respect to one of the two centers of similitude S_c, S_c', say S_c, of the two spheres (A), (B), hence the points of intersection X, Y of these planes with the line MS_c are homothetic, and the lines

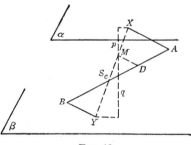

FIG. 48

AX, BY joining X, Y to the centers A, B of (A) (B) are parallel.

If D is the trace on AB of the parallel to AX through M we have

$$DA : DB = MX : MY = p : q,$$

hence the point D is determined, and the parallel to MD through A will meet S_cM in the point X of the plane α.

Now considering the two spheres (A), (C), we may determine a second point in α, in a similar manner. Through the two points draw a plane tangent to (A) and construct the homothetics of this plane with reference to the other two spheres. The three planes will constitute a solution of the problem.

The point D may be constructed on AB in two ways, and the point M may be joined to either of the two centers of similitude of (A), (B), hence we obtain four different positions for X. If we consider the spheres (A), (C), we obtain, in an analogous way, four points Z. Joining an X to a Z we obtain in all sixteen lines. Through each of these lines two tangent planes may be drawn to (A). Hence the problem may have thirty-two solutions.

489. Theorem. *The centers of the three spheres of similitude of three given spheres taken two-by-two are collinear.*

The plane determined by the centers of the given spheres cuts these spheres and their spheres of similitude along three great circles and their circles of similitude, hence the proposition (C. G., p. 197).

A second proof of this proposition will be given later (§ 596).

490. Definition. The tetrahedron determined by the centers of four given spheres will be referred to as the "central tetrahedron" of these spheres. The six lines joining their centers are thus the edges of the central tetrahedron.

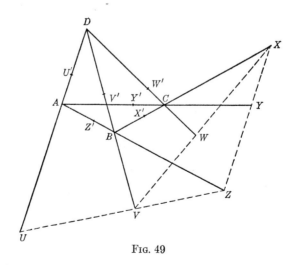

Fig. 49

491. Given four spheres (A), (B), (C), (D) (Fig. 49), let X, Y, Z, U, V, W, be the external centers of similitude of the pairs of spheres (B) (C); (C), (A); (A), (B); (D), (A); (D), (B); (D), (C); let X', Y', Z', U', V', W' be the corresponding internal centers of similitude. Taken in pairs the four spheres have thus 12 centers of similitude. The four faces BCD, CDA, DAB, ABC of the central tetrahedron contain each the four axes of similitude of the three spheres having their centers in the respective face (§ 482). The twelve centers of similitude are thus distributed on the 16 axes of similitude in the following way

	I.			II.			III.			IV.		
a.	X	V	W	Y	U	W	Z	U	V	X	Y	Z
b.	X'	V	W'	Y'	U	W'	Z'	U	V'	X'	Y	Z'
c.	X'	V'	W	Y'	U'	W	Z'	U'	V	X'	Y'	Z
d.	X	V'	W'	Y	U'	W'	Z	U'	V'	X	Y'	Z'

and we have the four groups of six coplanar points

$$\begin{array}{cccccc} X & V & W & X' & V' & W' \\ Y & W & U & Y' & W' & U' \\ Z & U & V & Z' & U' & V' \\ X & Y & Z & X' & Y' & Z' \end{array}$$

the planes being the faces of the central tetrahedron.

492. The first line of the group **I,** which line we may denote by **Ia,** and the lines **IIa, IIIa, IVa,** are such that each of them has a point in common with the remaining three lines, hence the four lines are coplanar, and we have the six coplanar points

$$X \quad Y \quad Z \quad U \quad V \quad W.$$

Thus: *The six external centers of similitude of four spheres taken in pairs are coplanar.*

493. Definition. The plane containing the six external centers of similitude of four spheres taken in pairs (§ 492) is called the *external plane of similitude* of the four spheres.

494. Consider the four groups of lines

Ia	IIc	IIIc	IVd
Ic	IIa	IIIb	IVb
Ib	IIb	IIIa	IVc
Id	IId	IIId	IVa

The group of lines in each row of this table is such that each line has a point in common with the remaining three lines, hence these lines are coplanar. Now each row involves six centers of similitude. We thus obtain the following groups of coplanar points

$$
\begin{array}{cccccc}
X & Y' & Z' & U' & V & W \\
X' & Y & Z' & U & V' & W \\
X' & Y' & Z & U & V & W' \\
X & Y & Z & U' & V' & W'
\end{array}
$$

From this table we see that *given four spheres, if we take any group of three of these spheres, the three external centers of similitude of these three spheres taken two-by-two and the internal centers of similitude of the fourth sphere with each sphere of the group are six coplanar points.*

The proposition may also be stated as follows. *The plane determined by the three internal centers of similitude located on three concurrent edges of the central tetrahedron contains the external centers of similitude located on the remaining three edges.*

495. Definition. A plane of this type (§ 494) will be referred to as a *mixed plane of similitude* of the four given spheres.

496. From the table (§ 491) we may derive again the following groups of lines

$$
\begin{array}{cccc}
\text{Id} & \text{IIb} & \text{IIIb} & \text{IVd} \\
\text{Ic} & \text{IIc} & \text{IIId} & \text{IVc} \\
\text{Ib} & \text{IId} & \text{IIIc} & \text{IVb}
\end{array}
$$

By the same reasoning as before (§ 494) we arrive at the following groups of coplanar points

$$
\begin{array}{cccccc}
X & Y' & Z' & U & V' & W' \\
X' & Y' & Z & U' & V' & W \\
X' & Y & Z' & U' & V & W'
\end{array}
$$

From this table we derive the following

THEOREM. *If four given spheres are divided into two groups, the external centers of similitude of these two groups and the four internal centers of similitude of the pairs of spheres obtained by combining each sphere of the first group with each sphere of the second group are six coplanar points.*

497. Definition. A plane of this type (§ 496) will be referred to as an *internal plane of similitude* of the four given spheres.

It may be observed that an internal plane of similitude is determined by two external centers of similitude located on a pair of opposite edges of the central tetrahderon and the four internal centers of similitude not relative to the external centers of similitude considered.

498. The relations between the centers, axes, and planes of similitude of four spheres (the centers of which are not coplanar) obtained above (§§ 491–497) may also be arrived at in the following manner.

Instead of taking the tetrahedron determined by the centers of the four spheres, consider four parallel radii of the four spheres, and take the tetrahedron determined by the ends of these radii.

The four ends of these radii lie by twos on six lines (the six edges of the tetrahedron) each of which passes through a center of similitude of the spheres, and again these six centers of similitude lie by threes in four planes (the faces of the tetrahedron) which contain each an axis of similitude (§ 481). These four axes intersect in the centers of similitude considered, hence they are coplanar, thus determining a plane of similitude.

With regard to these four parallel radii, we may have the following different cases.

(a) *The four radii are all drawn in the same sense.* We obtain the six external centers of similitude and the external plane of similitude containing the four external axes of similitude.

(b) *One of the four radii is drawn in the sense opposite to the sense of the remaining three.* The lines joining the end of this fourth radius to remaining three will pass through the internal center of similitude of fourth sphere with each of the first three. The corresponding plane of similitude will contain the three internal centers of similitude considered, and the three external centers of similitude of the first three spheres taken in pairs, these three centers of similitude being collinear.

The choice of the fourth radius may be made in four different ways, hence we obtain four planes of similitude of this kind.

(c) *Two of the four parallel radii have the same sense and the remaining two the opposite sense of the first two.* The corresponding plane of similitude will contain two external centers of similitude and four internal centers of similitude. The four axes of similitude lying in this plane of similitude will each contain one external center of similitude and two internal centers.

The grouping of the radii may, in this case, be made in three different ways, hence we have three planes of similitude of this kind.

499. Theorem. *If from the twelve centers of similitude of four spheres taken two-by-two we exclude any six lying in the same plane of similitude the remaining six lie on three concurrent (but not coplanar) lines.*

The proof may be obtained by verification.

500. Remark I. Each center of similitude lies in four planes of similitude.

Through each of the sixteen axes of similitude pass two planes of similitude.

501. Remark II. Given four spheres, the four faces of their central tetrahedron (§ 490) contain, by sixes, the twelve centers of similitude of the spheres taken two at a time (§ 491).

If we group the four spheres in sets of three (§ 494) we obtain again four planes forming a tetrahedron, the faces of which contain, by sixes, the twelve centers of similitude.

Finally, if we group the spheres in sets of two, we obtain three planes (§496) which, together with the external plane of similitude, form a tetrahedron of the same nature as the two tetrahedrons above.

The line of intersection of a face of one tetrahedron with the face of a second of these tetrahedrons lies in a face of the third tetrahedron.

Three such tetrahedrons are said to form a "desmic configuration."

502. Centers of Similitude of Imaginary Spheres. A real sphere and an imaginary sphere cannot be homothetic to each other with respect to a real center of similitude, for the homothetic of a real sphere is a real sphere, the ratio being real.

If both given spheres (A), (B) are imaginary we can determine on the line of centers AB a real point S such that $SA^2 : SB^2 = -a^2 : -b^2 = a^2 : b^2$, where $-a^2$, $-b^2$ are the squares of the radii of these spheres. Thus two imaginary spheres have the same centers of similitude as the two spheres respectively concentric with them and the squares of whose radii are equal to the squares of the respective given spheres, but opposite in sign.

Two imaginary spheres thus have a real sphere of similitude.

EXERCISES

1. (a) Through a given line to draw a plane cutting two given spheres along two circles the radii of which are proportional to the radii of the respective spheres. (b) Through a given point to draw a plane cutting three given spheres along three circles the radii of which are proportional to the radii of the respective spheres.

2. Find the locus of the centers of similitude of the two circles along which two given spheres are cut by a variable plane passing through a center of similitude of the given spheres.

3. If the radii of two spheres having for their centers two vertices of a given tetrahedron are proportional to the respective medians of the tetrahedron, the sphere of similitude of these two spheres passes through the centroid of the tetrahedron.

4. (a) If two medians of a tetrahedron are taken for diameters of two spheres, the sphere of similitude of these two spheres passes through the centroid of the tetrahedron. (b) More generally. If two medians of a tetrahedron are divided in the same ratio and the points of division taken for the centers of two spheres the radii of which are proportional to the respective medians of the tetrahedron, the sphere of similitude of these two spheres will pass through the centroid of the tetrahedron.

5. If three given spheres are touched by a fourth sphere, the plane determined by the three points of contact passes through an axis of similitude of the given spheres.

6. Through a given point to draw a plane tangent to two given spheres.

7. (a) The three lines joining the internal centers of similitude of four spheres taken two by two and located on the three pairs of opposite edges of the central tetrahedron are concurrent. (b) Find seven other similar triads of concurrent lines.

8. The six traces, on the edges of a tetrahedron, of the external bisectors of the angles which these edges subtend at a given point in space are coplanar. Consider also the traces of the internal bisectors.

9. A plane passing through a center of similitude of two spheres makes equal angles with these spheres and cuts them along circles whose radii are proportional to the radii of the respective spheres. Conversely.

10. If a plane makes equal angles with three given spheres it contains an axis of similitude of the three spheres.

11. Find a plane cutting four given spheres along four circles whose radii are proportional to the radii of the respective spheres.

7. *The Power of a Point with Respect to a Sphere*

503. Theorem. *The product of the distances of a given point from any two points on a given sphere collinear with the given point is constant.*

Let P be the given point and A, A'; B, B' any two pairs of points on the given sphere (O) collinear with P. The plane $PAA'BB'$ cuts (O) along a circle, and we have $PA \cdot PA' = PB \cdot PB'$

This equality shows that the product considered depends only upon the point P and the sphere (O), but not on the pair of points on (O), hence the proposition.

504. Definition. The product $PA \cdot PA'$ preceded by the sign plus, if P is outside of (O), and by the sign minus, if P is inside of (O), is called "*the* **power** *of the point* P *with respect to the sphere* (O)."

505. Consequence. If we consider a plane passing through P and cutting (O) along a great circle, we may show, as in plane geometry (C. G., p. 163), that *the power of a point with respect to a sphere is equal, both in magnitude and in sign, to* $d^2 - R^2$, *where d is the distance of the point from the center of the sphere, and R is the radius of the sphere.*

506. Remark I. If the radius of the sphere decreases so as to become zero, the sphere becomes a point sphere, but the last form (§ 505) of the power of a point with respect to a sphere remains applicable.

This form of the power of the point with respect to a sphere involves the *square* of the radius, hence we can apply this concept to an imaginary sphere, without any modification.

507. Remark II. The power of a point with respect to a sphere grows with the distance of the point from the center of the sphere. If the point lies on the (real) sphere, its power is equal to zero.

The power of the center of the sphere with respect to the sphere is equal to the square of the radius, with the sign changed.

The power of a point with respect to a sphere is equal to the power of this point with respect to any circle of the sphere coplanar with this point.

508. Theorem. *The power of a point with respect to a sphere is equal to the square of the radius of the sphere orthogonal to the given sphere and having for center the given point.*

Let P be the given point, (A) the given sphere, a^2 the square of the radius of this sphere. If p^2 is the square of the radius of the sphere having P for center and orthogonal to (A), we have

$$PA^2 = p^2 + a^2,$$

hence

$$p^2 = PA^2 - a^2.$$

But the right hand side of the last equality is precisely the power of P with respect to (A), hence the proposition.

REMARK. When the point P is outside of (A), the sphere (P) orthogonal to (A) and having P for center is real. But when P is inside of (A), p^2 is negative, and (P) is imaginary. However, in many cases it is convenient to refer to the sphere (P) orthogonal to (A), even if (P) is imaginary, although, strictly speaking, the reference is simply to the power of P with respect to (A).

509. Converse Theorem. *If the power of the center of one sphere with respect to another sphere is equal to the square of the radius of the first sphere, the two spheres are orthogonal.*

Let a be the square of the radius and A the center of the sphere (A), and let a also be the power of A with respect to (B). Now the power of A with respect to (B) is equal to $AB^2 - b$, where b is the square of the radius of (B), hence

$$a = AB^2 - b, \quad \text{or} \quad AB^2 = a + b,$$

hence the two spheres are orthogonal (§ 402).

This is an extension of the proposition of § 406.

510. Corollary I. *If one of two orthogonal spheres is imaginary, any two points of the real sphere collinear with the center of the imaginary sphere are inverse points with respect to the imaginary sphere.*

If E, F are two points on the real sphere (B) collinear with the center A of the imaginary sphere (A), the square of the radius of which is equal to $-a$, we have, expressing the power of A with respect to (B) in two different ways,

$$AE \cdot AF = -a,$$

hence E, F are inverse with respect to (A) (§ 462). This is an extension of the proposition of § 412.

511. Corollary II. *Conversely, if two points of a real sphere are collinear with the center of an imaginary sphere and are inverse with respect to that sphere, the two spheres are orthogonal.*

We have, by assumption, $AE \cdot AF = -a$. But $AE \cdot AF$ is the power of A with respect to (B), hence this power is equal to the square of the radius of (A), hence the spheres are orthogonal (§ 509).

This is an extension of the proposition of § 413.

512. Problem. *Find the locus of the center of the variable sphere which passes through a fixed point and such that the polar plane of another fixed point with respect to this sphere passes through a given fixed line.*

Let (M) (Fig. 50) be one position of the variable sphere passing through the given point A, and let β be the polar plane of the

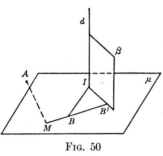

Fig. 50

other given point B with respect to (M). The center M of (M) lies on the perpendicular from B to β and the foot B' of this perpendicular is the inverse of B with respect to (M) (§ 424).

As the plane β varies turning about the given fixed line d, the locus described by B' is a circle (C) in the plane μ perpendicular to d through B. The trace I of d in μ is the diametric opposite of B on (C).

The sphere (S) determined by the circle (C) and the point A is orthogonal to (M) (§§ 413, 511), hence MA is tangent to (S) at A, i.e., M lies in the tangent plane to (S) at A, and therefore M lies on the line of intersection m of this tangent plane with μ.

Conversely, a sphere (M) having for center a point M of the line m and passing through A satisfies the conditions of the problem. For MA is tangent to (S), hence the line MB meets (C), and therefore (S), in a point B' such that $MA^2 = MB \cdot MB'$, i.e., B' is the inverse of B with respect to (M), hence the polar plane of B with respect to (M) will pass through B' and will be perpendicular to BB'. This plane will pass through the diametric opposite I of B on the circle (C), and therefore contain the line d. Thus the locus of M is the line m.

513. Theorem. *If two spheres are orthogonal, any two diametrically opposite points of one sphere are conjugate with respect to the other sphere.*

Let (A), (B) be two orthogonal spheres, one of which, say (B), is real, while the other may be real or imaginary.

The line EA joining any point E of (B) to the center A of (A) meets (B) again in the inverse F of E with respect to (A) (§ 510). Thus the polar plane of E with respect to (A) is perpendicular to

EA at *F*, hence, by elementary solid geometry, this plane passes through the diametric opposite *E'* of *E* with respect to (*B*), which proves the proposition (§ 433).

514. Converse Theorem. *If two diametrically opposite points of one sphere are conjugate with respect to another sphere, the two spheres are orthogonal.*

Let *E*, *E'* be two diametrically opposite points of the real sphere (*B*) and conjugate with respect to the sphere (*A*), real or imaginary.

The polar plane of *E* with respect to (*A*) cuts *EA* in the inverse *F* of *E* with respect to (*A*) and passes through *E'*, hence *EE'* subtends a right angle at *F* and therefore *F* lies on (*B*). Thus (*B*) passes through the two points *E*, *F*, inverse with respect to (*A*), hence (*B*) is orthogonal to (*A*) (§ 511).

515. On the Circle of Intersection of a Sphere with a Plane. Given the sphere (*O*) of radius *R* and a plane (*P*) cutting (*O*) along a real circle (*C*), the center *C* of (*C*) is the foot of the perpendicular *OC* from the center *O* of (*O*) upon (*P*), while the square of the radius of (*C*) is equal to $R^2 - OC^2$, i.e., to the power of *C* with respect to (*O*), with the sign changed.

Put in this form the notion of the circle of intersection of a plane with a sphere may be extended to include the case when the plane does not cut the sphere, and even to the case, when the sphere is wholly imaginary. The center of the circle of intersection is, by definition, the foot of the perpendicular dropped from the real center of the sphere upon the plane, hence a real point, and the square of the radius of the circle is equal to the negative of the power of this center with respect to the sphere.

516. The usefulness of this extended concept of the circle depends largely whether the theorems valid for the real circle may be applied to this new kind of circle. We shall proceed to prove the following

THEOREM. *Given a point and its polar plane with respect to a given sphere, a plane passing through the point cuts the sphere along a circle and the polar plane along a line which is the polar of the point with respect to the circle.*

It has been shown already (§ 426) that the proposition holds when the sphere is real and the secant plane cuts the sphere along a real circle. We shall now show that the proposition remains valid, when the circle of intersection of the plane with the sphere is imaginary, and when the sphere itself is imaginary.

Let (O) be the given sphere and let R be the square of its radius, positive or negative.

Let a plane (M) (Fig. 51) through the given point A cut (O) along the circle (C), and the polar plane of A with respect to (O) along a line u.

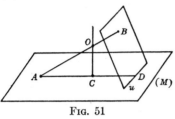

Fig. 51

The line OC joining the center O of (O) to the center C of (C) is perpendicular to the plane (M), and the polar plane of A with respect to (O) is perpendicular to OA at the inverse B of A with respect to (O), hence the line u is perpendicular to the plane AOC and therefore to the line AC.

Let D be the point common to u and AC. The line AO is perpendicular to BD, and we have from the two right triangles AOC, ABD

$$AD \cdot AC = AB \cdot AO,$$

or

$$(AC + CD)AC = (AO + OB)AO,$$
$$AC^2 + CD \cdot AC = AO^2 + AO \cdot OB,$$
$$AC^2 + CD \cdot AC = AC^2 + OC^2 + AO \cdot OB,$$
$$CD \cdot CA = OA \cdot OB - OC^2.$$

Now the points A, B are inverse with respect to (O), hence $OA \cdot OB = R$ and therefore

(1) $$CD \cdot CA = R - OC^2.$$

The power of C with respect to (O) is equal to $OC^2 - R$, hence $R - OC^2$ is the square of the radius of (C) (§ 515). We conclude therefore from (1) that the point D is the inverse of A with respect to (C), and since we have seen above that u is perpendicular to AC, the line u is the polar of A with respect to (C).

This proof is valid for the case when (O) is a real sphere and (M) cuts (O) along a real circle.

EXERCISES

1. If the sum of the powers of the center of one of two given spheres with respect to these two spheres is equal to zero, the two spheres are orthogonal.

2. The locus of the points having a constant power with respect to a given sphere is a sphere.

3. What is the locus of the center of the sphere with fixed radius and orthogonal to a given sphere?

4. The powers of a center of similitude of two given spheres with respect to these spheres are proportional to the squares of the radii of these spheres.

5. The power of a center of similitude of two spheres with respect to the variable sphere tangent to the two given spheres is constant, if the two points of contact are collinear with the center of similitude considered.

6. The square of the distance between two points which are inverse with respect to a given sphere is equal to the sum of the powers of these points with respect to the given sphere.

7. Through three given points to draw a sphere tangent to a given line.

8. Construct a sphere passing through two given points and orthogonal to a given circle.

9. A variable sphere passes through a fixed point, has its center in a fixed plane, and is tangent to another fixed plane. Find the locus of its point of contact with the fixed plane.

10. The power of the Monge point M of a tetrahedron (T) with respect to a sphere having for diameter a median of (T) is equal to one third of the power of M with respect to the circumsphere of (T). HINT. Use the formula for the square of the median of a triangle.

11. Find a necessary and sufficient condition that two given circles, real, imaginary, or one real and the other imaginary, shall lie on the same sphere.

12. The lines AM, BM joining two fixed points in space to a point M of a given sphere (S) meet (S) again in the points C and D, respectively. Determine the locus of M on (S) so that the ratio $AC : BD$ shall have a given value.

13. (a) The power of the vertex S of a trirectangular tetrahedron $SABC$ with respect to the sphere having the circumcircle of the base ABC of $SABC$ for great circle is equal to the square of the altitude of $SABC$, with the sign changed. (b) The square of the chord intercepted by this sphere on the altitude is equal to eight times the square of the altitude.

8. The Radical Plane of Two Spheres

517. Theorem. *The locus of the point which moves so that its powers with respect to two given spheres remain equal is a plane perpendicular to the line of centers of the given spheres.*

Let A, B be the centers and a, b the squares of the radii of the given spheres (A), (B). If X is a point of the required locus, we have, by assumption,

$$XA^2 - a = XB^2 - b,$$

hence the proposition (§ 18).

518. Definition. This plane (§ 517) is called the *radical plane* of the two spheres.

519. Remark I. The preceding theorem (§ 517) remains valid, if either a or b, or both, are zero, i.e., we may speak of the radical plane of a point and a sphere, or even of two points, in which case the plane is identical with the mediator of the two points.

Furthermore, the proposition retains its meaning, if either of the two quantities a, b, or both, become negative. We may thus consider the radical plane of a real sphere and an imaginary sphere, or the radical plane of two imaginary spheres.

520. Remark II. If the two spheres (A), (B) are real and intersect, every point of their common circle belongs to the required locus (§ 517), for the powers of a point common to two spheres with respect to these spheres are equal, namely both are zero (§ 507). Hence: *The radical plane of two intersecting spheres is the plane of their circle of intersection.*

When the two spheres, being real, do not intersect, or when one or both spheres are imaginary, the radical plane still contains the common circle of the two spheres, in the generalized sense of this term (§ 515), for the trace of the radical plane on the line of centers of the two spheres has the same power with respect to the two spheres.

521. Remark III. Two concentric spheres have no radical plane. If two spheres are tangent to each other, their radical plane is their common tangent plane at their point of contact.

522. Theorem. *The radical plane of two spheres is the locus of the centers of the spheres which are orthogonal to the two spheres.*

523. Corollary. *If a sphere having its center in the radical plane of two given spheres is orthogonal to one of these spheres it is also orthogonal to the second sphere.*

The proofs are the same as in plane geometry (C. G., p. 165).

524. Remark. If real spheres only are considered the above theorem (§ 522) must be qualified to read that only the points of the radical plane *which lie outside the given spheres* belong to the locus. The introduction of the imaginary sphere does away with this exception and gives the theorem all its generality, without loss of precision or definiteness.

525. Theorem. *The points from which tangents of equal length may be drawn to two given spheres lie in the the radical plane of the two spheres.*

526. Corollary. The radical plane bisects all the common tangents of the two spheres.

527. Theorem. *The two polar planes, with respect to two given spheres, of any point in the radical plane of these spheres are coaxal with the radical plane.*

Let P be a point in the radical plane (R) of the two given spheres (A), (B), and let Q be any point of the line of intersection u of the polar planes of P with respect to (A), (B).

The points P, Q are conjugate with respect to both (A) and (B), hence the sphere (PQ) having PQ for diameter is orthogonal to both (A) and (B) (§ 514), and the center M of (PQ) lies in (R) (§ 522); now since P lies in (R), by assumption, the point Q, collinear with P and M, also lies in (R). Thus any point Q of u lies in (R), hence the proposition.

OTHERWISE. The radical plane (R) cuts the two polar planes of P with respect to (A), (B) along the polar u of P with respect to the common circle (C) of (A) and (B) (§§ 516, 520), hence the proposition.

Notice that both above proofs are valid, whatever the nature of the two given spheres may be.

528. Theorem. *Two antihomologous chords of two spheres intersect in the radical plane of these spheres.*

The two pairs of points determining the two chords are concyclic (§ 476), hence their point of intersection has equal powers with respect to the two spheres.

529. Theorem. *Two antihomologous planes of two spheres intersect in the radical plane of these spheres.*

The two planes are determined by the three pairs of antihomologous chords (§ 474). The chords in each of these pairs intersect in the radical plane of the two spheres (§ 528), hence the line of intersection of the two planes lies in the radical plane of the two spheres.

530. Theorem. *The tangent planes to two spheres at two antihomologous points on these spheres are coaxal with the radical plane of these spheres.*

The two given antihomologous points P, Q' on the two spheres are antihomologous points on the two circles along which any plane (M) through the line PQ' cuts the given spheres (§ 470). The same plane (M) will cut the tangent planes to the spheres along the tangents to these circles at P and Q' respectively. Now these tangents intersect on the radical axis of these two circles

(C. G., p. 167), which radical axis lies in the radical plane of the two spheres, hence the proposition.

531. Remark. This proposition may be considered as a limiting case of the proposition § 529.

532. Theorem. *If through a line in the radical plane of two spheres a tangent plane is drawn to each of the two spheres, the points of contact are antihomologous points on the two spheres.*

Let P be the point of contact of the tangent plane through the given line s to the sphere (A). The point P has two antihomologous points Q', R' on the second sphere (B), relative to the two centers of similitude of (A) and (B). Now the tangent planes to (B) at Q', R' pass through the line of intersection s of the tangent plane at P to (A) and the radical plane of (A), (B) (§ 530), and only two tangent planes may be drawn from s to (B) (§ 448), hence the proposition.

533. Definition. A sphere (A) is said to be "*bisected*" by another sphere (B), if the circle of intersection of the two spheres is a great circle of (A).

The sphere (B) is the *bisecting* sphere and (A) the *bisected* sphere.

Two spheres cannot bisect each other, for if they did their common circle would have to be a great circle on both spheres, and the spheres would be identical.

534. Let a, b be the squares of the radii of the two spheres (A), (B) (§ 533), and d the square of their line of centers AB. From the right triangle formed by the centers A, B of the two spheres and any point on their common circle we have

$$b = a + d, \qquad \text{or} \qquad d = b - a.$$

Thus: *The square of the line of centers is equal to the difference between the squares of the radii of the bisecting and the bisected spheres.*

535. The formula $b = d + a$ may be taken as the definition of the sphere (B) bisecting the sphere (A). Since this formula involves the squares of the radii of the two spheres, it may be applied to imaginary spheres as well as to real spheres.

If the given sphere (A) is real, any point in space B may be taken as the center of a real sphere bisecting (A).

If the given sphere is imaginary, b will be positive only if d

is numerically greater than a, hence a bisecting sphere of an imaginary sphere may be either real or imaginary.

536. Definition. The symmetric of the radical plane of two spheres with respect to the mid-point of the line of centers of the two spheres will be referred to as the *antiradical* plane of these spheres.

The antiradical plane of the two spheres (A, a), (B, b) is the radical plane of the two spheres (A, b), (B, a) having for centers the same points A, B and for the squares of their radii b and a respectively.

For any point P of the antiradical plane of the two spheres (A, a), (B, b) we have

$$PA^2 - PB^2 = b - a \qquad \text{or} \qquad PA^2 + a = PB^2 + b.$$

537. Problem. *Find the locus of the center of the variable sphere which bisects two given spheres.*

Let A, B, be the centers and a, b the radii of the two given spheres (A), (B). If P is a point of the required locus and p the radius of the corresponding sphere we have

$$p^2 = PA^2 + a^2 = PB^2 + b^2,$$

hence the required locus is the anti-radical plane of the two given spheres (§ 536).

538. Theorem. *The radical plane of the two spheres having for diameters two medians of a tetrahedron coincides with the Monge plane which is perpendicular to the edge joining the two vertices considered.*

Let G_a, G_b (Fig. 52) be the centroids of the faces BCD, CDA of the tetrahedron $ABCD$, let C'' be the mid-point of CD, and P, Q the feet of the perpendiculars dropped from G_a, G_b

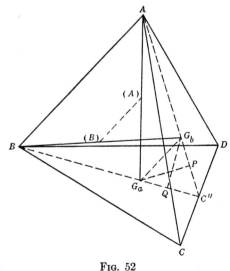

Fig. 52

upon AG_b, BG_a, respectively. The spheres (A), (B) having AG_a, BG_b for diameters pass respectively through P, Q, and from the two pairs of similar triangles $C''AB$, $C''G_aG_b$ (§ 176); $C''PG_a$, $C''QG_b$ we have

$$C''A : C''B = C''G_b : C''G_a = C''Q : C''P,$$

hence

$$C''A \cdot C''P = C''B \cdot C''Q$$

i.e., C'' is a point of the radical plane of (A), (B) (§ 517).

On the other hand the line of centers of (A), (B) is parallel to the edge AB, therefore the radical plane of the two spheres is perpendicular to AB, hence the proposition.

539. Theorem. *The inverses, with respect to two given spheres, of a point on the sphere of similitude of these two spheres are symmetrical with respect to the radical plane of the given spheres.*

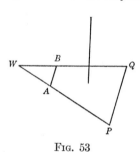

Let P, Q (Fig. 53) be the inverse points of the point W with respect to the two given spheres (A), (B) having A, B for centers and a, b for the squares of their radii. We have then

(1) $AP \cdot AW = a$, $BQ \cdot BW = b$,

hence

$$\frac{AP}{BQ} \cdot \frac{AW}{BW} = \frac{a}{b},$$

FIG. 53

and now if W is a point on the sphere of similitude (S) of (A), (B), we have (§§ 479, 502)

$$WA^2 : WB^2 = a : b$$

hence

$$\frac{AP}{BQ} \cdot \frac{AW}{BW} = \frac{AW^2}{BW^2},$$

and therefore

(2) $AP : BQ = AW : BW.$

This proportion shows that the line PQ is parallel to AB and therefore perpendicular to the radical plane of (A), (B).

Any sphere passing through W, P, Q is orthogonal to the spheres (A), (B) (§ 413), hence the axis of the triangle WPQ lies in the radical plane of (A), (B) (§ 522). But this axis also lies in the mediator of the segment PQ and is perpendicular to PQ, therefore also to AB, hence this mediator coincides with the radical plane, which proves the proposition.

This proof is valid whether (A), (B) are both real or both imaginary. In either case the points P, Q lie on the same side of the line AB.

540. Theorem. *The locus of the point the sum of whose powers with respect to two given spheres is constant is a sphere having for its center the mid-point of the line of centers of the two given spheres.*

The proof is left to the reader. HINT. Use Art. 17.

541. Remark. If p, q are the squares of the radii of the two spheres (§ 540), d the square of their line of centers, and s the sum of the powers of any point of the locus with respect to the two given spheres, the square of the radius of the sphere representing the locus is given by the expression

$$\tfrac{1}{2}(s + p + q) - \tfrac{1}{4}d.$$

The locus therefore will be real if

$$s + p + q > \tfrac{1}{2}d.$$

542. Theorem. *The locus of the point the powers of which with respect to two given spheres are equal in magnitude and opposite in sign is a sphere having for its center the mid-point of the line of centers of the two spheres.*

Indeed, the sum of the powers of the variable point with respect to the two given spheres is constant, namely equal to zero, hence the proposition (§ 540).

543. Definition. This sphere (§ 542) is called the **radical sphere** of the two given spheres.

544. Remark I. If p, q are the squares of the radii of the two given spheres, and d the square of the line of centers, the square of the radius of the radical sphere of these two spheres is given by the formula (§ 541)

$$\tfrac{1}{2}(p + q) - \tfrac{1}{4}d.$$

545. Remark II. *If the two given spheres intersect, their radical sphere passes through their common circle.*

Indeed, the powers of a point of the circle of intersection of the two spheres with respect to these spheres are both zero (§ 507).

546. Theorem. *If a plane cuts two given spheres along two orthogonal circles, the sum of the powers of the center of either circle with respect to the two spheres is zero.*

Let u, v be the squares of the radii of the two orthogonal circles (C), (D) along which a given plane cuts the two given spheres (A), (B). The power of the center C of (C) with respect to the circle (C), and therefore also with respect to (A) (§ 507), is equal to $- u$ (§ 515). On the other hand, the power of C with respect to the circle (D), and therefore with respect to (B) is equal to u (§ 508), hence the sum of the powers of C with respect to the two spheres is zero. Similarly for the center D of (D).

547. Corollary. *If a plane cuts two given spheres along two orthogonal circles, the centers of these circles lie on the radical sphere of the two spheres.*

548. Consequence. A necessary condition for the possibility of cutting two given spheres along two orthogonal circles is that their radical sphere shall be real, i.e. (§ 544), $p + q > \frac{1}{2}d$. This inequality cannot be satisfied unless one of the given spheres is real, a result that could be foreseen, since two imaginary circles cannot be orthogonal (§ 465).

549. Theorem. *If the radical sphere of two given spheres is real, through every point of the radical sphere two planes may be drawn cutting the given spheres along two orthogonal circles.*

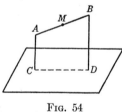

FIG. 54

Let C be a point on the radical sphere (M), supposed real, of the two given spheres (A), (B) (Fig. 54). Let u, v be the squares of the radii of the two circles (C), (D) along which (A), (B) are cut by the plane perpendicular at C to the line CA joining the center C of (C) to the center A of (A). The powers of C with respect to (C), (D) are respectively $- u$ and $CD^2 - v$, where D is the center of (D). But the powers of C with respect to (C), (D) are also the powers of C with respect to (A), (B) (§ 507), and since C is a point on (M) the sum of the powers of C with respect to the two spheres is zero, hence

$$- u + CD^2 - v = 0, \quad \text{or} \quad CD^2 = u + v,$$

hence (C), (D) are orthogonal.

Similarly the plane through C and perpendicular to CB cuts (A), (B) along two orthogonal circles.

550. Problem. *Through a given line to draw a plane cutting two given spheres along two orthogonal circles.*

In the plane (P) perpendicular to the given line s and passing through the center A of one of the two given spheres (A), (B) construct the circle (AL) having for diameter the perpendicular AL from A upon s. Let (C) be the circle common to the plane (P) and the radical sphere (M) of (A), (B). If T is a point common to (C) and the circle (AL), the plane s–T satisfies the conditions of the problem.

The problem may have two solutions.

551. Theorem. *If the chords determined on a line by two spheres are harmonic, the mid-points of these chords lie on the radical sphere of the two given spheres.*

Let PP', QQ' be the two chords determined on the line s by the given spheres (A), (B), and let U, V be the mid-points of PP', QQ'.

The powers of U with respect to (A), (B) are

$$- UP^2, \qquad UQ \cdot UQ'.$$

Now if PP', QQ' are harmonic, we have (C. G., p. 135)

$$UP^2 = UQ \cdot UQ',$$

hence the sum of the powers of U with respect to (A), (B) is zero, and U lies on the radical sphere of (A), (B) (§§ 542, 543).

Similarly for V. Hence the proposition.

EXERCISES

1. The power, with respect to either of two orthogonal spheres, of the point of intersection of their line of centers with their radical plane is equal to the product of the distances of this point from the centers of two spheres.

2. The foot of the radical plane of two spheres on the line of centers divides this segment in the same ratio in which this point divides the segment determined by the poles of the radical plane with respect to the two given spheres.

3. Construct a sphere orthogonal to two given circles.

4. Through an arbitrary point common to two given spheres an arbitrary secant is drawn meeting the two spheres again in the points E, F, respectively. Show that the locus of the mid-point of EF is the radical sphere of the given spheres.

5. All the planes which pass through a given point and cut two given spheres along two orthogonal circles are tangent to a fixed cone of second degree.

6. Find a plane having a given orientation and cutting two given spheres along two orthogonal circles.

7. If the two chords determined on a given line by two spheres are harmonic, the plane passing through this line and perpendicular to the line joining the mid-point of one chord to the center of the corresponding sphere cuts the two spheres along two orthogonal circles.

8. The lines on which two given spheres (A), (B) determine pairs of harmonic chords and which pass through the same given point L form, in general, a cone of the second degree (L) having L for its vertex. The two spheres having for diameters LA, LB cut the radical sphere (M) of (A), (B) along two circles belonging to the cone (L). If L lies on (M), the cone (L) degenerates into two planes. Consider the case when (A), (B) are orthogonal.

9. A line s parallel to the line of centers AB of two given spheres (A), (B) meets the radical plane of these spheres in L. The line ML joining L to the mid-point M of AB meets the sphere of similitude of (A), (B) in W. Prove that the lines WA, WB meet s in the inverses of W with respect to (A), (B).

10. The lines joining the centers A, B of two given spheres (A), (B) to a point on their sphere of similitude meet the spheres in X, X'; Y, Y', respectively. Show that two of the four lines XY, $X'Y'$, XY', $X'Y$ are parallel to AB, and the remaining two intersect in the radical plane of (A), (B).

11. Find the locus of the centers of the spheres which (a) bisect two (or three) given spheres; (b) which are bisected by two (or three) given spheres.

12. If two spheres are tangent to each other, any sphere passing through their point of contact and tangent at this point to their line of centers is orthogonal to both spheres. Conversely. If a sphere is orthogonal to two tangent spheres it passes through their point of contact and is tangent at this point to their line of centers.

13. Through two points, antihomologous on two given spheres, it is possible to draw one and only one sphere tangent at these points to the given spheres.

14. Two planes coaxal with the radical plane of two given spheres cut these two spheres along four circles. Show that any two of these circles situated in different planes are cospherical.

15. The antiradical plane of two spheres having for diameters two opposite edges of a given tetrahedron passes through the circumcenter of the tetrahedron.

16. The radical plane of two spheres having for diameter two opposite edges of a given tetrahedron passes through the Monge point of the tetrahedron.

17. The four orthogonal projections, upon the four faces of a given tetrahedron, of the mid-point of the segment determined by the centers of two spheres each touching the four faces of the tetrahedron, are coplanar.

18. If the polar plane of the center of one sphere with respect to a second sphere (not concentric with the first) coincides with the radical plane of the two spheres the spheres are orthogonal.

19. (a) A plane passing through the center of one of two given orthogonal spheres cuts these spheres along two orthogonal circles. (b) Conversely.

If a plane cuts two orthogonal spheres along two orthogonal circles, the plane passes through the center of at least one of the two spheres.

20. If the spheres (A), (B) are orthogonal, the perpendicular dropped from the center of (A) upon a plane (P) passing through the center of (B) has for its polar reciprocal, with respect to (B), the line of intersection of (P) with the radical plane of (A), (B).

9. Coaxal Pencils of Spheres

552. Definition. A system of spheres is said to form a *coaxal pencil*, if the same fixed plane is the radical plane of any two spheres of the system.

This radical plane is called the *radical plane of the pencil*.

Any given point of the radical plane has the same power with respect to all the spheres of the pencil.

553. Theorem. *The centers of a coaxal pencil of spheres are collinear.*

554. Definition. The line containing the centers of the pencil of spheres is called the *line of centers of the pencil*.

555. Theorem. *A coaxal pencil of spheres is determined by two spheres of the pencil, or by one sphere and the radical plane of the pencil.*

556. Discussion. There are three types of coaxal pencils of spheres.

(a) If the two spheres (or the sphere and the plane) which determine the pencil intersect along a real circle, every sphere of the pencil will pass through this circle, *the basic circle of the pencil*, and the pencil is called an "*intersecting* coaxal pencil of spheres."

(b) If the two given spheres (or the sphere and the plane) are tangent to each other, every sphere of the pencil will touch the given spheres at the same point, and we have a "coaxal pencil of tangent spheres."

(c) If the circle of intersection of the two spheres (or the plane and the sphere) is imaginary, they determine a "*non-intersecting* coaxal pencil of spheres."

Any two spheres of the pencil have this imaginary circle in common and have no real points in common.

An imaginary sphere may belong to a pencil of this type, while it cannot belong to the first two types.

N. B. What follows refers only to types (a) and (c), unless otherwise stated.

557. Limiting Points. The concept of the limiting points of a coaxal pencil of spheres may be arrived at by considering the limiting points of the coaxal pencil of circles obtained as the intersection of the given pencil of spheres with a plane passing through the line of centers of the given pencil.

If we make use of the notion of an imaginary sphere, the limiting points determine the segment which contains the centers of the imaginary spheres belonging to the pencil, while the points of the line of centers lying outside this segment are the centers of the real spheres belonging to the pencil. The limiting points themselves are then to be considered as the centers of the spheres of radius zero belonging to the coaxal pencil.

Let H be the trace of the radical plane of the given coaxal pencil of spheres upon the line of centers, and let p be the power of this point with respect to the spheres of the pencil. If there exists a sphere (L) of the pencil of radius zero and of center L we must have

$$HL^2 = p.$$

If p is negative, i.e., if the pencil is an intersecting one, the distance HL is imaginary, and such a system has no (real) limiting points. If p is positive, i.e., if the pencil is a non-intersecting one, we obtain two real limiting points L and L'.

558. Theorem. *Any plane cuts a coaxal pencil of spheres along a coaxal pencil of circles.*

For the secant plane cuts the radical plane of the pencil of spheres along a line any point of which has the same power with respect to all the circles of intersection of the secant plane with the spheres of the pencil, hence this line is the radical axis of the system of circles, the line of centers of the coaxal pencil of circles being the orthogonal projection of the line of centers of the pencil of spheres upon the secant plane.

559. Problem. *Through a given point in space to draw a sphere belonging to a given coaxal system.*

The plane determined by the given point and the line of centers of the given pencil of spheres cuts this pencil along a coaxal pencil of circles (§ 558), and the circle of this pencil (C. G., p. 182) passing through the given point is a great circle of the required sphere.

Consider the case when the given point lies: (a) in the radical plane; (b) on the line of centers.

REMARK. This is also the solution of the problem: *Construct a sphere passing through a given point and a given imaginary circle.*

560. Theorem. *The limiting points of a coaxal pencil of spheres are a pair of inverse points with respect to every sphere of the pencil.*

561. Conversely. *If two points are inverse with respect to the spheres of a given system, the system is a coaxal pencil.*

562. Corollary I. Each limiting point has the same polar plane with respect to all the spheres of the pencil.

563. Corollary II. A sphere passing through the limiting points of a coaxal pencil of spheres is orthogonal to each sphere of the pencil.

564. Corollary III. A coaxal pencil of spheres cannot have more than one pair of limiting points.

565. Problem. *Construct a sphere belonging to a given coaxal pencil and tangent to a given plane.*

The pencil of spheres determines in the given plane a coaxal pencil of circles (§ 558). The plane through a limiting point of this pencil of circles and perpendicular to the line of centers of the pencil of spheres meets this line in the center of the required sphere.

OTHERWISE. The point of contact T of the given plane (P) with the required sphere lies on the orthogonal projection u of the line of centers of the coaxal pencil of spheres upon the plane (P). If M is any point of the trace of (P) on the radical plane of the pencil, and m the power of M with respect to any sphere of the pencil, we have $MT^2 = m$. Hence T is the point of intersection of the line u with the circle drawn in (P) having M for center and m for the square of its radius.

How many solutions may the problem have? Are these solutions always real?

566. Theorem. *A sphere orthogonal to two spheres of a coaxal pencil is orthogonal to every sphere of the pencil.*

567. Theorem. *A sphere orthogonal to one sphere of a coaxal pencil and having its center in the radical plane of the pencil is orthogonal to every sphere of the pencil.*

568. Theorem. *If three spheres have their centers on a straight line and are orthogonal to the same sphere, they are coaxal* (C. G., p. 188).

569. Theorem. *The sphere having for diameter the line of centers of two given orthogonal spheres is coaxal with the given spheres.*

This proposition has been proved already in the case when both given spheres are real (§ 409). We shall now give a proof which is valid whatever the nature of the spheres.

Let A, B be the centers and a, b the squares of the radii of the given spheres (A), (B). If M is the mid-point of the line of centers AB and P any point in space, we have, by the formula for the median of a triangle,

$$PA^2 + PB^2 = 2PM^2 + \tfrac{1}{2}AB^2,$$

hence

$$(PA^2 - a) + (PB^2 - b) = 2PM^2 + \tfrac{1}{2}AB^2 - a - b.$$

The two parentheses of the left hand side of this equality represent the powers of P with respect to (A), (B). If we assume that P lies in the radical plane of the two spheres these powers are equal to each other. Let p represent their common value. The two spheres being orthogonal, we have

$$AB^2 = a + b.$$

Thus we have

$$2p = 2(PM^2 - \tfrac{1}{4}AB^2).$$

Now this last parenthesis is precisely the power of the point P with respect to the sphere (AB) having AB for diameter, and the last equality shows that the power of P with respect to (AB) is the same as with respect to (A), (B); the proposition is proved.

570. Remark. It may be observed that the sphere (AB) (§ 569) is the radical sphere of (A), (B), for it has for its center the mid-point M of AB and passes through the points A, B, and the sum of the powers of either of these two points with respect to the given spheres is zero.

571. Converse Theorem. *If the sphere having for diameter the line of centers of two given spheres is coaxal with these spheres, the two given spheres are orthogonal.*

The proof is obtained by reversing the steps in the proof of the direct theorem.

572. Theorem. *The square of the distance between two points conjugate with respect to a sphere is equal to the sum of the powers of these points with respect to the sphere considered.*

Let A, B be two points conjugate with respect to a given sphere (S). The sphere (AB) having AB for diameter is orthogonal to (S) (§ 514), and if we consider the spheres (A), (B) having for centers the points A, B and orthogonal to the sphere (S), we have three spheres (A), (B), (AB) the centers of which are collinear and which are orthogonal to the same sphere (S), hence these three spheres are coaxal (§ 568), consequently the spheres (A), (B) are orthogonal (§ 571).

Thus AB^2 is equal to the sum of the squares of the radii of (A), (B) (§§ 402, 465). But the squares of these radii are the powers of the points A, B with respect to (S) (§ 508), hence the proposition.

573. Corollary. *Two spheres orthogonal to a third sphere and having for their centers two points conjugate with respect to this third sphere are orthogonal to each other.*

574. Remark. The reader should observe that the generality of the last two propositions is made possible by the consideration of the imaginary sphere. Otherwise the propositions would have to be restricted to the case when the two given points both lie outside the given sphere. The cases when one of the points lies inside the given sphere would have to be studied separately and the results formulated in different terms.

575. Converse Theorem. *If the sum of the powers of two points with respect to a given sphere is equal to the square of the distance between these points, the points are conjugate with respect to the sphere.*

By hypothesis, the spheres (A), (B) (§ 572) are orthogonal to each other (§§ 508, 465), hence the sphere (AB) is coaxal with them and therefore orthogonal to (S) (§ 566), and the points A, B are conjugate with respect to (S) (§ 513).

576. Corollary. *If three spheres are mutually orthogonal, the centers of any two of them are conjugate points with respect to the third sphere.*

577. Theorem. *The polar planes of a point with respect to the spheres of a coaxal pencil are coaxal.*

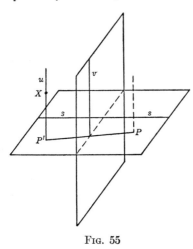

Fig. 55

The given point P (Fig. 55) and the line of centers s of the coaxal pencil of spheres determine a plane Ps cutting these spheres along a coaxal pencil of circles (§ 558) which are great circles on the respective spheres. The plane Ps cuts the polar planes of P with respect to the spheres of the pencil along the polars of P with respect to the respective circles of the coaxal pencil of circles (§ 426). Now the polars of P with respect to these circles pass through a fixed point P' (C. G., p. 188). Hence the polar planes of P with respect to the coaxal pencil of spheres pass through the line u perpendicular at P' to the plane Ps.

EXERCISE. Consider the case when the point P lies (a) in the radical plane of (S); (b) on the line of centers of (S).

578. Remark. If (P) (Fig. 55) is the sphere of the given coaxal pencil passing through P (§ 559), the tangent plane to (P) at P passes through the line u, for this plane is the polar plane of P with respect to (P) (§ 430).

Let v be the trace of this tangent plane in the radical plane of the given pencil of spheres (S). The point P and any point X of u are conjugate with respect to all the spheres of the pencil, hence the sphere having PX for diameter is orthogonal to all the spheres of (S) (§ 514), and therefore has its center in the radical plane of (S) (§§ 522, 566), i.e., on the line v. Thus the line u is the symmetric, with respect to v, of the parallel to v through P.

579. Converse Theorem. *If the centers of three spheres are collinear, and the polar planes of a given point with respect to these spheres are coaxal, the spheres form a coaxal pencil.*

The plane Ps (Fig. 55) determined by the given point P and the line of centers s of the three given spheres cuts the axis u of the three polar planes in a point P' which is conjugate to P with respect to each of the given spheres. Therefore these spheres are orthogonal to the sphere having PP' for diameter (§ 514), hence the three spheres are coaxal (§ 568).

580. Theorem. *The power of a point with respect to a sphere diminished by the power of the same point with respect to a second sphere is equal, in magnitude and in sign, to twice the distance of the point from the radical plane of the two spheres (the beginning of the segment being the point in the radical plane), multiplied by the line of centers of the spheres (the beginning being the center of the first sphere considered).*

Let A, B (Fig. 56) be the centers and a, b the squares of the radii of the two given spheres (A) and (B), O the trace on AB of the radical plane of (A) and (B), M, N the feet of the perpendiculars PM, PN dropped from the given point P upon the line

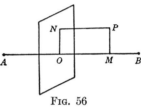

Fig. 56

AB and upon the radical plane of the given spheres. Denoting by d the required difference, we have

$$d = (PA^2 - a) - (PB^2 - b) = (PA^2 - PB^2) - (a - b).$$

From the right triangles PMA, PMB we have

$$PA^2 = PM^2 + AM^2, \qquad PB^2 = PM^2 + BM^2,$$

hence

$$PA^2 - PB^2 = AM^2 - BM^2.$$

The powers of O with respect to the spheres being equal, we have

$$OA^2 - a = OB^2 - b, \quad \text{or} \quad OA^2 - OB^2 = a - b.$$

Thus we have

$$d = (AM^2 - BM^2) - (OA^2 - OB^2).$$

From this relation we obtain successively, both in magnitude and in sign,

$$d = (AM + MB)(AM - MB) - (AO + OB)(AO - OB)$$
$$= AB[AM - MB - AO + OB]$$
$$= AB[(AO + OM) - (MO + OB) - AO + OB]$$
$$= 2AB \cdot OM = 2AB \cdot NP.$$

581. Corollary I.   *The power, with respect to a sphere, of a point on another sphere is equal, in magnitude and in sign, to twice the distance of the point from the radical plane of the two spheres (the beginning of the segment being the point in the radical plane) multiplied by the line of centers of the two spheres (the beginning being the center of the sphere with respect to which the power is taken).*

Indeed, the power, with respect to a sphere, of a point on the sphere is zero (§ 507).

582. Corollary II.   If U is the mid-point of AB (§ 580), the length of the segment UO, both in magnitude and in sign, is given by the formula

$$UO = (a - b) : 2AB.$$

Indeed, the difference of the powers of U with respect to (A) and (B) is equal to

$$(UA^2 - a) - (UB^2 - b) = - (a - b),$$

since U is the mid-point of AB.   On the other hand this difference is equal to $2 \cdot AB \cdot OU$ (§ 580).   Equating the two values for this difference we obtain the announced relation.

583. Theorem.   *If a sphere is coaxal with two given spheres, the powers of any point of this sphere with respect to the two given spheres are in a constant ratio.*

This ratio is equal, both in magnitude and in sign, to the ratio of the distances of the center of the sphere from the centers of the first and of the second given spheres.

Let P be any point on a sphere (S) coaxal with the two given spheres (A), (B), and let u, v be the powers of P with respect to (A), (B).   If N is the foot of the perpendicular from P upon the radical plane of the pencil (A), (B), (S), and A, B, S the centers of these spheres, we have, both in magnitude and in sign (§ 580),

$$u = 2NP \cdot AS, \qquad v = 2NP \cdot BS,$$

hence

$$u : v = AS : BS = SA : SB,$$

which ratio is independent of the position of P on (S).

584. Remark.   The ratio $u : v$ (§ 583) is negative, if S lies on the segment AB, and positive, if S lies outside this segment.

585. Converse Theorem. *The locus of a point the ratio of whose powers with respect to two given spheres is constant, both in magnitude and in sign, is a sphere coaxal with the given spheres.*

If P is a point on the locus, the sphere (S) passing through P and coaxal with the given spheres (A), (B) (§ 559) will have for its center the point S which divides the line of centers AB of the given spheres in the given ratio, internally, if the ratio is negative, and externally, if this ratio is positive (§ 584). Thus the position of the center S, and therefore of the sphere (S), is uniquely determined by the given ratio, independently of the position of P, hence the proposition.

586. Remark. If the ratio (§ 585) is given only in magnitude the locus of P consists of two spheres coaxal with the given spheres and having for their centers two points which divide the line of centers of the two given spheres internally and externally in the given ratio.

587. Corollary. *The locus of the point the ratio of whose powers with respect to two given spheres (A), (B) is equal to the ratio of the radii of these spheres, consists of two spheres (S), (S'), coaxal with (A), (B), and having for their centers the centers of similitude of (A), (B).*

588. Definition. The two spheres (S), (S') (§ 587) are called the ***spheres of antisimilitude*** of the given spheres (A), (B).

The direct, or external center of similitude of (A), (B) is the center of the "direct," or "external" sphere of antisimilitude, and the indirect, or internal center of similitude is the center of the "indirect," or "internal" sphere of antisimilitude of (A), (B).

589. Theorem. *The sphere of similitude of two spheres is coaxal with these spheres.*

Let A, B be the centers, and a, b the squares of the radii of the two given spheres (A), (B). If P is a point on their sphere of similitude, we have (§§ 479, 502)

$$PA^2 : PB^2 = a : b, \qquad \text{or} \qquad (PA^2 - a) : (PB^2 - b) = a : b.$$

Thus the ratio of the powers of any point P of the sphere of similitude of (A), (B) with respect to these two spheres is constant, hence the proposition (§ 585).

590. Remark. This proposition (§ 589) has already been proved for two real intersecting spheres (§ 480). The present proof shows that the proposition is valid for two non-intersecting spheres, or for two imaginary spheres (§ 502).

591. Converse Theorem. *The sphere of similitude of two given spheres is the only sphere which is coaxal with these spheres and which divides their line of centers harmonically.*

The spheres having for diameters the segments which divide harmonically the segment determined by the centers A, B of the two given spheres (A), (B) form a coaxal pencil (X) having A, B for its limiting points (§ 561), and the sphere of similitude (S) of (A), (B) belongs to the pencil (X).

On the other hand (S) belongs to the coaxal pencil (Z) determined by (A) and (B). But the two coaxal pencils (X), (Z) cannot have more than one sphere in common (§ 555), hence the proposition.

592. Theorem. *The radical sphere of two given spheres is coaxal with these spheres.*

The ratio of the powers of any point P of the radical sphere (M) of two given spheres (A), (B) with respect to these spheres is equal to -1 (§§ 542, 543), i.e., this ratio is constant, hence the proposition.

REMARK. This is a more general form of the proposition (§ 545).

593. Discussion. (a) If the two given spheres (A), (B) are both real, and intersect, the radical sphere (M) is real.

(b) If (A), (B) are real, but do not intersect, their radical sphere will be real, if the mid-point M of the line of centers AB does not fall between the limiting points of the coaxal system determined by (A), (B). This will always be the case, when the centers A, B lie on the same side of the radical plane; it may or may not take place, when A, B lie on opposite sides of the radical plane.

(c) If one of the given spheres is imaginary, (M) may be real or imaginary.

(d) If both given spheres are imaginary, their radical sphere is necessarily imaginary.

(e) When (A), (B) are orthogonal, the sphere (M) coincides with the sphere having AB for diameter (§ 570).

This discussion may be used to clarify further the solution of the problem of cutting two spheres along two orthogonal circles (§§ 548, 549).

594. Theorem. *Given five points in space, the sum of the inverses of the powers of each of these points with respect to the sphere determined by the remaining four points is zero.*

Let A_1, A_2, A_3, A_4, A_5 be the given points, and let O_1, O_2, $\cdots$ be the circumcenters, (O_1), (O_2), $\cdots$, the circumspheres, and V_1, V_2, $\cdots$, the volumes of the tetrahedrons $A_2A_3A_4A_5$, $A_3A_4A_5A_1$, $\cdots$.

The plane $A_2A_3A_4$ is the radical plane of the spheres (O_1), (O_5). If x, y denote the distances of the points A_1, A_5 from this plane, and p_1, p_5 the powers of A_1, A_5 with respect to (O_1), (O_5), we have, both in magnitude and in sign (§ 581),

$$p_1 = x \cdot 2O_1O_5, \qquad p_5 = y \cdot 2O_5O_1,$$

hence

$$p_5 : p_1 = - (y : x) = - (V_1 : V_5).$$

Similarly

$$p_5 : p_2 \qquad\qquad = - (V_2 : V_5)$$
$$p_5 : p_3 \qquad\qquad = - (V_3 : V_5)$$
$$p_5 : p_4 \qquad\qquad = - (V_4 : V_5).$$

Now $V_1 + V_2 + V_3 + V_4 = V_5$. This relation is valid whatever the position of the point A_5 may be with respect to the tetrahedron $A_1A_2A_3A_4$, due regard being paid to the signs of the volumes considered with regard to the volume V_5. Hence

$$p_5 \left(\frac{1}{p_1} + \frac{1}{p_2} + \frac{1}{p_3} + \frac{1}{p_4} \right) = - 1,$$

and therefore

$$\frac{1}{p_1} + \frac{1}{p_2} + \frac{1}{p_3} + \frac{1}{p_4} + \frac{1}{p_5} = 0.$$

595. Theorem. *If the centers of three given spheres are not collinear, the three radical planes of these spheres taken in pairs are coaxal.*

Any point P of the line of intersection u of the radical plane of the spheres (A), (B) with the radical plane of the spheres (B), (C) has equal powers with respect to (C), (A), hence the radical plane of these two spheres passes through u.

DEFINITION. The line u is called the *radical axis* of the three spheres.

The radical axis of three spheres is perpendicular to the plane determined by the centers of the three spheres.

COROLLARY I.   The radical axis of three spheres is the locus of the point which has equal powers with respect to the three spheres.

The radical axis of three spheres is also the locus of the points from which three equal tangents may be drawn to the three spheres.

COROLLARY II.   If a sphere is orthogonal to three spheres the centers of which are not collinear, the center of this sphere lies on the radical axis of the given sphere.

596. Theorem.   *The three spheres of similitude of three given spheres taken two-by-two are coaxal.*

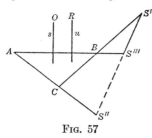

FIG. 57

Let (S'), (S''), (S''') be the spheres of similitude of the pairs of given spheres (B), (C); (C), (A); (A), (B) (Fig. 57).

Let (O) be a sphere passing through the centers A, B, C of the given spheres (A), (B), (C). The points B, C are inverse with respect to (S'), hence (O) is orthogonal to (S') (§§ 413, 511).   Similarly for (S''), (S''').

Let (R) be any sphere orthogonal to (A), (B), (C).   The sphere (S') is coaxal with (B), (C) (§ 589), hence (R) is orthogonal to (S') (§ 566).   Similarly for (S''), (S''').

The centers R, O of the spheres (R), (O) lie in the radical plane of (S'), (S'') (§ 522), and since R is any point of the radical axis u of (A), (B), (C) (§ 595), this plane must contain the line u. Similarly this plane must contain the axis s of the triangle ABC, hence the radical plane of (S'), (S'') is determined by the two parallel lines u, s.

In the same manner we may show that the plane us is also the radical plane of (S''), (S'''), and again of (S'''), (S'), hence the proposition.

EXERCISE.   When will the lines u, s coincide?   What becomes of the proposition in such a case?

597. Theorem.   *The radical planes of the spheres of a coaxal pencil with a sphere not belonging to the pencil are coaxal, and the* *axis of this pencil of planes lies in the radical plane of the coaxal pencil of spheres.*

Let (A), (B) be any two spheres of the pencil, and (S) a sphere not belonging to the given pencil. The three radical planes of the three pairs of spheres

(1) (S) (A); (S), (B); (A), (B),

have a common axis u (§ 595). Now if (C) is any other sphere of the coaxal pencil, the three radical planes of the three pairs of spheres

(2) (S), (A); (S), (C); (A), (C),

have in turn a common axis v. But two of the planes are the same in (1) and in (2), hence v is identical with u, which proves the proposition.

598. Remark. The line u (§ 597) is perpendicular to the plane determined by the center S of (S) and the line of centers of the given coaxal pencil.

599. Problem. *Construct a sphere belonging to a given coaxal pencil and tangent to a given sphere* (not belonging to the pencil).

If T, T' are the two points of contact of the tangent planes drawn to the given sphere (S) from the line u (§ 597), the two spheres of the given pencil which pass through the two points T, T' constitute the two solutions of the problem. There are no real solutions if u cuts (S).

600. Problem. *Construct a sphere belonging to a given coaxal pencil and orthogonal to a given sphere* (not belonging to the pencil).

The polar planes of the center P of the given sphere (P) with respect to the spheres of the given coaxal pencil (S) pass through a fixed line u perpendicular to the plane Ps determined by the line of centers s of (S) (§ 578).

The radical planes of (P) and the spheres of (S) pass through a fixed line v, also perpendicular to the plane Ps (§ 598). Now if (P) is orthogonal to the sphere (M) of (S), the radical plane of (P) and (M) passes through both u and v, hence the center M of (M) is the trace, on s, of the perpendicular from P upon the plane uv, or, what is the same thing, upon the line joining the traces of u and v in the plane Ps.   The problem has, in general, one solution.

If P lies in the radical plane of (S), then either (P) is orthogonal to all the spheres of (S), or the problem has no solution.

The reader may consider the case when P lies on s.

EXERCISES

1. The spheres having in common two fixed points and with respect to which another pair of points are conjugate form an intersecting pencil of coaxal spheres.

2. Construct a sphere passing through a given circle so that two given points shall be conjugate with respect to this sphere.

3. Construct a sphere tangent to a given plane so that it shall admit a given pair of perpendicular non-intersecting lines as a pair of conjugate lines.

4. Construct a sphere belonging to a given coaxal pencil and tangent to a given circle.

5. Given an intersecting coaxal pencil of spheres (S) and a fixed sphere (F) the center F of which lies on the line of centers of (S).   If P is any point of the basic circle of (S), the distance of the center of any sphere of (S) from F is inversely proportional to the distance of P from the radical plane of this sphere and the sphere (F).

6. The pole of the radical plane of two spheres (A), (B), with respect to one of the spheres of antisimilitude of (A), (B), coincides with the center of the second sphere of antisimilitude of (A), (B).

7. If P is a point common to all the spheres of a coaxal pencil, the tangent planes to these spheres at P form a coaxal pencil of planes.

8. If tangents can be drawn to two given real spheres from a point of their sphere of similitude, the ratio of these tangents is equal to the ratio of the radii of these spheres.

9. Let u be the axis of the pencil of polar planes of a given point P with respect to the spheres of a coaxal pencil.   Show that the mid-point of the segment joining P to any point of u lies in the radical plane of the pencil of spheres.

10. A variable sphere passes through a fixed circle (C).   Find the locus of the circle of contact of this sphere with the circumscribed cone having for vertex a given point in the plane of (C).

11. A variable sphere passes through a fixed circle.   Find the locus of the line of intersection of the two tangent planes to this sphere at two fixed points on the fixed circle.

12. Find the locus of the points of contact of the spheres of a coaxal pencil with the pairs of tangent planes drawn to them from a line in the radical plane of the pencil.

13. Find the locus of the point whose powers with respect to three given spheres are to each other as the squares of the radii of these spheres.

14. The orthogonal projections of a fixed point of the line of centers of two spheres upon all the planes which touch both spheres lie on a fixed sphere.

15. Draw a sphere belonging to a given coaxal pencil and bisecting a given sphere.

16. Determine the sphere of a given coaxal pencil which is bisected by a given sphere.

17. A non-intersecting coaxal pencil of spheres is determined (a) by the two limiting points of the pencil; (b) by one limiting point and a sphere of the pencil.

18. The locus of the inverse of a given point with respect to the spheres of a coaxal pencil is a circle.

19. If two lines, at right angles to each other, pass each through a limiting point of a coaxal pencil of spheres, and are perpendicular to the line joining these two points, they are conjugate with respect to every sphere of the pencil. Conversely.

20. In two given coaxal pencils of spheres to determine two spheres so that (a) their line of centers shall pass through a given point; (b) their radical plane shall have a given orientation. Discussion.

21. Find the locus of the trace of the radical plane of two spheres upon their line of centers, if one of the spheres is fixed and the other describes a coaxal pencil.

22. The radical axis of three spheres, of which two are fixed and the third describes a given coaxal pencil, constantly passes through a fixed point.

23. The sphere having for ends of a diameter the two points determined on two fixed orthogonal skew lines by a variable plane of fixed orientation describes a coaxal pencil.

10. Coaxal Nets of Spheres

601. Definition. A system of spheres such that the same fixed line is the radical axis of any three spheres of the system is called a *coaxal net of spheres.*

The centers of a coaxal net are coplanar. For if (A), (B), (C), (D), $\cdots$ are the given spheres, and $A, B, C, D, \cdots$ their centers, the radical axis r of the three spheres (A), (B), (C) is perpendicular to the plane ABC (§ 595). Now, by definition, the radical axis of (A), (B), (D) coincides with r and is therefore perpendicular to the plane ABD. But one and only one plane may be drawn through the point A perpendicular to the line r, hence the planes ABC, ABD are identical, i.e., D lies in the plane ABC.

The plane $ABCD \cdots$ is called *the plane of centers* of the coaxal net.

602. Consequences. (a) Any point of the radical axis of a coaxal net has the same power with respect to all the spheres of the net.

(b) The radical plane of any two spheres belonging to a given coaxal net passes through the radical axis of the net.

(c) A coaxal net of spheres is determined by any three spheres of the net, the centers of which are not colinear.

(d) A coaxal net of spheres is determined by one sphere and the radical axis of the net.

(e) If two spheres belong to a given coaxal net, any sphere coaxal with these two spheres also belongs to the coaxal net.

(f) *The spheres orthogonal to a given sphere and having their centers in a given plane form a coaxal net.*

For the radical axis of any three of these spheres will coincide with the perpendicular from the center of the orthogonal sphere to the given plane of the centers of the spheres.

(g) *The spheres of a given coaxal net which have their centers in a straight line form a coaxal pencil of spheres.*

Indeed, the radical plane of this pencil is the plane passing through the radical axis of the given net and perpendicular to the line containing the centers of the spheres considered.

(h) *The spheres of a coaxal net which pass through a given point in space form a coaxal pencil.*

For any two of these spheres have the same radical plane, namely the plane determined by the point considered and the radical axis of the net.

603. Definition. (a) The point common to the radical axis of a net of spheres and the plane of centers of the net may be called the *radical center* of the net.

(b) The circle having for its center the radical center of the net, situated in the central plane of the net, and orthogonal to the spheres of the net, is called the **limiting circle** of the net.

604. Discussion. Let R (Fig. 58) be the radical center of a coaxal net of spheres and p the power of R with respect to the spheres of the net.

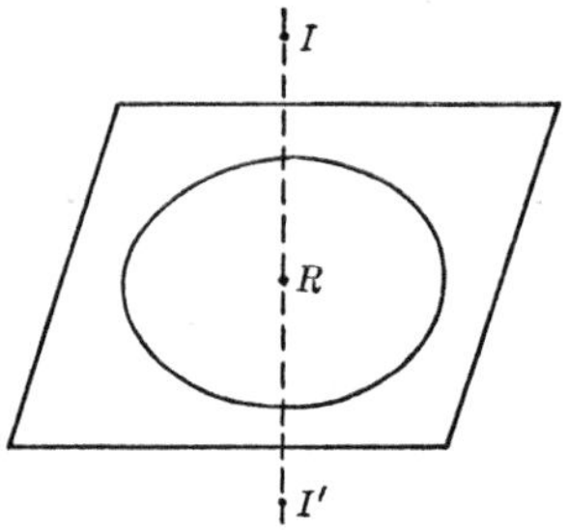

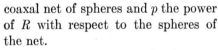

(a) p IS POSITIVE. The limiting circle (R) of the net is real. Every point of the plane of centers (P) which lies outside of (R) is the center of a real sphere of the net, and every point inside of (R) is the center of an imaginary sphere of the net, while every point on (R) may be said to be the center of a sphere of radius zero, or a "null sphere" of the net, or a "point sphere" of the net.

Fig. 58

Since p is positive, the point R lies outside every real non-null sphere of the net. Thus the radical axis r of the net does not meet the spheres. On the other hand, if three spheres of the net had a point in common, this point would have equal powers with respect to these spheres, and therefore be a point of the radical axis of the net (§ 595). Thus the spheres of the net have no points in common. The net is called a *non-intersecting net* or *of the non-intersecting type.*

(b) p IS NEGATIVE. The limiting circle (R) is imaginary, and every point of the plane of centers is the center of a real sphere of the net.

Since p is negative, R lies inside every sphere of the net, hence the radical axis r of the net meets the spheres in pairs of real points. It is readily seen that these pairs of points are identical. Indeed, a point common to r and one sphere of the net must have the power zero with respect to all the spheres of the net [§ 602(a)], i.e., it must lie on every sphere of the net. Thus the spheres of the net have two points I, I' in common. These points are determined by the relation $RI^2 = RI'^2 = -p$. This type is called the *intersecting coaxal net* or *the intersecting type.*

(c) $p = 0$. All the spheres of the net pass through R and are tangent at this point to the radical axis of the net. This is called the *tangent type* of net.

The three types of nets may thus be defined as follows:

(a) The net formed by the spheres orthogonal to the same (real) circle;

(b) The net formed by the spheres having two real points in common;

(c) The spheres tangent to the same line at the same point.

Thus each type may be characterized separately in terms of real geometric elements. By making use of the imaginary circle and the null-circle we may give one and the same characterization for all the three types by saying that a net of spheres is constituted by all the spheres orthogonal to a fixed circle, which circle may be real, imaginary, or a null circle.

Another way of stating the same thing would be to say that a coaxal net of spheres consists of all the spheres which have two points in common, which points may be real and distinct, real and coincident, or imaginary.

605. Theorem. *Through any two points in space not coplanar with the radical axis one and only one sphere may be drawn belonging to a given coaxal net.*

Construct the inverse points A', B' of the given two points A, B with respect to the sphere (L) having for great circle the limiting circle (R) of the net. The four points A, A', B, B' are concyclic (§ 399). The perpendicular erected to the plane $AA'B$ at the center of the circle $AA'BB'$ meets the plane of centers of the net in the center M of the required sphere (M). Indeed, (M) is orthogonal to (L) (§ 413), hence it is orthogonal to the limiting circle (R).

This solution fails, if the plane $RAA'BB'$ is perpendicular to the plane of centers, i.e., when the radical axis r of the net lies in the plane RAB.

606. Corollary. *Through a given point in space an infinite number of spheres may be drawn belonging to a given coaxal net.*

EXERCISE. State the above proof without making use of the sphere (L), or the limiting circle (R). Use the radical center R and the power p of R with respect to the spheres of the net.

607. Problem. *Find the locus of the points of contact of a fixed plane with the spheres of a given coaxal net.*

The power, with respect to any sphere (S) of the net tangent to the given plane, of the point I common to this plane and the radical axis of the net is equal to the square of the segment IT joining I to the point of contact T of (S) with the plane. Now I has equal powers with respect to all the spheres of the net, hence the locus of T is a circle having I for center and for the square of its radius the power of the point I with respect to the spheres of the net.—When will this locus be real?

EXERCISE. Consider the case when the given plane is parallel to the axis of the net; when it contains the axis.

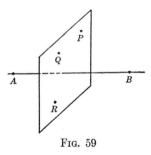

FIG. 59

608. Theorem. *The spheres orthogonal to the spheres of a given coaxal pencil form a coaxal net.*

Let (A), (B) (Fig. 59) be any two spheres of the given coaxal pencil, and let (P), (Q), (R) be any three spheres whose centers P, Q, R are not collinear and which are orthogonal to (A) and (B).

The center A of (A) is a point on the radical axis of the three spheres (P), (Q), (R) (§ 595), and so is the center B of (B), hence this radical axis coincides with the line of centers of the given pencil of spheres. Thus any three spheres (the centers of which are not collinear) which are orthogonal to the spheres of the given pencil have the same radical axis, hence the proposition.

Besides, we know (§ 522) that the centers of the spheres (P), (Q), (R), $\cdots$ lie in the same plane, namely the radical plane of the given pencil.

609. Definition. The coaxal pencil of spheres each member of which is orthogonal to the spheres of a given coaxal net (§ 608) is said to be *conjugate* to the net, and vice versa, the net is said to be *conjugate* to the pencil.

610. Consequences. From the last proposition (§ 608) and its proof follows: Given a coaxal net (N) and its conjugate coaxal pencil (P): (a) The radical plane of (P) is the plane of centers of (N); (b) The line of centers of (P) is the radical axis of (N); (c) If (P) is an intersecting pencil, (N) is non-intersecting, and the common circle of the spheres of (P) is the limiting circle of (N); (d) If (P) is a non-intersecting pencil, (N) is an intersecting net, and the limiting points of (P) are the points common to the spheres of (N).

611. Theorem. *The polar planes of a point with respect to the spheres of a coaxal net have a point in common.*

Let Q be the point of intersection of the polar planes of the given point P with respect to the three spheres (A), (B), (C) belonging to the given net and whose centers are not collinear. The points P, Q being conjugate with respect to these three spheres, these spheres are orthogonal to the sphere (PQ) described on PQ as diameter (§ 514), and therefore any other sphere (D) of the net is also orthogonal to (PQ), hence P, Q are conjugate with respect to (D) (§ 513), and the polar plane of P with respect to (D) will pass through Q.

612. Remark. The mid-point of PQ, which is the center of (PQ), lies on the radical axis of the given net (§ 595).

613. Theorem. *The radical plane of a fixed sphere and a variable sphere belonging to a given coaxal net passes through a fixed point on the radical axis of the given net.*

Let I be the trace of the radical axis of the net in the radical plane of the sphere (A) of the net with the sphere (S) not belonging to the net. The point I has equal powers with respect to (A) and (S), and also with respect to (A) and any other sphere (B) of the net, hence the powers of I with respect to (S) and (B) are equal, and therefore the radical plane of (S) and (B) passes through I. The sphere (B) being any sphere of the net, the proposition is proved.

614. Corollary. *The locus of the point of contact of a given sphere with a variable sphere belonging to a given coaxal net is a circle.*

If T is the point of contact of the sphere (S) (§ 613) with any sphere (M) of the net, the tangent plane to the spheres (S), (M) at T is the radical plane of these two spheres, hence this plane passes through I. Thus T is the point of contact of the tangent IT from I to (S), hence T lies on the circle of intersection (T) of the sphere (S) with the polar plane of I with respect to (S).

615. Remark. The centers of all the spheres of the net which are tangent to (S) lie on the cone having for vertex the center S of (S) and passing through the circle (T).

616. Theorem. *The six spheres of antisimilitude of three given spheres taken in pairs belong to the coaxal net of spheres determined by the three given spheres.*

Indeed, each of the spheres of antisimilitude is coaxal with two of the given spheres (§§ 587, 588).

617. Remark. *The three spheres of similitude of the three given spheres taken in pairs also belong to this coaxal net* (§ 589).

618. Corollary I. *Three spheres of antisimilitude of three given spheres taken in pairs are coaxal, if their centers lie on the same axis of similitude of the given spheres.*

619. Corollary II. *The three circles* (real or imaginary) *obtained as the intersections of each of three given spheres with the internal sphere of antisimilitude of the other two spheres are cospherical.*

The lines joining the centers A, B, C of the given spheres (A), (B), (C) to their internal centers of similitude meet in a point S, the trilinear pole, with respect to the triangle ABC, of the external axis of similitude of the three given spheres.

The sphere (S) having S for center and belonging to the coaxal net determined by (A), (B), (C) is coaxal with the sphere (A) and the internal sphere of antisimilitude (X') of the two spheres (B), (C). Similarly (S) is coaxal with the spheres (B), (Y'); and again with (C), (Z'), hence the proposition.

EXERCISE. Extend this proposition to any three of the six spheres of antisimilitude the centers of which are not collinear.

620. Problem. *Find a sphere common to two given coaxal nets.*

(a) The required sphere (S) must be orthogonal to the two limiting circles (L), (L'), of the two given nets (N), (N') (§ 604), or, what is the same thing, to the two spheres (R), (R') having (L), (L') for diametral circles. Thus the center S of (S) lies in the radical plane of the two spheres (R), (R'), and since S necessarily lies in the planes of centers of both (N) and (N'), the center S is common to three known planes. The problem has, in general, one and only one solution.

(b) SPECIAL CASE. The three planes considered will be coaxal, if the radical plane of (R), (R') passes through the line of intersection u of the planes of centers of (N) and (N') (Fig. 60). The line LL' joining the centers L, L'

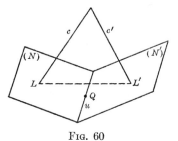

FIG. 60

of (R), (R') will be perpendicular to u, and since the radical axes c, c' of (N), (N') are obviously perpendicular to u, these two axes lie in the plane through LL' perpendicular to u, i.e., c and c' are coplanar.

If (Q) is a sphere having its center Q on u and belonging to both given nets, the sphere (Q) is orthogonal to the spheres of the two coaxal pencils (P), (P'), conjugate to these nets. In particular (Q) will be orthogonal to the spheres (F), (F') of (P), (P') having for center the point cc'. But the point cc' is the center of only one sphere orthogonal to (Q), hence (P), (P') have a sphere in common, i.e., (L) and (L') are cospherical.

Thus, the lines c and c' being coplanar, the problem has no solution, if the circles (L), (L') are not cospherical. If these two circles are cospherical, every point Q of u is the center of a sphere satisfying the conditions of the problem, i.e., the two nets have a coaxal pencil of spheres in common.

When the basic points of both (N) and (N') are real, the above results are immediately apparent.

621. Problem.   *Construct a sphere orthogonal to two given circles.* This problem was solved in connection with the solution of the problem of § 620.

622. Problem.   *In each of three given coaxal pencils of spheres to determine a sphere so that the three spheres shall be coaxal.*

The two conjugate nets of the two given pencils of spheres (A), (B) have a sphere (R) in common [§ 620 (a)] which is orthogonal to all the spheres of both (A) and (B).   Now if a sphere of the third pencil (C) is coaxal with a sphere of (A) and a sphere of (B), that sphere is also orthogonal to (R).   Hence the following solution of the problem.

Determine the sphere (R) orthogonal to spheres of the two given pencils (A), (B).   In the third given pencil (C) determine the sphere (F) orthogonal to (R) (§ 600) and through the center F of (F) draw the line meeting the lines of centers u, v of (A), (B), in the points D, E.   The spheres (D), (E) belonging to (A), (B) and having D, E for centers constitute, together with the sphere (F), the solution of the problem.

It is clear that in the above solution we could have considered first any two of the three pencils of spheres (A), (B), (C).

623. Special Cases.   (a) The lines u, v intersect, and the basic circles (a), (b) of the two pencils (A), (B) are not cospherical. In this case the sphere (R) does not exist [§ 620 (b)].

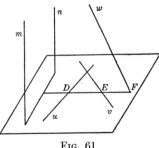

FIG. 61

Let (F) (Fig. 61) be the sphere of the pencil (C) having for center the trace F of the line of centers w of (C) in the plane uv. The radical planes of (F) with the spheres of (A) have a line m in common perpendicular to the plane Fu and situated in the radical plane of (A) (§ 598).   Let n be the analogous line relative to (B).

The two lines m, n being perpendicular to the same plane $Fu \equiv Fv \equiv uv$, are coplanar.   The perpendicular from F upon the trace of

mn in the plane uv meets the lines u, v in the points D, E. The spheres (D), (E) of (A), (B) having D, E for centers, and the sphere (F) constitute a solution of the problem.

(b) The lines u, v are coplanar, and (a), (b) belong to the same sphere (S). The two pencils (A), (B) thus belong to the same net (N).

The sphere (S) and any sphere of the pencil (C) constitute a (degenerate) solution of the problem, and these are the only solutions, if the sphere (F) of (C) having its center F in the plane uv does not belong to (N). But if (F) belongs to (N), the problem has also the solutions consisting of (F) and any two spheres of (A) and (B) whose centers are collinear with F.

(c) The lines u, v are not coplanar, and the radical plane of (C) passes through R. The problem has no solution, if the sphere (R) does not belong to the conjugate net of (C).

If (R) belongs to this net, then (R) is orthogonal to all the spheres of the three pencils (A), (B), (C), and therefore also to the three basic circles (a), (b), (c) of these pencils. Let D, E, F be the points in which a line t meets the lines u, v, w. The three spheres having D, E, F for centers and belonging to (A), (B), (C), respectively, constitute a solution of the problem, for their centers are collinear and they are orthogonal to the same sphere (R). We obtain an infinite number of solutions, as t describes the ruled system supplementary to the one determined by u, v, w.

(d) The reader may consider other special cases, as when the lines u, v, w are concurrent, or coplanar, when they are parallel to the same plane, when two of these lines coincide, etc.

624. Darboux's Problem. *Construct a circle intersecting three given (real) circles in space.*

If the circle (x) intersects each of the three given circles (a), (b), (c), it is cospherical with each of them, and the three spheres (D), (E), (F) so determined belong, respectively, to the three pencils of spheres (A), (B), (C) having (a), (b), (c) for basic circles. On the other hand (D), (E), (F) are coaxal, for they have the circle (x) in common. The problem of determining the circle (x) is thus reduced to the preceding one (§ 622).

The reader may find it instructive to discuss the special cases, with direct reference to the circle (x).

625. Problem. *Construct a circle whose projections upon three given planes from three given points, respectively, shall be circles.*

If (U), (V), (W) are the cones determined by the given points A, B, C and the required circle (s), (a) the plane of (s) is either antiparallel, with respect to the three cones, to the three given planes (P), (Q), (R), or (b) the plane of (s) is antiparallel to two of these planes and parallel to the third (§ 375).

(a) The plane touching the sphere $(D) \equiv A - (s)$ at the point A is antiparallel to the plane of (s) on (U), and therefore parallel to the plane (P). Hence (D) belongs to the coaxal pencil of spheres (A) passing through the point A and having their centers on the perpendicular a from A upon (P).

Thus consider the three pencils of spheres (A), (B), (C) having for their lines of centers the perpendiculars a, b, c from the points A, B, C upon the planes (P), (Q), (R) and tangent to these planes at the points A, B, C, respectively. In these three pencils determine three spheres (D), (E), (F) so that they shall be coaxal (§ 622). The circle common to these spheres is a solution of the problem.

(b) The plane of (s) is parallel, say, to the plane (P). The problem reduces to finding two spheres (E), (F), one belonging to the pencil (B) and the other to (C), so that the radical plane of (E), (F) shall be parallel to (P), or, what is the same thing, that the line of centers of these spheres shall be parallel to a. Let E, F be the points where a line parallel to a meets the lines b, c (§ 5). The circle common to the spheres (E), (F) having E, F for centers and passing, respectively, through the points B, C is a solution of the problem. Similarly for the planes (Q), (R).

The problem may thus have four solutions.

EXERCISES

1. The spheres with respect to which two given points I, J have the same powers p, q form a coaxal net.

2. Construct the sphere belonging to a given coaxal net and having for center a given point of the plane of centers of the net.

3. Find the locus of the centers of the spheres which admit two fixed pairs of conjugate points.

4. The locus of the centers of the spheres which are orthogonal to a given sphere and belong to a given coaxal net is a straight line.

5. The point common to the radical axis and the plane of centers of a coaxal net of spheres is the center of a sphere belonging to the net and also the center of a sphere belonging to the conjugate orthogonal pencil of the net.

Show that one of these two spheres is imaginary.   Find a relation between the radii of these two concentric spheres.   May these two spheres coincide?

6. Given the spheres (A), (B), (C), a sphere (B') is taken belonging to the coaxal pencil (A), (B), and a sphere (C') belonging to the coaxal pencil (A), (C).   Show that the two coaxal pencils of spheres (B), (C); (B'), (C') have a sphere in common; the same is true about the two coaxal pencils (B), (C'); (B'), (C).

7. The spheres which admit three fixed pairs of conjugate points form a coaxal pencil.   Determine the circle common to these spheres.

8. The spheres of a coaxal net which are tangent to a given plane touch also another fixed plane.

9. Find the locus of the trace of the radical plane of two spheres upon their line of centers, if one of these spheres is fixed and the other describes a coaxal net.

10. The polar conjugate of the line of centers of a coaxal pencil with respect to a given sphere of the conjugate net of spheres lies in all the radical planes of this sphere with the spheres of the pencil.

11. If a variable circle has a pair of points in common with each of two given fixed circles, its plane passes through a fixed point.

12. If a line s coplanar with the axis of a given coaxal net touches a sphere of the net, at a point P, every sphere of the net passing through P is tangent to s at P.

13. Construct a sphere orthogonal to three given spheres and tangent to a given line.

14. Construct a sphere belonging to a given coaxal net, passing through a given point, and tangent to a given plane.

15. Determine the sphere belonging to a given coaxal net and orthogonal to two given spheres.

16. Construct a sphere passing through two given points and tangent to two given planes.

17. All the spheres passing through two given points and having their centers on a straight line form a coaxal pencil.   Construct the common circle of these spheres.

18. Find a necessary and sufficient condition for two coaxal pencils of spheres to belong to the same coaxal net.

19. Find the locus of the centers of the spheres belonging to a given coaxal net and having equal radii.

20. The locus of the inverses of a given point with respect to the spheres of a given coaxal net is a sphere.

11. Four Spheres

626. Theorem.   *The six radical planes of four spheres taken two-by-two have a point in common.*

The radical axis of three of the four given spheres and the radical plane of one of these three spheres with the fourth sphere meet in a point which has equal powers with respect to the four given spheres, hence this point is common to the six radical planes of the given spheres taken in pairs.

627. Definitions.   The point common to the six radical planes of four spheres taken two-by-two is called the *radical center* of the four spheres.

The radical center of four spheres is the center of a sphere, real or imaginary, which is orthogonal to the four given spheres. This sphere is called the *orthogonal sphere* of the four given spheres.

628. Theorem.   *If each of four given spheres touches the remaining three, their six points of contact lie on their orthogonal sphere.*

If Z is the point of contact of the two given spheres (A), (B), the plane perpendicular at Z to the line AB joining the centers A, B of the two spheres is the radical plane of (A), (B) and therefore contains the radical center R of the four given spheres. Now RZ is a tangent drawn from R to the sphere (A), hence RZ is a radius of the orthogonal sphere (R) of the four given spheres. Similarly for the other points of contact.

629. Corollary I.   The radius RZ (§ 628) of (R) is perpendicular to the line AB, hence: *The orthogonal sphere (R) touches the six lines determined by the centers of the given spheres at the points where the given spheres touch each other.*

630. Corollary II.   Let A, B, C, D (Fig. 35) be the centers of the given spheres (§ 628), and let U, V, W, X, Y, Z be the points of contact of (R) with the edges DA, DB, DC, BC, CA, AB of the tetrahedron $DABC$.   The plane ABC cuts (R) along the inscribed circle of the triangle ABC, which circles touches BC, CA, AB in X, Y, Z, hence the lines AX, BY, CZ are concurrent (C. G., p. 129).   Similarly for the other faces of $ABCD$.   Hence (§ 348): *The lines UX, VY, WZ have a point M in common.*

631. Corollary III.   *The tangent planes to the sphere (R) along the edges of $ABCD$ (§ 630) meet the respectively opposite edges in six coplanar points.*

The tangent planes to (R) at U and X pass, respectively, through the edges DA, BC of $DABC$ and intersect in the conjugate t of UX with respect to (R).   Hence the trace $X' \equiv (t, BC)$, on

BC, of the tangent plane to (R) at U is conjugate to the point M (§ 630) with respect to (R). Thus X' and its five analogous points lie in the polar plane of M with respect to (R).

632. Definitions. The sphere determined by the centers of four given spheres may be referred to as the *central sphere* of the four given spheres.

The radical plane of the central sphere and the orthogonal sphere of four given spheres will be referred to as the *Newtonian plane* of the four given spheres.

633. Neuberg's Theorem. *The distances of the centers of four spheres from the Newtonian plane of these spheres are proportional to the squares of the radii of the respective spheres.*

Let A, B, C, D be the centers and a, b, c, d the squares of the radii of the four given spheres (A), (B), (C), (D). Let (R) be their orthogonal sphere and (O) their central sphere.

If R, O are the centers of the spheres (R), (O), and p the distance of A from the Newtonian plane of the given spheres (§ 632), the quantity $2p \cdot RO$ is equal to the difference of the powers of A with respect to (R) and (O) (§ 580). Now these powers are respectively equal to a and zero, hence

$$a = 2p \cdot RO, \qquad \text{or} \qquad p : a = 1 : 2RO.$$

Since the right hand side of this equality is constant, the proposition is proved.

634. Theorem. *The six spheres of similitude of four given spheres taken in pairs belong to the same coaxal net.*

The sphere of similitude (S_{ab}) of the two given spheres (A), (B) is coaxal with these spheres (§ 589), hence (S_{ab}) is orthogonal to any sphere which is orthogonal to (A) and (B) (§ 566), and in particular to the orthogonal sphere (R) of the four given spheres (A), (B), (C), (D).

The centers of similitude of (A), (B) are harmonically separated by the centers A, B, therefore these centers of similitude are conjugate with respect to the central sphere (O) of the four given spheres. Hence (S_{ab}) is orthogonal to (O) (§ 514).

Thus each of the six spheres of similitude of the four given spheres taken in pairs is orthogonal to the same two spheres (R) and (O), hence the proposition (§ 608).

635. Corollary. *The centers of the six spheres of similitude of four given spheres taken in pairs lie in the Newtonian plane of the given spheres.*

Indeed, these spheres of similitude being orthogonal to (R) and (O), have their centers in the radical plane of the latter spheres.

636. Remark. This proposition (§ 635) is an extension to space of the corresponding proposition in the plane (C. G., p. 197). The line of centers of the three circles of similitude is often referred to as the "Newtonian line," and this is the justification of the name of the corresponding plane in space.

637. Definition. The limiting points of the coaxal pencil of spheres determined by the central sphere and the orthogonal sphere of four given spheres will be referred to as the *isodynamic points* of the four given spheres.

The isodynamic points of four spheres are common to the six spheres of similitude of the four given spheres taken in pairs (§ 634).

638. Theorem. *The four inverses, with respect to four given spheres, of a (real) isodynamic point of these spheres determine a sphere concentric with the orthogonal sphere of the given spheres.*

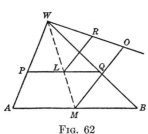

FIG. 62

Let P, Q (Fig. 62) be the inverses of the isodynamic point W of the given spheres (A), (B), (C), (D), with respect to (A) and (B). The lines PQ, AB are parallel (§ 539), hence the midpoints L, M of PQ, AB are collinear with W, and we have

$$WP : WA = WL : WM.$$

Also the mediators of the segments PQ, AB are parallel.

The mediator of AB contains the center O of the central sphere (O) of the four given spheres; the mediator of PQ coincides with the radical plane of (A), (B) (§ 539) and therefore contains the radical center R of the four given spheres; furthermore the three points W, O, R are collinear (§ 637). Hence OM is parallel to RL, and we have

$$WL : WM = WR : WO,$$

hence

$$WP : WA = WR : WO.$$

This proportion shows that the lines OA, RP are parallel, and we have

$$RP : OA = WR : WO.$$

The last three terms of this proportion do not depend upon the sphere (A) considered, hence RP is constant, which proves the proposition.

639. Remark. The point W divides the line of centers RO of the sphere (O) and the sphere (R') determined by the inverses of W with respect to the four given spheres, in the ratio of the radii of the spheres (O), (R'), hence W *is a center of similitude of these two spheres.*

640. Theorem. *The distances of a* (real) *isodynamic point of four spheres from the centers of these spheres are proportional to the respective radii of these spheres.*

The isodynamic point W of the four spheres (A), (B), (C), (D) is common to the six spheres of similitude of these four spheres taken in pairs (§ 637), hence if A, B are the centers and a, b the radii of (A), (B), we have (§ 479)

$$WA : WB = a : b, \quad \text{or} \quad WA : a = WB : b$$

and similarly

$$WA : a = WC : c = WD : d.$$

OTHERWISE. From the preceding paragraph (§ 639) we have

$$AW : AP = OW : OR.$$

The points P, W being inverse with respect to (A), we have

$$AW \cdot AP = a^2$$

hence

$$AW^2 : a^2 = OW : OR.$$

The left hand side of this proportion does not depend upon the particular sphere considered, hence the proposition.

REMARK. The second proof also provides an interpretation of the constant $WA : a$.

641. Theorem. *If the radii of four spheres with fixed centers vary so as to remain proportional, the orthogonal sphere of these four spheres describes a coaxal pencil.*

The ratio of the radii of any two of these spheres being constant, the centers of similitude of these two spheres are fixed, and

therefore the same holds for the center of their sphere of similitude.
Thus the four spheres have a fixed Newtonian plane (N) (§ 635).

The centers of the four spheres being fixed, their central sphere
is fixed, hence their orthogonal sphere belongs to the coaxal pencil
determined by (O) and (N) (§ 555).

642. Problem. *With four given points as centers to describe
four spheres so that one of their planes of similitude shall coincide
with a given plane.*

Let U, V, W, X, Y, Z (Fig. 49) be the traces, in the given plane,
of the edges DA, DB, DC, BC, CA, AB of the tetrahedron $DABC$
determined by the four given points D, A, B, C. If $U', V', \cdots$
are the harmonic conjugates of these traces with respect to the
corresponding pairs of vertices of $DABC$, let $(UU'), \cdots$ denote
the spheres having for diameters the segments $UU', \cdots$.

An arbitrary sphere (D) having D for center, and the three
spheres $(A), (B), (C)$ having A, B, C for centers and respectively
coaxal with the pairs of spheres $(D), (UU'); (D), (VV'); (D),$
(WW') are four spheres satisfying the conditions of the problem.

Indeed, the sphere (UU') is coaxal with $(D), (A)$ and divides the
line of centers of these two spheres harmonically, hence (UU') is
the sphere of similitude of $(D), (A)$ (§ 591), and therefore U is a
center of similitude of these two spheres. Similarly the points
V, W are, respectively, centers of similitude of the pairs of spheres
$(D), (B); (D), (C)$. Now the points U, V, Z are collinear, being
common to the two planes UVW and DAB, and U, V are centers
of similitude of the two pairs of spheres $(D), (A); (D), (B)$, hence
Z is a center of similitude of $(A), (B)$ (§ 481). Similarly the points
X, Y are, respectively, centers of similitude of the pairs of spheres
$(B), (C); (C), (A)$. Thus the given plane UVW is a plane of
similitude of the spheres $(D), (A), (B), (C)$.

The radius of the sphere (D) was chosen arbitrarily, hence any
four spheres $(D'), (A'), (B'), (C')$ whose radii are proportional to
the radii of $(D), (A), (B), (C)$, constitute a solution of the
problem.

643. Theorem. *The six external spheres of antisimilitude of
four given spheres taken in pairs form a coaxal net.*

The external sphere of antisimilitude of any two of the given
spheres is coaxal with these two spheres and therefore orthognal
to any sphere orthogonal to these two spheres. In particular the

sphere of antisimilitude is orthogonal to the orthogonal sphere (R) of the four given spheres.

On the other hand, the six external centers of similitude of the four given spheres taken in pairs are coplanar (§ 492), hence the proposition [§ 602 (f)].

644. Remark. The proposition is valid for any six of the twelve spheres of antisimilitude the centers of which are coplanar (§§ 491 ff.).

645. Theorem. *Four given spheres may be arranged in groups of two in three different ways. In each arrangement we have two internal spheres of antisimilitude, and we consider the coaxal pencil determined by these two spheres. The three coaxal pencils thus obtained have a sphere in common.*

In the first place the lines of centers of these three coaxal pencils have a point P in common (§ 496). On the other hand, all the spheres of antisimilitude considered are orthogonal to the orthogonal sphere (R) of the four given spheres. Hence the sphere (P) having P for center and orthogonal to (R) belongs to each of the three pencils considered (§ 568).

646. Theorem. *If the radii of four spheres with fixed centers vary so that the sum of the powers of each center with respect to the other three spheres is the same for the four centers, the radical center of the four spheres remains fixed.*

Let A, B, C, D be the centers and p, q, r, s the squares of the radii of the four given spheres (A, p), (B, q), (C, r), (D, s). For the points A and B we have, by assumption,

$$AB^2 - q + AC^2 - r + AD^2 - s = BA^2 - p + BC^2 - r + BD^2 - s$$

or

$$(1) \qquad AC^2 + AD^2 + p = BC^2 + BD^2 + q.$$

If V is the mid-point of CD we have, applying the formula for the median to AV, BV in the triangles ACD, BCD,

$$(2) \quad CD^2/2 = AD^2 + AC^2 - 2AV^2 = BD^2 + BC^2 - 2BV^2,$$

hence, from (1) and (2),

$$AV^2 + p/2 = BV^2 + q/2.$$

Thus the point V has the same powers with respect to the two spheres $(A, -p/2)$, $(B, -q/2)$ having for centers A, B and for the squares of their radii $-p/2$, $-q/2$, hence the radical plane of these two spheres is the plane through V perpendicular to AB, consequently this plane passes through the Monge point M of the tetrahedron $ABCD$ (§ 228).

On the other hand this radical plane determines on AB the point X such that

$$UX = (-p/2 + q/2)/2AB,$$

where U is the mid-point of AB (§ 582), while the radical plane of the spheres (A, p), (B, q) determines on AB the point Y such that

$$UY = (p - q)/2AB,$$

hence

$$UY = -2UX.$$

Now the plane perpendicular to AB at U passes through the circumcenter O of the tetrahedron $ABCD$, hence the radical plane of (A, p), (B, q) meets the line OM in a point N such that

$$ON = -2OM.$$

Thus the point N is independent of the radii of the spheres considered and also independent of the particular edge AB which we considered, hence the proposition is proved.

647. Remark. The point N lies on the Euler line of $ABCD$, and if G is the centroid of $ABCD$ we have

$$GN : GO = 5 : 1.$$

EXERCISES

1. If the orthogonal sphere of four spheres is imaginary, there is a real sphere concentric with it which is bisected by each of the given spheres.

2. The isodynamic points of four spheres are inverse both with respect to the orthogonal sphere and the central sphere of the four given spheres.

3. Find a point the distances of which to four given points are proportional to four given quantities (segments).

4. The radical center of the four escribed spheres of an isosceles tetrahedron coincides with the centroid of the tetrahedron.

5. (a) With the four vertices of a tetrahedron as centers spheres are drawn having for their radii the respective medians of the tetrahedron; show that the radical center of these four spheres lies on the Euler line of the tetrahedron. Locate this radical center with reference to the known points on the Euler line. (b) Show that the proposition is valid if the radii are taken proportionally to the medians. For what value of the factor of proportionality will the radical center coincide with the Monge point of the tetrahedron? With the circumcenter?

6. If the distances of a point to the centers of four given spheres bear a constant ratio to the radii of the respective spheres, the point is an isodynamic point of the four given spheres.

7. The six radical planes of the central sphere of four given spheres with the six spheres of similitude of the given spheres taken in pairs, have a point in common. What is the relation of this point to the Newtonian plane of the given spheres?

8. The tetrahedron determined by the centers of four given spheres and the tetrahedron whose faces are the radical planes of these spheres with their orthogonal sphere (R) are polar reciprocal tetrahedrons with respect to (R).

9. Four spheres have the point M in common and intersect by threes in the points A, B, C, D. A fifth sphere (U) passing through M cuts the spheres $MBCD, MCDA, MDAB, MABC$ along circles lying in the planes $(P), (Q), (R), (S)$. Show that the four lines of intersection of these planes with the planes BCD, CDA, DAB, ABC, respectively, are coplanar.

10. Find a point whose powers with respect to four given spheres are proportional to the radii of these spheres.

11. The radical center of four equal spheres is the center of two spheres each of which is tangent to the four given spheres.

12. If the four polar planes of a point P with respect to four spheres (whose centers are not coplanar) have a point Q in common, the two points P, Q are the ends of a diameter of the orthogonal sphere of the four given spheres. Conversely.

13. Given four mutually tangents spheres $(A), (B), (C), (D)$, the mediator of the line UX joining the point of contact U of $(A), (D)$ to the point of contact X of the two remaining spheres $(B), (C)$ cuts the two lines of centers AD, BC of these two pairs of spheres in the points U', X'. Show that the pair of points U', X', and the two analogous pairs of points all lie in the same plane.

14. Each of four given spheres touches the remaining three externally; if each center is joined to the Gergonne point of the triangle formed by the remaining three centers, the four lines thus obtained are concurrent.

15. Construct a sphere which shall divide harmonically each of four given segments in space.

16. Given the four spheres $(A), (B), (C), (D)$, find a fifth sphere (L) such that the radical planes of the pairs of spheres $(L), (A); (L,) (B); (L), (C); (L), (D)$ shall pass, respectively, through the four given points P, Q, R, S.

17. Let the line joining a given point L to the center A of the given sphere (A) meet (A) in the points A', A'' (the points A' and L lying on the same side of A). Given the four spheres $(A), (B), (C), (D)$, determine the point L so that the two tetrahedrons $A'B'C'D', A''B''C''D''$ shall be homothetic with respect to L.

18. The four points P, Q, R, S are marked on the four radical axes of four given spheres taken three-by-three. Find a fifth sphere (M) such that the points P, Q, R, S shall be the respective radical centers of (M) and of the given spheres taken three-by-three.

19. Given a tetrahedron $ABCD$ and a point P not on its faces. Draw through P the three lines, each meeting a pair of opposite edges. Express the ratios in which the latter will be divided by the points of intersection, in terms of four quantities a, b, c, d, the edge AB being divided in the ratio $a : b$, etc.

20. Given four mutually tangent spheres, (a) the distance of the point of contact of two of these spheres from the Newtonian plane of the four spheres is equal to the product of the radii of the two spheres considered divided by twice the distance between the radical center and the center of the central sphere of the four spheres; (b) the product of the distance considered in (a) by the analogous distance relative to the point of contact of the remaining two spheres is independent of the choice of the first two spheres; (c) state and prove analogous propositions for the mid-points of the lines of centers of the given spheres.

21. Four spheres whose radii are a, b, c, d, respectively, are such that each touches the other three externally. In the space between these four, another sphere, radius r, is described touching all four externally. Show that

$$\frac{1}{r^2} - \frac{1}{r} \Sigma \frac{1}{a} + \Sigma \frac{1}{a^2} - \Sigma \frac{1}{ab} = 0.$$

22. If four spheres with radii, a, b, c, d touch one another externally, and r is the radius of the sphere which cuts them orthogonally, then

$$\frac{4}{r^2} = 2\Sigma \frac{1}{ab} - \Sigma \frac{1}{a^2}.$$

MISCELLANEOUS EXERCISES

1. The plane (T) touches a given sphere (A) of a coaxal pencil (X) at the point P. Show that the point P has the same polar p with respect to all the circles of intersection of (T) with the spheres of (X), and that p is parallel to the trace t of (T) in the radical plane of (X).

2. Through each vertex of a triangle a sphere is drawn tangent to the plane of the triangle and so that the three spheres are tangent to each other. Find the radii of these spheres in terms of the sides of the triangle.

3. The Monge point of a tetrahedron is the radical center of the four spheres having for diameters the four medians of the tetrahedron.

4. Two skew lines AP, BQ passing through two fixed points A, B vary so that their common perpendicular PQ passes through a fixed point L and the ratio $PL : LQ$ remains constant. Find the locus of P and Q.

5. Through a fixed point I, within a sphere (S), an arbitrary plane (P) is drawn cutting (S) along a circle (C). An infinite number of triangles may be inscribed in (C) having I for their incenter. If a, b, c are the sides of such a triangle, the value of the expression

$$\frac{1}{bc} + \frac{1}{ca} + \frac{1}{ab}$$

is the same whatever the triangle, and whatever the position of (P).

6. On the three edges of a trihedral angle to mark three points so that their six orthogonal projections upon these edges shall lie on the same sphere.

7. A variable sphere (P) cuts a given sphere (S') along a great circle and has its center on a fixed sphere (S). Show that the radical plane of the two spheres (S), (P) is tangent to a fixed sphere concentric with (S').

8. If p, q are the squares of the radii of two spheres (real, imaginary, or one sphere real and the other imaginary), d the square of their line of centers, and s the square of the radius of their circle of intersection, we have

$$4ds = 4pq - (p + q - d)^2.$$

Consider the case of two orthogonal spheres.

9. Two spheres passing through two circles of an orthogonal link are orthogonal.

10. Two circles forming an orthogonal link with the same third circle are cospherical.

11. If L is a limiting point of two spheres, centers A, B, radii a, b, we have, both in magnitude and in sign,

$$b^2 = (1 - k)(a^2 - k \cdot AL^2),$$

where $k = AB : AL$.

12. If two orthogonal spheres determine on a straight line two harmonic chords, the two planes determined by this line and the centers of the two spheres are rectangular. Conversely.

13. (a) Through a given line to draw a plane cutting two given spheres along two equal circles. Show that the problem may have two solutions. (b) The planes passing through a given point P and cutting two given spheres along two equal circles are tangent to an oblique circular cone the base of which lies in the radical plane of the two given spheres. (c) Each element of this cone determines equal chords in the two spheres, and these are the only lines passing through P and having this property. (d) State and prove the corresponding propositions, when the radii of the two circles of intersection, instead of being equal, have a given ratio.

14. To a given sphere to draw a tangent plane which shall pass through the inaccessible point of intersection of three given planes.

15. If the sphere (A) passes through the center of the sphere (B), the plane of the points of contact of the sphere (A) with the common circumscribed cone of the two spheres is tangent to the sphere (B).

16. Given the two non-coplanar circles (C), (C'), construct the two spheres (P), (Q) passing through (C) and tangent to (C'); also the two spheres (P'), (Q') passing through (C') and tangent to (C). Show that the angle of intersection of the spheres (P), (Q) is equal to the angle of intersection of the spheres (P') and (Q'). What is the exceptional case?

17. If $A'B'C'D'$ is the tetrahedron formed by the polar planes of A, B, C, D with respect to the sphere (N), the parallels through the center N of (N) to the lines joining the points A, B, C, D to a point P on the sphere $ABCD$ meet the respective faces of $A'B'C'D'$ in four coplanar points.

18. Given two circles (a), (b) in space, construct a circle (1) which shall be tangent to (a) and (b); (2) which shall bisect (a) and (b); (3) which shall be bisected by (a) and (b).

19. If a plane cuts two orthogonal spheres along two orthogonal circles, twice the product of the distances of this plane from the centers of the two spheres is equal, in magnitude and in sign, to the sum of the squares of the radii of the spheres diminished by the square of their line of centers. Discussion.

20. Given four coaxal spheres, if there is a sphere, not coaxal with them, whose four radical planes with the four given spheres are harmonic, then the same will hold for any other sphere, and the polar planes of any point with respect to the given spheres will form a harmonic pencil.

21. If I is the incenter of the tetrahedron $ABCD$, the centers of the four spheres $IBCD$, $ICDA$, $IDAB$, $IABC$ determine a sphere whose center coincides with the circumcenter O of $ABCD$. If u is the radius of this sphere, and R, r the circumradius and the inradius of $ABCD$, we have $OI^2 = R^2 - 2ur$. HINT. Use § 580.

22. The diameter of the circumsphere (O) of the tetrahedron $ABCD$ perpendicular to the face BCD meets (O) in A', A''. Let (A'), (A'') be the spheres having A', A'' for centers and passing through the vertices B, C, D of $ABCD$. The three other faces of $ABCD$ give rise to three analogous pairs of spheres. Show that these eight spheres may be grouped by fours so that the radical centers of these groups will coincide with the centers of the eight spheres touching the four faces of $ABCD$.

23. Given the tetrahedron $ABCD$ and the point M in space, let $A'B'C'D'$ be the tetrahedron formed by the four planes through A, B, C, D and perpendicular to the lines AM, BM, CM, DM. If r is the circumradius of $ABCD$, M' the symmetric of M with respect to the circumcenter O of $ABCD$, and P, Q, R, S the projections of M upon the faces BCD, CDA, DAB, ABC, we have

$$MO^2 = r^2 - MP \cdot M'A' = r^2 - MQ \cdot M'B' = \cdots.$$

Consider the special case when M coincides with the center of a sphere touching the four faces of $ABCD$.

24. If each of the six quadrilaterals forming the faces of a hexahedron is cyclic, the eight vertices of the hexahedron lie on a sphere.

25. If on each edge of a tetrahedron two points are marked so that the four points marked on any two coplanar edges are concyclic, all the twelve marked points lie on a sphere.

26. If a tetrahedron varies so that its circumsphere and its centroid remain fixed, the spheres having for diameters the medians of the tetrahedron are orthogonal to a fixed sphere and have their centers on another fixed sphere.

27. Three equal spheres are circumscribed to the faces ABC, ACD, ADB of the tetrahedron $ABCD$. Prove that the three tangent planes to these spheres at the diametric opposites of A on the respective spheres meet on the common chord of the three spheres.

28. The plane of a triangle ABC cuts the spheres (P), (Q), (R) at equal angles. If through AB a pair of tangent planes be drawn to (R), through BC a pair of tangent planes to (P), and through AC a pair of tangent planes to (Q), prove that the six tangent planes so drawn touch the same sphere.

29. Determine four equal spheres orthogonal to a given sphere and touching three faces of a given tetrahedron.

30. If two spheres belonging to two given coaxal pencils of spheres are tangent to each other, their point of contact lies, in general, on a fixed sphere.

31. A variable line u is tangent to a fixed sphere (S) and meets two fixed tangents to (S). (a) The locus of the points of contact of u with (S) is composed of two circles; (b) all the lines u which have their point of contact on the same circle are tangent to an infinite number of other spheres besides (S).

32. Given the tetrahedron $ABCD$, let P, Q, R, S be the centers of four equal spheres each passing through three of the vertices of $ABCD$. These spheres intersect by threes in the points A', B', C', D'. Show that the centers of the three spheres $ABCD$, $PQRS$, $A'B'C'D'$ are collinear.

33. A variable tetrahedron $ABCD$ is inscribed in the fixed sphere (O) and circumscribed about the fixed sphere (O') interior to (O). Consider the three spheres (Q), (R), (S) having their centers on (O), passing respectively through the points (C, A, D), (D, A, B), (B, A, C) and intersecting in a point, K, inside of $ABCD$. Let M denote the second point of intersection of AK with (O). (a) The spheres (Q), (R), (S) are orthogonal to a fixed sphere concentric with (O'); (b) the polar planes of the center O of (O) with respect to (Q), (R), (S) are tangent to a fixed sphere; (c) if three positions of $ABCD$ are considered, the radical axis of the three spheres having M for center and MK for radius passes through a fixed point P; (d) the radical planes of the spheres (O) and (M) are tangent to a fixed sphere having P for center.

34. If two perspective tetrahedrons have the same circumsphere, their center and plane of perspectivity are pole and polar plane with respect to this sphere.

35. (a) The four lines joining the vertices of a tetrahedron to the poles, with respect to a sphere, of the respectively opposite faces form a hyperbolic group. (b) The polar planes, with respect to a given sphere, of the vertices of a tetrahedron meet the respectively opposite faces of the tetrahedron in four lines forming a hyperbolic group.

36. The planes through O perpendicular to OA, OB, OC, OD meet the corresponding faces of $ABCD$ in four lines forming a hyperbolic group.

CHAPTER VIII

INVERSION

648. Definition. As in plane geometry, given the fixed point O, the *center*, or *pole of inversion*, and the constant k, the *power*, or *constant of inversion*, the point P' is said to be the *inverse* of the given point P, if the points P, P' are collinear with O, and if $OP \cdot OP' = k$.

If k is positive, the points P, P' lie on the same side of O. If k is negative, P and P' lie on opposite sides of O.

If k is positive, the points of the sphere (O) having O for center and k for the square of its radius are their own inverses. The sphere (O) is called the *sphere of inversion.*

If k is negative, the sphere of inversion is imaginary, and the inversion involves no points which are their own inverses. However, whether the sphere of inversion be real or imaginary, two inverse points, as defined here, are inverse with respect to the sphere of inversion, in the sense in which inverse points with respect to a sphere were defined before (§ 462).

Inversion in the plane is a part of the theory of inversion in space and will be assumed to be familiar to the reader. Moreover, the proofs of many of the propositions of inversion in space are analogous to the proofs of the corresponding propositions in the plane, and will be omitted on that account. The reader, however, may find it instructive to state these proofs explicitly.

649. Theorem. *The inverse of a plane passing through the center of inversion is the plane itself.*

650. Remark. The above statement (§ 649) asserts that a point P of the given plane has for its inverse a point P' of the same plane. The two points P, P' are, in general, distinct.

The case is different with the sphere of inversion (when this sphere is real). Every point of this sphere coincides with its inverse point (§ 648).

651. Theorem. *The inverse of a plane not passing through the center of inversion is a sphere through the center of inversion.*

652. Theorem. *The inverse of a sphere passing through the center of inversion is a plane not passing through the center of inversion.*

653. Theorem. (a) *The inverse of a sphere not passing through the center of inversion is a sphere.*

(b) *The center of inversion is a center of similitude of the given sphere and its inverse.*

(c) If R is the radius of the given sphere, R' the radius of the inverse sphere, k the constant of inversion, and p the power of the center of inversion with respect to the given sphere (§ 504), we have

$$R' : R = k : p.$$

(d) *The inverse of the center of the given sphere is the inverse, with respect to the inverse sphere, of the center of inversion.*

(e) If the constant of inversion is equal to the power of the center of inversion with respect to the given sphere, this sphere is its own inverse; in other words: *A sphere orthogonal to the sphere of inversion is its own inverse.*

654. Theorem. *A plane and a sphere may, in general, be considered as two inverse figures, in two different ways.*

The poles of inversion are the ends of the diameter of the sphere which is perpendicular to the plane.

655. Theorem. *Two given spheres may, in general, be considered as the inverses of one another, in two different ways, and in two ways only.*

656. Theorem. *The inverse of a circle, when the center of inversion does not lie in the plane of the circle, is a circle.*

For the inverse of the given circle (C) is the circle of intersection (C') of the inverse spheres (P'), (Q') of any two spheres (P), (Q) passing through (C).

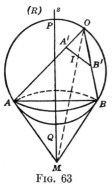

FIG. 63

657. Remark I. The spheres (P), (Q) (§ 656) have their centers P, Q (Fig. 63) on the axis s of (C), hence the centers P', Q' of (P'), (Q') lie in the plane Os determined by s and the center of inversion O. Thus the center I of (C') lies in the plane Os, and the plane of (C') is perpendicular to the plane Os.

Let A, B be the ends of the diameter of (C) lying in Os, and A', B' their inverse points. These points lie on (C'), and since the center of (C') also lies in Os, the points A', B' are diametrically opposite on (C'). We have thus a construction for the center I of (C').

658. Remark II. *The axes of two inverse circles are coplanar and their plane contains the center of inversion.*

659. Chasles' Theorem. *The center of the inverse circle of a given circle lies on the line joining the center of inversion to the pole of the plane of the given circle with respect to the sphere determined by this circle and the pole of inversion.*

The plane Os (§ 657) cuts the sphere (S) determined by O and (C) along a great circle (R) circumscribed about the triangle OAB (Fig. 63). The line $A'B'$ is antiparallel to AB with respect to OA, OB, and since the center I of (C') is the mid-point of $A'B'$ (§ 657), the line OI is a symmedian of OAB (C. G., p. 222). Thus OI passes through the pole M of AB with respect to (R) (C. G., p. 226), and since M is also the pole of the plane of (C) with respect to (S), the proposition is proved.

660. Theorem. *Two inverse circles are cospherical.*

The planes of the two circles (C), (C') (§ 659) are perpendicular to the plane OAB, and these circles have for diameters the lines AB, $A'B'$. Now the points A', B' being the inverses of A, B, these four points are concyclic, and the sphere on which $AA'BB'$ is a great circle obviously both passes through (C) and (C').

OTHERWISE. The circles (C) and $AA'BB'$ have the points A, B in common, hence they determine a sphere (U). Now $OA \cdot OA'$ is the constant of inversion and also the power of O with respect to (U), hence (U) is its own inverse (§ 654), and since (U) contains (C), it also contains the inverse (C') of (C).

661. Converse Theorem. *Any two circles of the same sphere may, in general, be considered as the inverses of each other, in two different ways.*

The plane SCD determined by the centers S, C, D of the given sphere (S) and the two circles (C), (D), given on (S) (Fig. 64),

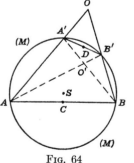

FIG. 64

cuts (C), (D) along the diameters AB, $A'B'$ and the sphere (S) along the great circle $(M) \equiv AA'BB'$. Consider now the inversion having for center the point $O \equiv (AA', BB')$, and for constant of inversion $k = OA \cdot OA' = OB \cdot OB'$. The planes of the circles (C), (D) being perpendicular to the plane SCD, the inverse of (C) coincides with (D) (§ 660).

The point $O' \equiv (AB', A'B)$ and the constant $k' = O'A \cdot O'B'$ $= O'A' \cdot O'B$ determine a second inversion in which to the circle (C) corresponds the circle (D).

662. Corollary. *Through two cospherical circles pass, in general, two cones.*

663. Remark. There can be no more than two such cones, for the two circles must be inverse with respect to the vertex of the cone, and this vertex must lie in the plane determined by the two inverse diameters AB, $A'B'$, of these two circles, hence this vertex coincides either with O or with O'.

If the two circles are tangent to each other, one of the points A, B coincides with one of the points A', B' (§ 661), and in such a case there is only one cone containing the two circles.

One of the two pairs of lines AA', BB'; AB', $A'B$ (§ 661) may be parallel. In that case one of the two cones passing through the two circles becomes a cylinder.

664. Theorem. *The tangents to two inverse curves at two corresponding points make equal angles with the radius vector.*

The proof remains the same as in the case of the plane although the curves considered may not be plane curves, for the two tangents at the two corresponding points A, A' are the limiting positions of the two secants AB, $A'B'$ which are coplanar, since the two lines AA', BB' pass through the center of inversion.

665. Remark. *The two tangents at two corresponding points are symmetrical with respect to the mediator of the segment joining the two points of contact.*

666. Through a given point M of a given surface (S) an infinite number of curves may be drawn on the surface. The tangents to these curves at the points M lie, in general, in the same plane, called the "tangent plane" to (S) at M.

Now let (S') be the inverse of (S) and M' the inverse of M. To the curves drawn on (S) through M correspond on (S') curves through M', and the tangents at M and M' to the pairs of corresponding curves are symmetrical with respect to the mediator of the segment MM'. Hence: *The tangent planes to two inverse surfaces at two corresponding points are symmetrical with respect to the mediator of the segment determined by the two points of contact.*

667. Definitions. The angle between two curves (surfaces) at a common point is the angle formed by the tangents (tangent planes) to the two curves (surfaces) at this point.

The angle between a curve and a surface at a point of their intersection is the angle formed by the tangent to the curve and the tangent plane to the surface at this point.

668. Theorem. *The angle between two curves which intersect in a given point is equal to the angle between the two inverse curves at the corresponding point.*

The tangents AS, AT to the two given curves at their common point A are the symmetrics of the tangents $A'S'$, $A'T'$ with respect to the mediator of AA' (§ 665), hence the angles SAT, $S'A'T'$ are equal.

669. Theorem. *The angle between a curve and a surface at a point of their intersection is equal to the angle between their inverses at the corresponding point.*

670. Theorem. *The angle between two surfaces at a point of their intersection is equal to the angle between their inverses at the corresponding point.*

The proofs of these two propositions are analogous to the proof of the one before (§ 668).

671. Remark. The last three propositions (§§ 668, 669, 670) may be expressed in the following succinct form: *In an inversion angles are preserved.*

As special cases of this proposition we have: (a) *In an inversion orthogonality is preserved.* (b) *In an inversion contact is preserved.*

672. Theorem. *Two inverse spheres and the sphere of inversion are coaxal.*

Let (P) be any sphere orthogonal both to the given sphere (S) and to the sphere of inversion (O). The sphere (P) is its own inverse [§ 653 (e)] and therefore will be orthogonal to the inverse (S') of (S) (§ 671); the sphere (O) remains fixed (§ 648). Thus the three spheres (O), (S), (S') have their centers collinear (§ 653) and are orthogonal to the same sphere (P), hence they are coaxal (§ 568).

673. Corollary I. *The sphere of inversion is a sphere of anti-similitude* (§ 588) *of the given sphere and its inverse,* for the center of inversion is a center of similitude of the two spheres [§ 653 (b)].

674. Corollary II. *The two inversions in which two given spheres correspond to each other* (§ 655) *have for spheres of inversion the two spheres of antisimilitude to the two given spheres.*

675. Theorem. *If two figures in space are such that to a point of one corresponds a point in the other, and that any two points of one and the corresponding two points of the other are concyclic, the two figures are inverse to each other.*

Let A, B (Fig. 65) be two points of the first figure, and A', B' their corresponding points in the other figure. The four points A, A'; B, B' are concyclic, by assumption, hence the lines AA', BB' are coplanar and meet in a point O, and we have $OA \cdot OA' = OB \cdot OB'$.

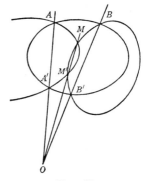

Now let M be any point of the first figure. Its corresponding point M' in the second figure lies on the circle $AA'M$ and also on the circle $BB'M$, hence the line MM' meets both AA' and BB',

FIG. 65

without necessarily lying in the plane of the circle $AA'BB'$ (otherwise both given figures would consist of the same circle, a hypothesis which we exclude), hence MM' passes through O, and we have

$$OM \cdot OM' = OA \cdot OA' = OB \cdot OB'.$$

Thus M' corresponds to M in the inversion having O for center and $OA \cdot OA'$ for constant of inversion.

If the two lines AA', BB' do not intersect, they are parallel. It is readily shown that in that case the two figures are symmetric with respect to a plane.

EXERCISES

1. A sphere of antisimilitude of two intersecting spheres bisects the angles between these spheres.

2. Through a given point A a variable line m is drawn meeting two given planes in two points P, Q. Find the locus of m, if the product $AP \cdot AQ$ is constant.

3. If p, q are the radii and d the length of the line of centers of two given (intersecting) spheres, and p', q', d' are the corresponding elements of the inverses of these two spheres, we have

$$(p^2 + q^2 - d^2) : 2pq = \pm (p'^2 + q'^2 - d'^2) : 2p'q'.$$

Explain the meaning of the double sign in the formula.

4. The fourth power of the radius of a sphere of antisimilitude of two given spheres is equal to the product of the powers, with respect to the two given spheres, of the center of the sphere of antisimilitude considered.

5. Find an inversion such that the inverses of three given points shall be the vertices of an equilateral triangle.

6. The angle of intersection of any two of the four circles determined by four given points (coplanar or not) is equal to the angle of intersection of the remaining two circles. State this proposition with reference to the circumcircles of the faces of a tetrahedron.

7. If three circles are inverse in pairs, their axes are either concurrent, or coplanar, in which case their plane contains the three centers of inversion.

8. Prove by inversion that the locus of the point of contact of a fixed sphere with the spheres passing through two fixed (real) points is a circle.

9. Two given spheres and the two spheres obtained in transforming them by inversion are four spheres belonging to the same coaxal net.

10. If two spheres (A), (B) are inverse with respect to a third sphere (S), the radical plane of (A), (B) and the sphere of similitude of (A), (B) are inverse to one another with respect to (S).

11. Through a given circle to pass a sphere (a) tangent to a given sphere; (b) orthogonal to a given sphere; (c) making a given angle with a given sphere. HINT. Invert the figure with respect to a point on the given circle taking for constant of inversion the power of this point with respect to the given sphere.

12. If a variable sphere is orthogonal to two given spheres and is tangent to a third fixed sphere, the locus of its point of contact with this third sphere is a circle. HINT. Invert the figure with respect to either a limiting point or a point common to the two given spheres.

13. If two spheres, each tangent to two given spheres, are also tangent to each other, their point of contact lies on a sphere of antisimilitude of the two given spheres.

14. An orthogonal link is, in general, transformed, by inversion, into an orthogonal link. Consider the case when the center of inversion is taken on one of the circles.

15. The locus of the centers of the antiparallel circular sections of an oblique circular cone is the line joining the vertex V of the cone to the pole of the plane of the base with respect to the spheres determined by V and the circle of the base.

16. If four coplanar circles have a common radical center, it is possible to find four planes which intersect, two and two, at angles equal to those at which the circles intersect, but not otherwise.

676. Problem. *To transform, by inversion, three given spheres into three spheres having their centers on a straight line.*

If the transformed spheres have their centers on a straight line t, this line is orthogonal to each of the transformed spheres (§ 667), hence the three original spheres (A), (B), (C) are orthogonal to the inverse of t, i.e., to a circle (T) passing through the center of inversion S. Thus S must lie on the circle (T) orthogonal to the three great circles along which (A), (B), (C) are cut by the plane determined by their centers, or, what is the same thing, S must lie on the limiting circle of the coaxal net determined by the given spheres.

It is clear that this condition for the position of S is sufficient. The problem either has an infinite number of solutions, or no solutions at all, according as the circle (T) is real, or not. The constant of inversion is arbitrary.

If the centers of the three given spheres are collinear, the point S must be taken on their common line of centers.

677. Theorem. *The inverses of the spheres of a coaxal pencil form, in general, a coaxal pencil of spheres.*

Let (P) be the given coaxal pencil and (N) the coaxal net conjugate to (P) (§ 609). Let S be the center of inversion. It is assumed that S is neither common to all the spheres of (P), nor to all the spheres of (N).

Let (A), (B), (C) be any three spheres of (N) whose centers are not collinear. The centers of the three inverse spheres (A'), (B'), (C') will, in general, not be collinear (§ 682). Now if (M) is any sphere of (P), its inverse (M') will be orthogonal to (A'), (B'), (C') (§ 671), and therefore belong to the coaxal pencil (P') conjugate to the coaxal net determined by the spheres (A'), (B'), (C'). Conversely, the inverse (M) of any sphere (M') of the pencil (P') will be orthogonal to the spheres (A), (B), (C) (§ 671), and therefore belong to the pencil (P). Hence the proposition.

678. Definition. The two pencils (P), (P') (§ 677) are said to be *inverse* to one another.

679. Theorem. *The spheres belonging to a coaxal net invert, in general, into spheres forming a coaxal net.*

With the same notations as before (§ 677), any sphere of the net (N) will invert into a sphere orthogonal to the spheres of the pencil (P') and therefore belonging to the coaxal net (N') conjugate to the pencil (P').

Conversely, any sphere of (N') inverts into a sphere orthogonal to the spheres of the inverse pencil (P) of (P') and therefore belonging to the net (N).

680. Definition. The two nets (N), (N') (§ 679) are said to be *inverse* to one another.

681. Corollary. From the last two propositions (§§ 677, 679) we have: *A coaxal net of spheres and its conjugate pencil of spheres invert, respectively, into a coaxal net and a coaxal pencil, and the two are conjugate to one another.*

682. Special Cases. (a) *If the spheres of the pencil (P) (§ 679) have a real circle (C) in common, and the center of inversion S is taken on (C), the spheres of (P) will invert into planes (§ 652) having a line in common, namely, the inverse r of (C).*

The circle (C) is the limiting circle of the net (N) conjugate to (P) (§ 610), hence the inverses of the spheres of (N) will be orthogonal to the inverse r of (C), i.e., the centers of the inverse spheres lie on the line r. Thus the pencil of spheres (P) inverts into a coaxal pencil of planes, the axis of which is the line of centers of the inverses of the spheres of (N).

(b) If the pencil (P) (§ 679) has two limiting points A, B, these two points are common to all the spheres of (N) (§ 610), and if one of these two points, say A, is taken as the center of inversion, the spheres of (N) will invert into planes (§ 652) having a point in common, namely the inverse B' of B. The inverse (M') of any sphere (M) of the pencil (P) is orthogonal to all the planes passing through B' (§ 671), hence (M') has its center at B'. Thus (P) *inverts into a system of concentric spheres.*

683. Definition. A sphere which makes equal angles with two or more given spheres is said to be *isogonal* to the given spheres.

684. Theorem. *A sphere passing through two antihomologous points of two given spheres is isogonal to these spheres.*

The two antihomologous points P, Q' on the two given spheres (A), (B) are inverse with respect to one of the two spheres of antisimilitude, say (S), of (A), (B) (§§ 673, 474), hence in the inversion determined by (S) the sphere (C) passing through P, Q'

is its own inverse [§ 653 (e)] and the angle between (A) and (C) is equal to the angle between (B) and (C) (§ 671).

685. Corollary I. *If a sphere cutting two given spheres is orthogonal to one of their spheres of antisimilitude, it is isogonal to the given spheres.*

686. Corollary II. If the two circles of intersection of two given spheres with a third sphere pass through one pair of antihomologous points on the two given spheres, the two circles are inverse with respect to the corresponding sphere of antisimilitude of the two given spheres.

687. Theorem. *If a sphere is isogonal to two given spheres its two circles of intersection with these spheres are inverse with respect to one of the spheres of antisimilitude of the two given spheres.*

The plane of centers of the three spheres cuts the two given spheres (A), (B) along two great circles (U), (V), and the sphere (M) isogonal to (A) and (B) along a circle (X) isogonal to (U) and (V). Let $C, D; C', D'$ be the pairs of points of intersection of (X) with (U) and (V), and furthermore, let C, C' be the points at which the angles of intersection of (X) with (U), (V) are of opposite senses. The same will be the case at the points D and D'.

Let S be the point of intersection of the lines CC', DD'. If we take S for the center of inversion and $k = SC \cdot SC' = SD \cdot SD'$ for the constant of inversion, the circle (X) will invert into itself, and the circle (U) will invert into a circle (U') passing through C' and D' and making, at these points, with (X) angles equal in magnitude and in sense to those (V) makes with (X) at these points, hence (U') is identical with (V). Thus S is a center of similitude of (U) and (V), and therefore also of (A) and (B), and the inversion considered is one of the two inversions which transform the two given spheres into one another (§ 655). Hence the proposition.

688. Corollary. *If a sphere is isogonal to two given spheres it is orthogonal to one of the two spheres of antisimilitude of the two given spheres.*

689. Consequence. The spheres isogonal to two given spheres are divided into two groups: the spheres orthogonal to the external sphere of antisimilitude of the two given spheres, and those orthogonal to the internal sphere of antisimilitude.

The spheres tangent to the two given spheres are a special case of isogonal spheres. A sphere tangent to two given spheres belongs to the first or the second group according to whether its two contacts with the given spheres are of the same kind (both external, or both internal), or of opposite kinds (one internal and one external).

690. Theorem. *The spheres isogonal to three given spheres form four coaxal nets. These nets are respectively conjugate to the four coaxal pencils of spheres determined by the spheres of antisimilitude of the given spheres and having for their lines of centers the four axes of similitude of the three given spheres.*

Indeed, if a sphere (S) is isogonal to the three given spheres (A), (B), (C), it is orthogonal to three of their six spheres of antisimilitude (§ 688). If these three spheres of antisimilitude are coaxal (§ 618), the sphere (S) belongs to one of the nets referred to. If these three spheres of antisimilitude are not coaxal, they determine the same net of spheres (N), as do the spheres (A), (B), (C) (§ 616), hence (S) belongs to the coaxal pencil (P) conjugate to (N), and therefore (S) belongs to all four nets determined by the spheres of antisimilitude, since these six spheres all belong to the net (N).

691. Remark. The four nets (§ 690) have in common the coaxal pencil of spheres conjugate to the net determined by the three given spheres.

The planes of centers of these four nets are the planes perpendicular to the respective axes of similitude of the three given spheres and passing through the radical axis of the given spheres.

692. Consequence. The four nets (§ 691) include, as special cases, the spheres which are tangent to the three given spheres. Now the locus of the points of contact of one of the given spheres, say (A), with the spheres (S) of one of the four nets is a circle (§ 614), hence: *The locus of the points of contact of each of three fixed spheres with the spheres which touch these three spheres consists of four circles.*

693. Theorem. *The isogonal conjugate spheres of four given spheres form eight coaxal pencils of spheres. The radical plane of each pencil is a plane of similitude of the four spheres, and the orthogonal sphere of these four spheres belongs to each of the eight pencils.*

Each plane of similitude of the four spheres (A), (B), (C), (D) contains the centers of six of the twelve spheres of antisimilitude of the four given spheres taken in pairs, and these six spheres of antisimilitude form a coaxal net (§ 644). A sphere of the coaxal pencil conjugate to this net will be isogonal to the given spheres (§ 690). The orthogonal sphere (O) of (A), (B), (C), (D) is orthogonal to each of the six spheres of antisimilitude considered (§ 616), hence (O) belongs to the conjugate coaxal pencil of the net considered.

Let us now show that any sphere (S) isogonal to (A), (B), (C), (D) belongs to one of these eight pencils. The sphere (S) is, by assumption, isogonal to the three spheres (A), (B), (C), hence (S) belongs to a coaxal net having for radical axis an axis of similitude u of these three spheres (§ 691), and u contains therefore one of the two centers of similitude of the two spheres (A), (B), say the external center of similitude S_{ab}. Again (S) is isogonal to the three spheres (A), (B), (D), hence (S) belongs to a coaxal net having for radical axis an axis of similitude v of these three spheres, and v contains the same external center of similitude S_{ab} of the two spheres (A), (B) (§ 689). Thus the coaxal pencils of spheres having for lines of centers the lines u, v and conjugate respectively to the coaxal nets considered have in common the external sphere of antisimilitude of the two given spheres (A), (B). Hence the coaxal nets considered have a coaxal pencil of spheres in common [§ 620 (b)], and (S) belongs to this pencil. This pencil is conjugate to the coaxal net determined by the coaxal pencils u and v. Now uv is a plane of similitude of the four given spheres, hence the proposition.

694. Problem of Apollonius. *Construct a sphere tangent to four given spheres.*

Consider the coaxal pencil of spheres Σ determined by the orthogonal sphere (O) of the four given spheres (A), (B), (C), (D) and a plane of similitude of these spheres. Let (T) and (T') be the two spheres of Σ tangent to (A) (§ 599). These two spheres will also be tangent to (B), (C), (D) (§ 693). Considering the eight planes of similitude of the four given spheres (§§ 492 ff.) we may have sixteen spheres satisfying the conditions of the problem.

695. Some of the properties of the oblique circular cone we derived before (Chapter VI) may readily be obtained by inversion.

THEOREM. *A sphere passing through the base of an oblique circular cone cuts the cone again along a circle.*

Take the vertex V of the given cone (V) for the center of inversion, and the power of V with respect to the given sphere (S) as the constant of inversion. In this inversion both (V) and (S) are transformed into themselves, hence their second curve of intersection, besides the basic circle (C) of (V), is the inverse of (C), and therefore a circle (C') (§ 656).

696. Remark. Since any plane parallel to the plane of (C) (§ 695) may be taken for the base of (V), the preceding proposition may also be stated as follows: *If a cone contains a circle of a given sphere, it cuts the sphere again along a second circle.*

697. Corollary. *The plane of the circle (C') (§ 695) is antiparallel (§ 369) to the base of the cone.*

Indeed, the principal plane of (V) contains both the center of inversion and the axis of (C), hence it contains also the axis of (C') (§ 658).

698. Theorem. *A plane antiparallel to the base of an oblique circular cone cuts this cone along a circle.*

Let A, B be the ends of the principal diameter of the base (C) of the oblique circular cone (V), and let A', B' be the traces on VA, VB of the plane (P) antiparallel to (C).

The points A, A', B, B' are concyclic. Let $k = VA \cdot VA' = VB \cdot VB'$. In the inversion having V for center and k for constant of inversion to the circle (C) corresponds a circle (C') passing through A', B', and, furthermore, since the axis of (C) lies in the plane VAB, the plane of (C') is perpendicular to the plane VAB (§ 657), i.e., the plane of (C') coincides with the plane (P), hence the proposition.

699. Theorem. *A circular section of an oblique circular cone is either parallel or antiparallel to the base.*

Let (C') be a circular section of the cone (V) not parallel to the base (C). Through any point D of (C) draw a plane (P) parallel to the plane of (C'). The plane (P) cuts (V) along a circle (C''), and the circle (C) in two points D, E, which obviously belong also to (C''). The two circles (C), (C'') having two points in common lie on the same sphere (S), hence they may be considered as the inverse of one another with respect to the vertex V of (V) (§ 661). Thus the plane of (C'') is antiparallel to the base (C) (§ 697), and the same is therefore true about (C').

700. Corollary. *Two circular sections of an oblique circular cone, not situated in parallel planes, are cospherical.*
The proof is left to the reader.

701. Definition. Consider a sphere (O) and a diametral plane (P) of this sphere (Fig. 66). Let V be one of the two poles of the circle of intersection of (O) and (P). To every point M of (O) we make correspond the trace M' of VM in (P). The point M' is called the **stereographic projection** of M.

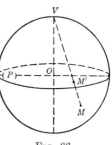

If M describes a curve (C) on (O), the point M' describes a curve (C') in (P), the stereographic projection of (C) on (P).

Fig. 66

702. From this definition (§ 701) it follows that the plane (P) is the inverse of the sphere (O) with respect to the center of inversion V, the constant of inversion being equal to $VO \cdot VV'$, where O is the center of (O) and V' the diametric opposite of V on (O).

This observation gives immediately the fundamental properties of the mode of projections considered.

(a) *The stereographic projection preserves angles* (§ 671).

(b) *The stereographic projection of a circle is a circle* (§ 656) *or a straight line.*

(c) *The center of the projected circle lies on the line joining the center of projection to the pole of the plane of the given circle with respect to the sphere* (§ 659).

Stereographic projections are used in map making.

703. Lemma. (a) *If on the sides A_2A_3, A_3A_1, A_1A_2 of the triangle $A_1A_2A_3$ are marked the points B_1, B_2, B_3, the three circles $A_1B_2B_3$, $A_2B_3B_1$, $A_3B_1B_2$ have a point C in common.*

(b) CONVERSELY. *Given three circles having a point C in common and having by twos the points B_1, B_2, B_3 in common, an infinite number of triangles $A_1A_2A_3$ may be drawn whose sides pass through B_1, B_2, B_3, and whose vertices lie on the three given circles.*

The proof follows immediately from the observation that the angles around C are supplementary to those of the triangle $A_1A_2A_3$.

704. If the figure of converse proposition [§ 703 (b)] is projected stereographically upon a sphere, the given circles will project into circles, and the sides of $A_1A_2A_3$ will invert into three circles passing through the center of projection, so that we obtain the proposition:

Given, on a sphere, three (small) circles having a point C in common and intersecting in pairs in the points B_1, B_2, B_3. If three other circles are drawn on the sphere intersecting in pairs in the points A_1, A_2, A_3, on the three given circles, and passing through the points B_1, B_2, B_3, the three new circles $A_1B_2A_3$, $A_2B_3A_1$, $A_3B_1A_2$ have a point D in common.

705. Roberts' Theorem. *If a point is marked on each edge of a tetrahedron and a sphere is passed through each vertex and the points on the three adjacent edges, the four spheres so obtained have a point in common.*

Let B_{12}, $\cdots$ be the points marked on the edges A_1A_2, $\cdots$ of the tetrahedron $A_1A_2A_3A_4$. Consider the four spheres $C_1 \equiv A_1B_{12}B_{13}B_{14}$, $C_2 \equiv A_2B_{21}B_{23}B_{24}$, $\cdots$. The face $A_1A_2A_3$ cuts the three spheres C_1, C_2, C_3 along three circles which pass through the vertices of the triangle $A_1A_2A_3$ and intersect in pairs in the points B_{12}, B_{23}, B_{31}, hence these three circles have a point D_4 in common [§ 703 (a)], and D_4 is of course also common to the three spheres. Similarly we obtain analogous points D_1, D_2, D_3 in the other three faces of the tetrahedron.

Now consider the three circles along which the sphere C_4 is cut by the three faces of the tetrahedron passing through the vertex A_4. These three circles have the point A_4 in common, intersect in pairs in the points B_{41}, B_{42}, B_{43}, and pass respectively through the points D_1, D_2, D_3, hence the three circles $D_2B_{41}D_3$, $D_3B_{42}D_1$, $D_1B_{43}D_2$ have a point E in common (§ 704). But these circles lie, respectively, on the spheres C_1, C_2, C_3, hence the proposition.

EXERCISES

1. If two spheres are to be inverted into two concentric spheres, it is both necessary and sufficient to take as center of inversion one of the limiting points of the two spheres.

2. If four spheres are to be inverted into four spheres with coplanar centers, it is both necessary and sufficient to take as center of inversion a point of the orthogonal sphere of the four given spheres.

3. Consider a coaxal pencil of spheres (P) tangent to a fixed plane at a given point F. The conjugate net of spheres (N) will consist of the spheres tangent at F to the line of centers s of (P).

4. The vertices of the two cones which pass through the two circles of intersection of two given spheres with a sphere orthogonal to them coincide with the centers of similitude of the given spheres.

5. Construct three spheres tangent to each other and each touching the same given plane in a given point. HINT. Invert the figure with respect to one of the three given points.

6. (a) Through a given point to draw a sphere tangent to three given spheres. HINT. Invert the figure with respect to the given point. (b) *Problem of Apollonius.* Draw a sphere tangent to four given spheres.

7. (a) A necessary and sufficient condition for inverting two given spheres into two equal spheres is that the center of inversion shall lie on one of the spheres of antisimilitude of the two given spheres. (b) Find a center of inversion with respect to which four given spheres may be inverted into four equal spheres. Show that the inverse spheres may be made to be equal to one of the given spheres. (c) *Problem of Apollonius.* Construct a sphere tangent to four given spheres.

8. Construct a sphere which shall cut four given spheres along four circles of given radii.

CHAPTER IX

RECENT GEOMETRY OF THE TETRAHEDRON

A. THE GENERAL TETRAHEDRON

1. Harmonic Points and Planes

a. Tetrahedral Poles and Polar Planes

706. Theorem. *If a line meets two opposite edges of a tetrahedron, its two harmonic conjugates with respect to the other two pairs of edges* (§ 48) *coincide*

Let U', X' be the traces of the given line $U'X'$ on the opposite edges DA, BC of the tetrahedron $DABC$. The harmonic conjugate of $U'X'$ with respect to AB, DC is determined by the harmonic conjugates U, X of U', X' with respect to the pairs of points A, D; B, C. But the harmonic conjugate of the line $U'X'$ with respect to the pair of lines AC, BD is also determined by the points U, X as is readily seen by considering the transversals $AU'D$, $BX'C$, hence the proposition.

707. Definition. For the sake of brevity we shall say that "UX is the *harmonic conjugate* of $U'X'$ with respect to the tetrahedron $DABC$."

It is clear that the relation between $U'X'$ and UX is reciprocal.

Two harmonic conjugate lines with respect to a tetrahedron meet the same pair of opposite edges of the tetrahedron and form a harmonic hyperbolic group with each of the other two pairs of opposite edges of the tetrahedron.

CONSEQUENCES. Let a, a'; b, b'; c, c' be the three pairs of opposite edges of a tetrahedron (T).

(a) If a line p meets a, a', the harmonic conjugate p' of p with respect to (T) passes through the two harmonic conjugate points, with respect to b, b'; c, c', of any point on p.

(b) p' lies in the two harmonic conjugate planes, with respect to b, b'; c, c' (§ 46), of any plane passing through p.

708. Definition. The plane determined by the three harmonic conjugates of a given point with respect to the three pairs of opposite edges of a tetrahedron is referred to as the **harmonic**

plane, or the *polar plane,* or the **tetrahedral polar plane** of the given point with respect to the tetrahedron.

709. Theorem. *The harmonic conjugates, with respect to a tetrahedron, of the three lines passing through a given point and meeting the three pairs of opposite edges of the tetrahedron lie in the harmonic plane of the given point with respect to the tetrahedron.*

Let d, e, f be the lines passing through the given point O and meeting the three pairs of opposite edges a, a'; b, b'; c, c' of the tetrahedron (T). The harmonic conjugate d' of d with respect to (T) passes through the two harmonic conjugates of O with respect to b, b'; c, c' [§ 707 (a)], hence d' lies in the harmonic plane of O with respect to (T) (§ 708). Similarly for e and f. Hence the proposition.

710. Definition. The point determined by the three harmonic conjugates of a given plane with respect to the three pairs of opposite edges of a tetrahedron is referred to as the **harmonic pole,** or the **tetrahedral pole,** or the **pole** of the given plane with respect to the tetrahedron.

711. Theorem. *The harmonic conjugates, with respect to a tetrahedron, of three coplanar lines meeting respectively the three pairs of opposite edges of the tetrahedron pass through the pole, with respect to the tetrahedron, of the plane containing the three given lines.*

Let p, q, r be the given lines lying in the plane λ and meeting the three pairs of opposite edges a, a'; b, b'; c, c' of the tetrahedron (T).

The harmonic conjugate p' of p with respect to (T) lies in the two harmonic conjugate planes of λ with respect to b, b'; c, c' [§ 707 (b)], hence p' passes through the pole of λ with respect to (T). Similarly for q and r. Hence the proposition.

712. Theorem. *If μ is the polar plane of the point M with respect to a tetrahedron, then M is the pole of the plane μ with respect to this tetrahedron.*

Let u', v', w' (Fig. 67) be the three lines passing through M meeting the three pairs of opposite edges DA, BC; DB, CA; DC, AB of the tetrahedron $DABC$. The harmonic conjugates u, v, w of u', v', w' with respect to $DABC$ lie in the plane μ (§ 709).

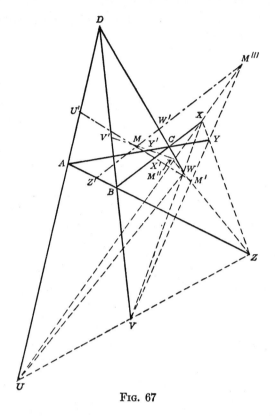

FIG. 67

On the other hand the harmonic conjugates of u, v, w with respect to $DABC$ pass through the pole of μ with respect to $DABC$ (§ 711). But these harmonic conjugates coincide with u', v', w', for the relation between conjugate lines is reciprocal (§ 707), hence the pole of μ with respect to $DABC$ coincides with M.

713. If U', X'; U, X (Fig. 67) are the traces of the lines u', u (§ 712) on the edges DA, BC, the two groups of points (DA, UU'), (BC, XX') are harmonic. Similarly for the traces V', Y'; V, Y of v', v on the edges DB, CA, and again for the traces W', Z'; W, Z of w', w on DC, AB. Hence the following table of groups of harmonic points:

(A) (DA, UU'), (DB, VV'), (DC, WW')
        (BC, XX'), (CA, YY'), (AB, ZZ')

714. The six pairs of points U, U'; V, V'; $\cdots$ (§ 713) are distributed in the faces of $DABC$ in the following way:

$$
\text{(H)} \quad
\begin{array}{ll}
ABC & XYZX'Y'Z' \\
BCD & XVWX'V'W' \\
CDA & UYWU'Y'W' \\
DAB & UVZU'V'Z'
\end{array}
$$

715. The harmonic conjugates M', M'', M''' of M (Fig. 67) with respect to the three pairs of points U', X'; V', Y'; W', Z' (§ 713) lie in the polar plane μ of M with respect to the tetrahedron $DABC$ so that we have (§ 713)

$$\mu \equiv M'M''M''' \equiv UVWXYZ.$$

The points M'', M''' are the traces on $u \equiv UX$ of the lines $v' \equiv V'Y'$, $v \equiv VY$ [§ 707 (a)]. But these two lines form a harmonic hyperbolic group with the pair of edges DA, BC, hence M'', M''' are harmonically separated by U, X. Similarly for the lines $v \equiv VY$, $w \equiv WZ$. We arrive thus at the following table of harmonic groups of points:

$$
\text{(B)} \quad
\begin{array}{lll}
(MM', & U'X'), & (MM'', \ V'Y'), & (MM''', \ W'Z') \\
(M''M''', \ UX), & (M'M''', \ VY), & (M'M'', \ WZ)
\end{array}
$$

716. Theorem. *The trilinear pole, with respect to a face of a given tetrahedron $ABCD$, of the line of intersection of this face with a given plane μ is collinear with the vertex opposite the face considered and the pole of μ with respect to $ABCD$.*

The pole M of the given plane μ lies on the line $U'X'$, $V'Y'$, $W'Z'$ (§ 715), hence the trace of DM in ABC is the point S (Fig. 68) common to the lines AX', BY', CZ'. Now the trace of μ in ABC contains the points X, Y, Z, hence S is the trilinear pole of XYZ (C. G., p. 220).

717. Theorem. *The trilinear polar, with respect to a face of a given tetrahedron $ABCD$, of the trace in this face of the line joining the opposite vertex to a given point M lies in the polar plane of M with respect to $ABCD$.*

The trace S of DM on ABC (§ 716) is common to the lines AX', BY', CZ', hence the trilinear polar of S with respect to ABC is determined by the points X, Y, Z (C. G., p. 220), and these points lie in the polar plane μ of M with respect to $ABCD$.

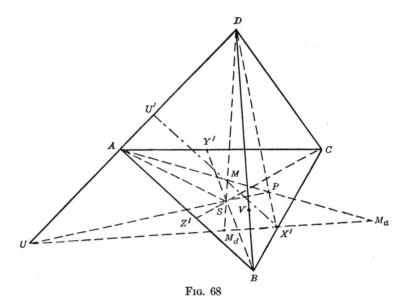

FIG. 68

718. Theorem. *The polar plane of a point with respect to a tetrahedron coincides with the polar plane of this point with respect to the cevian tetrahedron (§ 338) of the point considered.*

The feet S, P (Fig. 68) of the lines DM, AM (§ 717) fall on the lines AX', DX', hence $X'U'$ meets PS, say in U''. Thus the cevians $X'U'$, AP, DS of the triangle $X'AD$ meet in M, hence the line PS meets the side DA in the harmonic conjugate of U' with respect to D, A (C. G., p. 221), i.e., PS passes through U (§ 713), and this point is therefore the harmonic conjugate of U'' with respect to P, S.

In a similar way we may show that the line $X'U'$ will meet the line QR joining the feet Q, R of the cevians BMQ, CMR in a point X'', and that the harmonic conjugate of X'' with respect to Q, R coincides with the point X. Thus the line $MU''X''$ through M meets the opposite edges PS, QR of the tetrahedron $PQRS$ in the points U'', X'', and the harmonic conjugate of the line $MU''X''$ with respect to $PQRS$ coincides with UX. Similarly for the other two pairs of opposite edges of $PQRS$. Hence the proposition.

719. Corollary. The harmonic conjugate of M with respect to U'', X'' coincides with the harmonic conjugate M' of M with respect to U', X'.

720. Theorem. *The polar plane of a point with respect to a tetrahedron is the plane of homology of the given tetrahedron and the cevian tetrahedron of the point with respect to the given tetrahedron.*

Indeed, the above proof (§ 719) shows that the pairs of corresponding edges of the tetrahedrons $DABC$, $PQRS$ meet in the polar plane of M with respect to $ABCD$.

721. Remark. The point M has, in turn, a cevian tetrahedron with respect to $PQRS$, and the polar plane of M with respect to this new tetrahedron is the same plane μ, for we may consider $PQRS$ as the basic tetrahedron. The process may be continued indefinitely.

b. *Desmic Systems of Tetrahedrons*

722. Definition. If the vertices of a tetrahedron (P) are the poles of the opposite faces of (P) with respect to a second tetrahedron (Q), then (P) is said to be ***self-polar*** or ***harmonic*** with respect to (Q).

723. The table (B) shows that through M' pass three lines $M'U'X'$, $M'VY$, $M'WZ$, and these meet the three pairs of opposite edges of $DABC$ in the three pairs of points U', X'; V, Y; W, Z; moreover (B) shows that the harmonic conjugates of M' with respect to these three pairs of points are M, M''', M'', respectively. Consequently $MM''M'''$ is the polar plane of M' with respect to $DABC$. Similarly for the points M'' and M'''. Hence: *The tetrahedron $MM'M''M'''$ (§ 715) is self-polar with respect to $DABC$.*

724. Corollary. We have thus (§ 723) the following groups of coplanar points in the faces of the tetrahedron $MM'M''M'''$, as seen by the table (B),

(K)		
	$MM'M''$	$U'V'WX'Y'Z$
	$M'M''M'''$	$UVWXYZ$
	$M''M'''M$	$UV'W'XY'Z'$
	$M'''MM'$	$U'VW'X'YZ'$

725. Theorem. *If the tetrahedron (P) is self-polar with respect to the tetrahedron (Q), then (Q) is self-polar with respect to (P).*

Given the tetrahedron $ABCD$ and the point M (§ 715), we constructed the tetrahedron $MM'M''M'''$, self-polar with respect to $ABCD$. It follows from this construction that M is the vertex

of one and only one such tetrahedron. Hence in order to prove
the present proposition it is sufficient to show that $ABCD$ is
self-polar with respect to $MM'M''M'''$.

From the harmonic group (DA, UU') of the table (A) and the
two harmonic groups $(MM', U'X')$, $(M''M''', UX)$ of the table
(B) it follows that the line DUU' meets the pair of opposite edges
MM', $M''M'''$ of the tetrahedron $MM'M''M'''$ in the points
U', U, and that A is the harmonic conjugate of D with respect
to U, U'. Considering the lines DVV', DWW' we may show
that the plane ABC and the point D are harmonically associated
with respect to the tetrahedron $MM'M''M'''$.

A similar reasoning may be applied to each of the points A, B,
C. Hence the proposition.

726. Let P, Q, R, S be the traces of the lines AM, BM, CM,
DM on the faces BCD, CDA, DAB, ABC of the tetrahedron
$ABCD$, and let M_a, M_b, M_c, M_d be the harmonic conjugates of M
with respect to the pairs of points $A, P; B, Q; C, R; D, S$ (Fig. 68).

The secant DM cuts the first three rays of the harmonic pencil
$X'(DA, U'U)$ (§ 713) in the points D, S, M, hence the harmonic
conjugate M_d of M with respect to D, S lies on $X'U$. Again
cutting the same harmonic pencil by the transversal AM we find
$X'U$ also passes through the harmonic conjugate M_a of M with
respect to A, P. Furthermore the group (UX', M_aM_d) is
harmonic, for it is the section of the harmonic pencil $M(UU',
AD)$.

By like considerations it may be shown that $U'X$ contains the
points M_b, M_c, and that the group $(U'X, M_bM_c)$ is harmonic.

If we apply the same reasoning to the pairs of lines $Y'V$, $V'Y$;
$Z'W$, $W'Z$, we finally arrive at the following table of harmonic
groups:

(C) (M_aM_b, ZW'), (M_aM_c, YV'), (M_aM_d, UX')
      (M_cM_d, WZ'), (M_bM_d, VY'), (M_bM_c, XU')

Now if we confront this table with the table (A) in the same
manner as we compared the tables (A) and (B) (§ 725), we find
that the tetrahedron $M_aM_bM_cM_d$ is self-polar with respect to
$DABC$, and by comparing the tables (B) and (C) that $M_aM_bM_cM_d$
is self-polar with respect to $MM'M''M'''$. Consequently (§ 725):
*The three tetrahedrons $DABC$, $MM'M''M'''$, $M_aM_bM_cM_d$ are
mutually self-polar.*

727. Corollary. We have thus (§ 726) the following groups of coplanar points in the faces of the tetrahedron $M_a M_b M_c M_d$, as seen by table (C):

$$
\text{(L)} \quad
\begin{array}{ll}
M_a M_b M_c & U'V'W'XYZ \\
M_b M_c M_d & U'VWXY'Z' \\
M_c M_d M_a & UV'WX'YZ' \\
M_d M_a M_b & UVW'X'Y'Z
\end{array}
$$

728. Definition. *Three mutually self-polar tetrahedrons are said to form a* **desmic system.**

The figure of § 726 was obtained from the tetrahedron $DABC$ and the point M. It could also have been obtained from the tetrahedron $DABC$ and the plane μ (§ 712), for this plane determines the point M. Hence: *A desmic system of three tetrahedrons is determined by one of these tetrahedrons and either a vertex or a face of another of these tetrahedrons.*

729. The three tables (A), (B), (C) may be rearranged in the following way:

$$
\text{(D)} \quad
\begin{array}{lll}
(UU',\ DA), & (UX,\ M''M'''), & (UX',\ M_a M_d) \\
(XX',\ BC), & (U'X',\ MM'), & (XU',\ M_b M_c)
\end{array}
$$

$$
\text{(E)} \quad
\begin{array}{lll}
(VV',\ DB), & (VY,\ M'M'''), & (VY',\ M_b M_d) \\
(YY',\ CA), & (V'Y',\ MM''), & (YV',\ M_a M_c)
\end{array}
$$

$$
\text{(F)} \quad
\begin{array}{lll}
(WW',\ DC), & (WZ,\ M'M''), & (WZ',\ M_c M_d) \\
(ZZ',\ AB), & (Z'W',\ MM'''), & (ZW',\ M_a M_b)
\end{array}
$$

Comparing to each other these tables of groups of harmonic points in the same way as we compared the tables (A), (B), (C) (§§ 725, 726), we conclude: *The three tetrahedrons $UU'XX'$, $VV'YY'$, $WW'ZZ'$ form a desmic system.*

Thus, for instance, the line UU' (D) meets the pair of opposite edges VV', YY' (E) of the tetrahedron $VV'YY'$ in the points D, A; the line UX (D) meets the edges VY, $V'Y'$ (E) of this tetrahedron in the points M''', M'', and the line UX' (D) meets the pair of edges YV', VY' in the points M_d, M_a, while the harmonic conjugates of U with respect to the pairs of points D, A; M'', M'''; M_a, M_d are, respectively, the points U', X, X' (D), hence the face $U'X'X$ of the tetrahedron $UU'XX'$ is the polar plane of the vertex U with respect to the tetrahedron $VV'YY'$ (§ 710).

730. Corollary. From the tables (D), (E), (F) we may derive the following groups of coplanar points, in the faces of the tetrahedrons $UU'XX'$, $VV'YY'$, $WW'ZZ'$:

	1	$UU'X$	$ADM_bM_cM''M'''$
(H')	2	$U'XX'$	BCM_bM_cMM'
	3	$XX'U$	$BCM_aM_dM''M'''$
	4	$X'UU'$	ADM_aM_dMM'
	1	$VV'Y$	$BDM_aM_cM'M'''$
(K').	2	$V'YY'$	ACM_aM_cMM''
	3	$YY'V$	$ACM_bM_dM'M'''$
	4	$Y'VV'$	BDM_bM_dMM''
	1	$WW'Z$	$CDM_aM_bM'M''$
(L')	2	$W'ZZ'$	ABM_aM_bMM'''
	3	$ZZ'W$	$ABM_cM_dM'M''$
	4	$Z'WW'$	CDM_cM_dMM'''

731. Theorem. *Given a desmic system of three tetrahedrons, through the line of intersection of any face of one tetrahedron with any face of one of the other two tetrahedrons passes a face of the third tetrahedron.*

This is readily verified in both sets of tables (H), (K), (L) and (H'), (K'), (L'). Thus, for instance, the face $UU'X$ of the tetrahedron $UU'XX'$ meets the face $VV'Y'$ of $VV'YY'$ along the line DM_bM'', as is seen from (H', 1) and (K', 4), and this line lies in the face $WW'Z$ (L', 1) of $WW'ZZ'$.

732. Theorem. *Given a system of desmic tetrahedrons, the line joining any vertex of one of these tetrahedrons to any vertex of one of the other two tetrahedrons passes through a vertex of the third tetrahedron.*

This may also be verified in both sets of tables (H), (K), (L); (H'), (K'), (L'). Thus consider the line AM'' joining the vertex A of the tetrahedron $ABCD$ to the vertex M'' of $MM'M''M'''$. By (H', 1) and (K', 2) we see that the vertex M_c of the tetrahedron $M_aM_bM_cM_d$ is collinear with A and M''.

733. Remark. In the above manner (§§ 731, 732) we may arrive at the following triads of collinear points:

(J)

$AMM_a,$	$BMM_b,$	$CMM_c,$	DMM_d
$AM'M_d,$	$BM'M_c,$	$CM'M_b,$	$DM'M_a$
$AM''M_c,$	$BM''M_d,$	$CM''M_a,$	$DM''M_b$
$AM'''M_b,$	$BM'''M_a,$	$CM'''M_d,$	$DM'''M_c$

(J')

$UVZ,$	$U'VZ',$	$XVW,$	$X'VW'$
$UV'Z',$	$U'V'Z,$	$XV'W',$	$X'V'W$
$UYW,$	$U'YW',$	$XYZ,$	$X'YZ'$
$UY'W',$	$U'Y'W,$	$XY'Z',$	$X'Y'Z$

734. Theorem. *Any two tetrahedrons of a desmic system are perspective in four different ways, the centers of perspectivity being the vertices of the third tetrahedron, and the planes of perspectivity being the respectively opposite faces of this third tetrahedron. Moreover all these perspectivities are harmonic.*

Through each of the four lines of intersection of the face ABC of the tetrahedron $DABC$ with the faces of the tetrahedron $MM'M''M'''$ passes a face of the tetrahedron $M_aM_bM_cM_d$ (§ 731), hence the faces of the two tetrahedrons $MM'M''M'''$, $M_aM_bM_cM_d$ intersect in pairs in the same plane ABC, therefore the two tetrahedrons are perspective (§ 62), and ABC is their plane of perspectivity.

The face $MM'M''$ meets ABC along the line $X'Y'Z$ (§§ 724, 714), and the plane $M_aM_bM_d$ also passes through this line (§ 727), hence $MM'M''$, $M_aM_bM_d$ are a pair of corresponding planes in the perspectivity considered, and therefore M''', M_c are a pair of corresponding vertices in this perspectivity. These two points are collinear with the vertex D opposite ABC in the tetrahedron $DABC$, as is readily seen by the table (J). Similarly for the other pairs of corresponding faces. Hence D is the center of perspectivity of the tetrahedrons $MM'M''M'''$, $M_aM_bM_cM_d$.

The line (DA, UU') (table A) meets the planes $MM'M''$, $M_aM_bM_d$ in the points U' (K, 1), U (L, 4), respectively, and U, U' are harmonically separated by D and A, i.e., by the center of perspectivity D and the plane of perspectivity ABC, hence this perspectivity is harmonic (§ 63).

735. Given the tetrahedron $DABC$, if the point M (§ 712) is taken to coincide with the incenter I of $DABC$ (§ 241), the points U, U', X, $\cdots$ will be the traces of the bisecting planes of the dihedral angles of $DABC$ on the respectively opposite edges, and the points M', $\cdots$, M_a, $\cdots$ will coincide with the centers of the escribed spheres of $DABC$ (§§ 257, 715, 726). Thus all the propositions concerning the configurations formed by these centers, and the configurations formed by the traces of the bisecting planes, are special cases of the theory of desmic tetrahedrons.

736. Given four spheres (A), (B), (C), (D), let U, U'; V, V'; W, W'; X, X'; Y, Y'; Z, Z' be the centers of similitude of these spheres taken in pairs. It is sufficient to prove that the external centers of similitude U, V, W, X, Y, Z are coplanar (§ 492), and all the propositions concerning the configurations formed by these twelve centers of similitude become special cases of the theory of desmic tetrahedrons.

EXERCISES

1. Two twin tetrahedrons are self-polar with respect to one another.

2. If a point describes a line passing through a vertex of a given tetrahedron, its polar plane with respect to this tetrahedron describes a coaxal pencil.

3. If a point varies on a line meeting a pair of opposite edges of a tetrahedron, its polar plane with respect to this tetrahedron describes a coaxal pencil.

4. Through a point M the three lines a, b, c are drawn meeting the three pairs of opposite edges of a given tetrahedron. If the line c remains fixed, and the point M varies on c, the plane ab describes a coaxal pencil.

5. If each of four given spheres touches the remaining three externally the three lines joining the points of contact of the four spheres grouped in pairs are concurrent.

6. Given an orthocentric tetrahedron, every point of its (real) conjugate sphere is the vertex of a tetrahedron inscribed in this sphere and harmonic to the given tetrahedron.

7. If two tetrahedrons of a desmic system are inscribed in the same sphere, the third tetrahedron of the system is polar with respect to this sphere.

2. Isogonal Points

737. Definition. Two planes which pass through the edge of a dihedral angle and are symmetric with respect to the bisecting plane of this angle are said to be *isogonal* with respect to the dihedral angle.

738. Theorem. *The distances, from the faces of a dihedral angle, of two points in two isogonal planes of this dihedral angle are inversely proportional, and conversely.*

Let MP, MQ; NR, NS (Fig. 69) be the two pairs of perpendiculars dropped from the points M, N upon the two faces of the given dihedral angle, and U, V the traces of the edge UV of this angle in the planes MPQ, NRS. These planes are perpendicular to UV and therefore cut all the dihedral angles involved along their plane angles. Furthermore these two planes are parallel. Hence the projection $N'S'R'V'$ of the figure in the plane $NSRV$ upon the plane $MPQU$ will be congruent to the figure $NSRV$. The consideration of the two figures $MPQU$, $N'S'R'V'$

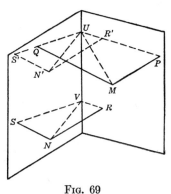

Fig. 69

(V' is identical with U) reduces the proof to the corresponding case in the plane (C. G., pp. 239–240).

739. Corollary. *The line joining the projections of a point upon the faces of a dihedral angle is perpendicular to the isogonal of the plane passing through the given point and through the edge of the dihedral angle.*

The proposition follows immediately from the corresponding proposition in the plane (C. G., p. 241).

740. Theorem. *If three planes passing through the three edges of a trihedral angle are coaxal, the isogonal planes of these three planes with respect to the corresponding dihedral angles are also coaxal.*

Let s be the line common to the three planes as, bs, cs passing through the edges a, b, c of the given trihedral angle, and let s' be the line of intersection of the two planes as', bs' isogonal to the planes as, bs with respect to the dihedral angles (ab, ac), (bc, ba).

Let M, M' be any two points on s and s', respectively, and let MD, ME, MF; $M'D'$, $M'E'$, $M'F'$ be the perpendiculars dropped from M, M' upon the planes bc, ca, ab. By assumption we have (§ 738)

$$ME : MF = M'F' : M'E', \qquad MF : MD = M'D' : M'F',$$

hence, multiplying these two proportions,

$$ME : MD = M'D' : M'E',$$

i.e., the planes cM, cM' are isogonal with respect to the dihedral angle (ca, cb) (§ 738), which proves the proposition.

741. Definition. The two lines s, s' (§ 740) may be said to be *isogonal* with respect to the given trihedral angle.

Every line within a trihedral angle and passing through its vertex has an isogonal line with respect to this angle.

742. Corollary. *The plane determined by the three projections of a point upon the faces of a trihedral angle is perpendicular to the isogonal line of the line joining the given point to the vertex of the trihedral angle.*

The lines DE, EF, FD (§ 740) are, respectively, perpendicular to the planes cM', aM', bM' (§ 739), hence the plane DEF is perpendicular to the line s' joining M' to the point abc.

743. Theorem. *The isogonal planes, with respect to the corresponding dihedral angles of a given tetrahedron, of the six planes passing through a given point and the six edges of the tetrahedron, have a point in common.*

Let $ABCD$ be the given tetrahedron, M the given point, p the isogonal conjugate of the line AM with respect to the trihedral angle A, and let q, r, s be the analogous lines in the trihedral angles B, C, D.

If we consider the trihedral angle A, the isogonal plane of ABM with respect to the dihedral angle AB will contain p, and if we consider the trihedral angle B, the isogonal of BAM with respect to the dihedral angle BA will contain q, hence p and q are coplanar. Thus any two of the lines p, q, r, s are coplanar, hence they have a point M' in common, which belongs to the six isogonal planes considered.

744. Remark. The four lines p, q, r, s (§ 743) may in some cases be parallel. It follows from the above proposition that if any two of these four lines are parallel, all four are parallel to each other.

745. Definition. The two points M, M' (§ 743) are said to be *isogonal* with respect to the tetrahedron.

Every point in space (not lying in a face of the tetrahedron) has an isogonal point with respect to the tetrahedron and only one.

746. Corollary. *The distances of two isogonal points from the faces of the tetrahedron are inversely proportional, and, **conversely,***

if the distances of two points from the faces of a tetrahedron are inversely proportional, the two points are isogonal with respect to the tetrahedron (§ 738).

747. Theorem. *The eight projections, upon the faces of a tetrahedron, of two isogonal points of the tetrahedron lie on a sphere having for center the mid-point of the segment determined by the two isogonal points.*

Let P, Q, R, S be the projections of the point M upon the faces BCD, CDA, DAB, ABC of the tetrahedron $ABCD$; let L be the center of the sphere $(L) \equiv PQRS$ and M' the symmetric of M with respect to L (Fig. 70). The projection P' of M' upon BCD is the symmetric of P with respect to the projection of L upon BCD, hence P' is the diametric opposite of P on the circle along which (L) is cut by BCD, hence P' lies on (L).

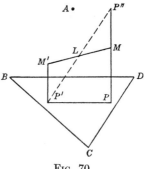

FIG. 70

The line MP meets (L) again in the diametric opposite P'' of P' on (L), as is readily seen by plane geometry, and we have $MP'' = M'P'$. Now if Q'', R'', S'' are the points analogous to P'' and relative to Q, S, R, we have, considering the power of M with respect to (L),

$$MP \cdot MP'' = MQ \cdot MQ'' = MR \cdot MR'' = MS \cdot MS'',$$

or

$$MP \cdot M'P' = MQ \cdot M'Q' = MR \cdot M'R' = MS \cdot M'S',$$

which shows that M and M' are isogonal with respect to $ABCD$ (§ 746), and the proposition is proved.

748. Remark. If the isogonal lines, with respect to the trihedral angles of a tetrahedron, of the lines joining the vertices of the tetrahedron to a given point M are parallel, the projections of M upon the faces of the tetrahedron are coplanar, and conversely.

The planes QRS, RSP (§ 747) are, respectively, perpendicular to the isogonals p, q of AM, BM, with respect to the trihedral angles A, B (§ 742), and if p, q are parallel, the four points P, Q,

R, S are coplanar.   Conversely, if these four points are coplanar, p, q are parallel.

The plane $PQRS$ suggests an analogy with the Simson line in the plane, and it might be expected that M is a point on the circumsphere of $ABCD$.   However this is not the case.   The locus of M is a surface of the third order.

749. Theorem.   *The four projections, upon the four faces of a tetrahedron, of the mid-point of the line of centers of two spheres which touch the four faces of the tetrahedron are coplanar.*

The projection of the mid-point of the line of centers of two such spheres upon one face of the tetrahedron is the mid-point of the segment determined by the points of contact of the two spheres with the face considered, hence this point has equal powers with respect to the two spheres, and therefore lies in their radical plane.

750. Theorem.   *If two points are isogonal with respect to a tetrahedron, each is the center of the sphere determined by the four symmetrics of the other with respect to the faces of the tetrahedron.*

Let P, Q, R, S be the projections of M upon the faces of $ABCD$, and P', Q', R', S' the symmetrics of M with respect to the corresponding faces.   The point M is the homothetic center of the two tetrahedrons $PQRS$, $P'Q'R'S'$, the homothetic ratio being $1 : 2$, therefore the circumcenter L' of $P'Q'R'S'$ is the symmetric of M with respect to the circumcenter L of $PQRS$ (§ 55), hence L' coincides with the isogonal M' of M with respect to $ABCD$ (§ 747).

751. Remark.   The two spheres of which the points M, M' are thus the centers (§ 750) are equal, for each radius is equal to twice the radius of the sphere (L) (§ 747).

752. Theorem.   *The radical center of the four spheres having for great circles the four intersections of the faces of a tetrahedron with a given sphere is the isogonal of the center of this sphere with respect to the tetrahedron.*

Let P, Q, R, S be the centers of the four circles along which the given sphere (M) is cut by the faces BCD, CDA, DAB, ABC of the given tetrahedron $ABCD$, and let (P), (Q), (R), (S) be the spheres having these circles for diametral circles.

The two pairs of spheres (M), (P); (M), (Q) have for their respective radical planes the faces BCD, CDA of $ABCD$, hence the radical plane of the two spheres (P), (Q) passes through the line CD, and this radical plane is necessarily perpendicular to the line of centers PQ of the two spheres. Thus this plane coincides with the isogonal plane of the plane CDM with respect to the dihedral angle (CDA, CDB) (§ 739). Hence the proposition.

753. Corollary. *The isogonal point of the circumcenter of a tetrahedron with respect to this tetrahedron is the radical center of the four spheres having for great circles the circumcircles of the four faces of the tetrahedron.*

754. Let M' be the radical center and (M') the orthogonal sphere of the four spheres (P), (Q), (R), (S) (§ 752). The two points M, M' being isogonal with respect to $ABCD$, the four points P, Q, R, S and the projections P', Q', R', S' of M' upon the faces of $ABCD$ lie on the same sphere (L) (§ 747).

THEOREM. *The sphere (L) is the radical sphere (§ 543) of the two spheres (M), (M').*

Indeed, the two spheres (M'), (P) are orthogonal, and the plane BCD passes through the center P of (P), hence BCD cuts (M') and (P) along two orthogonal circles (p. 176, Ex. 19). Thus the sum of the powers of P with respect to the two spheres (P), (M') is zero (§ 546). Now the powers of P with respect to the two spheres (P) and (M) are equal, hence the sum of the powers of P with respect to the two spheres (M), (M') is also zero, and the sphere (L) has for its center the mid-point of MM' (§ 747), hence the proposition (§ 542).

Thus given the sphere (M), the point M' and the sphere (L) may be constructed, and the sphere (M') is determined as the sphere with center M' and coaxal with (L) and (M) (§ 592).

755. Theorem. *The isogonal point O', with respect to a given tetrahedron, of the circumcenter O of this tetrahedron is the incenter of the tetrahedron formed by the projections of O' upon the faces of $ABCD$.*

The projections P', Q', R', S' of O' upon the faces BCD, CDA, DAB, ABC determine a tetrahedron whose faces are respectively perpendicular to the lines OA, OB, OC, OD (§ 742). Thus the planes $Q'R'S'$, $R'S'P'$, $S'P'Q'$ are parallel to the faces of the supplementary trihedral angle of the trihedral angle $O–ABC$. Now ABC is an isoclinal plane of $O–ABC$, for $OA = OB = OC$, and $S'O'$ is perpendicular to ABC, hence $S'O'$ is an axis of the trihedron $S'-P'Q'R'$ (§ 123), which proves the proposition (§ 240).

756. Theorem. *The four symmetrics of a given sphere with respect to the faces of a given tetrahedron have for radical center the isogonal conjugate of the center of the given sphere with respect to the tetrahedron.*

The symmetrics of the given sphere (M) with respect to the faces of $ABCD$ are equal to (M) and therefore equal to each other, hence the radical center U of these spheres is the center of the sphere $PQRS$ determined by their four centers. Now these centers are the symmetrics of the center M of (M) with respect to the faces of $ABCD$, hence they lie on a sphere having for center the isogonal conjugate M' of M with respect to $ABCD$ (§ 750), therefore U coincides with M', which proves the proposition.

757. Problem. *Find a point, inside a given tetrahedron, whose distances from the faces of the tetrahedron shall be proportional to the areas of these faces.*

The isogonal L of the required point K will have its distances to the faces of the tetrahedron $ABCD$ inversely proportional to the areas of these faces (§ 746), and therefore directly proportional to the altitudes $h_a, \cdots$ of the tetrahedron. If the factor of proportionality is m, and V is the volume of $ABCD$, we have

$$\text{vol. } LBCD = \tfrac{1}{3}mh_a \cdot BCD = mV.$$

Similarly,

$$\text{vol. } LCDA = \text{vol. } LDAB = \text{vol. } LABC = mV.$$

Thus vol. $LBCD = \tfrac{1}{4}V$, and the factor of proportionality m is equal to $\tfrac{1}{4}$, i.e., the distances of L from the faces of $ABCD$ are equal to $\tfrac{1}{4}$ of the respective altitudes of $ABCD$, hence L coincides with the centroid G of $ABCD$. Consequently the required point K is the isogonal point of the centroid of the tetrahedron.

EXERCISES

1. The three projections of a point of an axis of a trihedral angle upon the faces of this angle determine a plane perpendicular to the axis considered.

2. Two planes (P), (Q) intersect along the line s and cut a given sphere (O) along two circles (U), (V). The radical plane of the two spheres having (U), (V) for great circles passes through s and is the isogonal plane, with respect to the dihedral angle formed by (P) and (Q), of the plane Os passing through s and the center O of (O).

3. If P, Q, R, S are the projections of the point M upon the faces BCD, CDA, DAB, ABC of a given tetrahedron $ABCD$, the perpendiculars dropped from A, B, C, D upon the planes QRS, RSP, SPQ, PQR are concurrent.

4. (a) The two groups of points $MPQRS$, $M'P'Q'R'S'$ (§ 747) are such that the line joining two points of one group is perpendicular to the plane determined by the three non-homologous points of the other group. (b) If p, q, r, s are the lines of intersection of the corresponding faces of the two tetrahedrons $PQRS$, $P'Q'R'S'$, the planes Ap, Bq, Cr, Ds are perpendicular to the line MM'.

5. The four symmetrics of the circumsphere of a tetrahedron with respect to the faces of the tetrahedron have for their radical center the isogonal point of the circumcenter of the tetrahedron.

6. Consider the orthogonal sphere (R) of the four spheres having for great circles the intersections of four given planes with a variable sphere (M) having a fixed center. The sum of the squares of the radii of the two spheres (R), (M) is constant.

7. Given a tetrahedron (T) and a variable sphere (M) with a fixed center, the radical center of the four symmetrics of (M) with respect to the faces of (T) is fixed.

8. Find the locus of a point such that its three projections upon the faces of a trihedron shall determine a plane having a given orientation.

9. Given the tetrahedron $ABCD$, consider the isogonal conjugate AM of the altitude AA' of $ABCD$ in the trihedral angle A–BCD. If M is any point of AM show that (a) the projections of M upon the faces ABC, ACD, ADB determine a plane parallel to BCD; (b) the sphere determined by the four projections of M upon the faces of $ABCD$ passes through the foot A' of the altitude AA'.

3. Antiparallel Sections

758. Definitions. If the six points determined by two planes on the edges of a trihedral angle are cospherical, the two planes are said to be *antiparallel* with respect to the trihedral angle, and the two triangles determined in these planes by the edges of the trihedron are said to be *antiparallel sections* of the trihedral angle.

Given the tetrahedron $(T) \equiv ABCD$, if a plane antiparallel to the plane ABC with respect to the trihedral angle having D for its vertex cuts the edges DA, DB, DC in the points P, Q, R, the triangle PQR is said to be an *antiparallel section* of (T), or to be *antiparallel* to the triangle ABC. ˙

759. Theorem. *An antiparallel section of a tetrahedron relative to a given face is parallel to the tangent plane to the circumsphere of the tetrahedron at the vertex opposite the face considered.*

The line PQ (§ 758) is antiparallel to the side AB of the triangle DAB with respect to DA, DB and therefore parallel to the tangent u to the circle DAB at D (C. G., p. 85).

Similarly the lines QR, RP are parallel to the tangents v, w to the circles DBC, DCA at D. Now u, v, w lie in the tangent plane at D to the circumsphere of $DABC$, hence the proposition.

760. Theorem. *The sides of any antiparallel section of a tetrahedron are proportional to the products of the three pairs of opposite edges of the tetrahedron.*

If p denotes the power of D with respect to $(S) \equiv ABCPQR$ (§ 758), we have, with the usual notation for the length of the edges of (T) (§ 150),

(1) $$p = DP \cdot a' = DQ \cdot b' = DR \cdot c'.$$

On the other hand, from the similar triangles DAB, DPQ we have
$$DP : b' = PQ : c,$$
hence
$$DP = b' \cdot PQ : c = p : a',$$
or
$$PQ : cc' = p : a'b'c'.$$

Thus making use of the other two pairs of similar triangles we obtain

(2) $$\frac{QR}{aa'} = \frac{RP}{bb'} = \frac{PQ}{cc'} = \frac{p}{a'b'c'},$$

which proves the proposition.

Corollary. *All antiparallel sections of a tetrahedron are similar,* for their sides are proportional to the same three quantities aa', bb', cc'.

761. Theorem. *The symmedian points of the antiparallel sections relative to a given face of a tetrahedron lie on the line joining the symmedian point of the face considered to the opposite vertex of the tetrahedron.*

The oblique circular cone (D) having the point D (§ 759) for vertex and for base the circle ABC contains the circumcircle of PQR (§§ 758, 370, 698).

The tangent planes to (D) along the elements DA, DB, DC form a trihedral angle (T) the faces of which determine in the plane ABC the tangential triangle of the triangle ABC. Now the three lines joining the corresponding vertices of these two triangles meet in the symmedian point K_d of ABC (C. G., pp. 226, 228), hence the three planes determined by the three pairs of corresponding edges of the two trihedrons D and (T) have the line DK_d in common.

The trihedron (T) also determines in the plane PQR the tangential triangle of PQR, and it is now readily seen that the symmedian point of PQR coincides with the trace, in the plane PQR, of the line DK_d.

762. The plane PQR (§ 759) is perpendicular to the diameter DD' of the circumsphere (O) of (T) (§ 758), hence if L is the trace of DD' in PQR, we have, from the two similar right triangles DAD', DLP,

$$DD' \cdot DL = 2R \cdot DL = DP \cdot DA = p,$$

where R is the radius of (O), and p the power of D with respect to (S) (§ 760).

If V, V' are the volumes of the two tetrahedrons $DABC$, $DPQR$, we have

$$V' : V = DP \cdot DQ \cdot DR : a'b'c'.$$

Now we have (§ 760)

$$DP = p : a', \qquad DQ = p : b', \qquad DR = p : c',$$

hence

$$(a'b'c')^2 \cdot V' = p^3 \cdot V.$$

Let T denote the area of the triangle whose sides are numerically equal to aa', bb', cc', respectively. We have then (§ 760)

$$\text{area } PQR : T = PQ^2 : (cc')^2 = p^2 : (a'b'c')^2,$$

hence

$$3V' = DL \cdot \text{area } PQR = p^2 T \cdot DL : (a'b'c')^2.$$

Equating the two values of V' we obtain, after simplification,

$$3pV = T \cdot DL.$$

Now replacing p by $2R \cdot DL$, we obtain finally

$$6RV = T.$$

EXERCISES

1. Given the tetrahedron $ABCD$ and a point S, construct on SA, SB, SC, SD the points A', B', C', D' so that the planes $A'B'C'$, $B'C'D'$, $C'D'A'$, $D'A'B'$

shall be antiparallel, respectively, to the planes ABC, BCD, CDA, DAB with respect to the trihedral angles $S-ABC$, $S-BCD$, $S-CDA$, $S-DAB$.

2. Let U, V, W be any three points on the three perpendiculars from the given point M upon the faces DBC, DCA, DAB of the given trihedral angle $D-ABC$, and let M' be any point on the perpendicular from D upon the plane UVW. The projections of M' upon the faces of $D-ABC$ determine a plane which is antiparallel to UVW with respect to the trihedral angle $M-UVW$.

3. (a) In a tetrahedron the product of any pair of opposite edges is smaller than the sum of the products of the other two pairs of opposite edges. (b) The three angles formed by the three pairs of opposite edges cannot be equal unless they are right angles. Hint. Apply the law of cosines to the bimedians and derive the formula: $aa' \cos(aa') \pm bb' \cos(bb') \pm cc' \cos(cc') = 0$.

4. The altitude of a trirectangular tetrahedron contains the centroid of any antiparallel section relative to the base, and also the center of the sphere determined by this section and the vertex of the right angle of the tetrahedron.

5. In a trirectangular tetrahedron the median issued from the vertex of the right angle is perpendicular to the sections antiparallel to the base and is the locus of the orthocenters of these sections.

6. In a tetrahedron the centroids of the antiparallel sections relative to the same trihedral angle lie on a line passing through the vertex of the trihedral angle considered. The four lines thus obtained form a hyperbolic group supplementary to the hyperbolic group formed by the lines joining the vertices of the tetrahedron to the symmedian point of the faces of the tetrahedron.

4. Spheres Related to the Tetrahedron

a. Analogues of the Nine-Point Circle

763. The mid-points of the sides of a triangle are the projections, upon the sides, of the circumcenter of the triangle, and these three projections determine the nine-point circle of the triangle. By analogy, consider the sphere (O'') passing through the projections O_a, O_b, O_c, O_d of the circumcenter O of the tetrahedron $(T) \equiv ABCD$ upon the faces BCD, CDA, DAB, ABC of (T).

These four points are the centers of the circumcircles of the faces of (T). Consider the four spheres having these four circles for diametral sections. The radical center O' of these four spheres is the isogonal point of O with respect to (T) (§ 752). Hence the projections of O' upon the faces of (T) also lie on the sphere (O'') (§ 747). The symmetrics, with respect to O'', of the eight projections of O and O' upon the faces of (T) obviously lie on (O'').

The sphere (O'') is the radical sphere of (O) and (O') (§ 754), and is referred to as the **sixteen point sphere** of the tetrahedron.

764. The centroids of the faces of a tetrahedron (T) may also be considered as the analogues of the mid-points of the sides of a triangle. Hence the sphere (L) determined by the four centroids of the faces of (T) may be considered as a second analogue (§ 763) of the nine-point circle of a triangle.

The sphere (L) is the homothetic of the circumsphere (O) of (T) with respect to the centroid G of (T), the homothetic ratio being $- 1 : 3$ (§ 176). Hence the center L of (L) lies on the Euler line OG of (T) (§ 229), and $LG : GO = 1 : 3$ (Fig. 71).

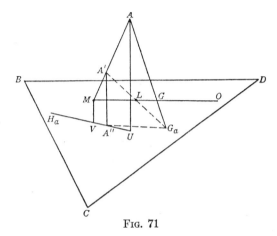

FIG. 71

The Monge point M of (T), being the symmetric of O with respect to G (§ 230), divides the segment LO externally in the ratio $1 : 3$, hence M is the external center of similitude of the two spheres (L), (O). Thus the sphere (L) passes through the point A' such that $MA' : MA = 1 : 3$, and through the three analogous points B', C', D', respectively relative to the vertices B, C, D.

The sphere (L) is known as the **twelve point sphere** of the tetrahedron. The center L of (L) divides the segment MO in the ratio of $1 : 2$. The radius of (L) is equal to one third of the radius of (O).

765. *The point A' (§ 764) and the centroid G_a of BCD are diametrically opposite on the sphere* (L).

Indeed, the three points A', L, G_a are collinear, as is readily seen by Menelaus' theorem applied to the triangle AMG and the transversal $A'G_a$.

766. *The sphere* (L) *passes through the projection* A'' *of* A' *upon* BCD (§ 765) *and through the three analogous points of* A'' (Fig. 71). Indeed, the diameter $A'G_a$ of (L) subtends a right angle at A''. We have thus twelve points on (L), which justifies the name given to this sphere.

767. *The point* A'' (§ 766) *is the harmonic conjugate of the orthocenter of* BCD *with respect to the projections, upon* BCD, *of the vertex* A *and the Monge point of the tetrahedron.*

Indeed, the projections U, V of A and the Monge point M are collinear with A'', and we have (Fig. 71)

$$VA'' : A''U = 1 : 2.$$

On the other hand, by Mannheim's theorem (§ 232) U, V are collinear with the orthocenter H_a of BCD, and V is the mid-point of UH_a (§ 233), hence the proposition.

b. *The Apollonian Spheres of the Tetrahedron*

768. Definition. Given the tetrahedron $(T) \equiv ABCD$, let (A), (B), (C), (D) be the spheres described with A, B, C, D as centers, and with radii proportional to the corresponding altitudes of (T). The six spheres of similitude (§ 478) of the four given spheres taken in pairs are, by definition, the **Apollonian spheres** of (T).

The six Apollonian spheres of (T) have their centers on the edges of (T). Each sphere will be said to be "relative" to or to "correspond" to the edge which contains its center.

769. Theorem. *An edge of a tetrahedron is met by the two bisecting planes of the opposite dihedral angle of the tetrahedron in two points diametrically opposite on the Apollonian sphere relative to the edge considered.*

Given the tetrahedron $(T) \equiv ABCD$, let X' (Fig. 72) be the trace on BC of the internal bisecting plane of the dihedral angle (DA). We have, by Gergonne's theorem (§ 235),

$$BX' : CX' = \text{area } DAB : \text{area } DAC = h_b : h_c,$$

where h_b, h_c are the altitudes of (T) issued from B and C. Hence X' is the internal center of similitude of the spheres (B), (C) (§ 467). Similarly the trace X on BC of the external bisecting plane of the angle (DA) is the external center of similitude of (B), (C). Hence the proposition (§ 478).

770. Remark I. This theorem (§ 769) shows that the Apollonian spheres of a tetrahedron may be defined as spheres directly associated with the tetrahedron, independently of the spheres (A), (B), (C), (D) (§ 768).

771. Remark II. In the light of the last theorem (§ 769) the propositions concerning the traces of the bisecting planes of the dihedral angles of a tetrahedron upon the respectively opposite edges (§§ 237 ff.) become special cases of the propositions relating to the centers of similitude of four spheres (§§ 491 ff.).

772. Theorem. *The centers of the six Apollonian spheres of a tetrahedron are coplanar.*

Indeed, the plane is the Newtonian plane of the four spheres (A), (B), (C), (D) (§ 632).

773. Corollary. *The six segments determined on the edges of a tetrahedron by the pairs of bisecting planes of the dihedral angles of the tetrahedron have their mid-points in the same plane.*

774. Definition. The last proposition (§ 773) shows that the plane of centers of the Apollonian spheres of a tetrahedron may be defined directly with reference to the tetrahedron, without making use of the spheres (A), (B), (C), (D) (§ 768). We shall refer to this plane as the *Apollonian plane* of the tetrahedron.

It should be observed that the Apollonian plane cuts the edges of the tetrahedron outside the tetrahedron, for the points X', X (§ 769) being harmonically separated by B, C, the mid-point X_0 of XX' lies outside of the segment BC.

775. Theorem. *The distances of the vertices of a tetrahedron from the Apollonian plane of the tetrahedron are proportional to the squares of the corresponding altitudes of the tetrahedron.*

Let X_0 (Fig. 72) be the mid-point of XX' (§ 769). The perpendiculars dropped from B, C upon the Apollonian plane are the sides of two similar right triangles of which BX_0, CX_0 are the hypotenuses, hence the ratio of these perpendiculars is equal to

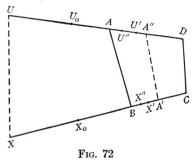

Fig. 72

$BX_0 : CX_0$. Now (§ 769)

$$BX' : CX' = h_b : h_c,$$

hence (§ 49)

$$BX_0 : CX_0 = h_b{}^2 : h_c{}^2.$$

OTHERWISE. This is a special case of Neuberg's theorem (§ 633).

776. Theorem. *The Apollonian spheres of a tetrahedron are orthogonal to the circumsphere of the tetrahedron* (§ 634).

777. Theorem. *The six Apollonian spheres of a tetrahedron form a coaxal net, the plane of centers of which is the Apollonian plane of the tetrahedron, and the radical axis of which is the perpendicular dropped from the circumcenter of the tetrahedron upon the Apollonian plane* (§ 634).

778. Definition. This radical axis (§ 777) will be referred to as the *Apollonian diameter* of the tetrahedron.

779. Theorem. *The six radical planes of the circumsphere of a tetrahedron with the six Apollonian spheres of the tetrahedron have a point in common.*

The circumsphere (O) being orthogonal to the Apollonian spheres (§ 776), the radical plane of (O) with an Apollonian sphere is the polar plane of the center of the latter sphere with respect to (O), hence this plane passes through the pole of the Apollonian plane with respect to the sphere (O).

780. Definition. This point (§ 779) may ᐧbe called the **Apollonian point** of the tetrahedron.

The Apollonian point of a tetrahedron lies on the Apollonian diameter and is the inverse, with respect to the circumsphere, of the trace of this diameter in the Apollonian plane.

781. Theorem. *The six Apollonian spheres of a tetrahedron have two points in common.*

782. Definition. By analogy with the case of the plane these two points (§ 781) may be called the **isodynamic points** of the tetrahedron.

The isodynamic points of a tetrahedron lie on the Apollonian diameter of the tetrahedron.

783. Contrary to what takes place in the plane, the isodynamic points W, W' of a tetrahedron are not necessarily real.

Given the triangle ABC, draw in its plane an arbitrary circle (r) so that the circles (a), (b), (c) orthogonal to (r) and having for centers the vertices A, B, C shall not cut the respectively opposite sides of ABC. The three circles of similitude (a'), (b'), (c') of the circles (a), (b), (c) taken in pairs have in common the limiting points of (r) with the circumcircle of ABC, hence these points may be either real or imaginary.

Now consider the spheres (A), (B), (C) having (a), (b), (c) for diametral sections. Through BC draw a tangent plane to (A), and similarly for CA and AB with respect to (B) and (C). If D is the point common to these three planes, the spheres (A), (B), (C) have for radii the corresponding altitudes of the tetrahedron $DABC$, and the spheres (A'), (B'), (C') having (a'), (b'), (c') for diametral circles are the spheres of similitude of (A), (B), (C) taken in pairs, hence they are Apollonian spheres of $DABC$, and thus may, or may not, have real points in common, depending upon the position of (r).

784. When the isodynamic points W, W' of a tetrahedron are real, they are symmetric with respect to the Apollonian plane of the tetrahedron and are inverse with respect to the circumsphere of $ABCD$.

The distances of a (real) isodynamic point from the vertices of the tetrahedron are proportional to the respective altitudes of the tetrahedron (§ 479), and therefore inversely proportional to the areas of the faces of the tetrahedron. Thus if (A), (B), (C), (D) are these areas, we have

$$WA \cdot (A) = WB \cdot (B) = WC \cdot (C) = WD \cdot (D),$$

and similarly for W'.

785. Theorem. *The centroid of a tetrahedron and the harmonic pole of the Apollonian plane are isogonal points with respect to the tetrahedron.*

The sphere (X_0) having XX' for diameter (§ 774) is orthogonal to the sphere (A') having BC for diameter (§ 413) (Fig. 72, p. 253), hence the radical plane of these two spheres is the polar plane of X_0 with respect to (A') and therefore meets BC in a point X'' which is the harmonic conjugate of X_0 with respect to B, C, and also the harmonic conjugate of the mid-point A' of BC with respect to X, X'. Let U'' be the point analogous to X'' on the edge DA.

The points A', X'' being harmonically separated by X, X', che planes DAA', DAX'' are harmonically separated by the bisecting planes DAX, DAX' of the dihedral angle (DA), hence the planes DAA', DAX'' are isogonal with respect to (DA) (§§ 41, 737). Similarly the planes BCA'', BCU'' are isogonal with respect to the dihedral angle (BC). But the two planes DAA', BCA'' intersect along the bimedian $A'A''$ of the tetrahedron, and the centroid G of the tetrahedron lies on $A'A''$ (§ 171), hence the isogonal point of G with respect to $ABCD$ lies on $X''U''$ and on the analogous lines $Y''V''$, $Z''W''$ relative to the pairs of opposite edges DB, CA; DC, AB.

Now the points X_0, X'' being harmonic with respect to B, C, and the points U_0, U'' being harmonic with respect to D, A, the line $X''U''$ is the harmonic conjugate of X_0U_0 with respect to $DABC$. Similarly for the analogous pairs of lines $Y''V''$, Y_0V_0; $Z''W''$, Z_0W_0. But the lines X_0U_0, Y_0V_0, Z_0W_0 lie in the Apollonian plane of $DABC$ (§ 774), hence the point common to the lines $X''U''$, $Y''V''$, $Z''W''$ is the harmonic pole of the Apollonian plane with respect to the tetrahedron.

B. SPECIAL TETRAHEDRONS

1. The Circumscriptible Tetrahedron

786. Definition. A tetrahedron whose six edges (not produced) are tangent to the same sphere will be referred to as *circumscriptible by the edges*, or, more briefly, *circumscriptible*.

787. Theorem. *In a tetrahedron circumscriptible by the edges the three sums of the three pairs of opposite edges are equal.*

We observe, in the first place, that the three tangents issued from a vertex of the tetrahedron $ABCD$ to the sphere (U) which touches its edges are equal [§ 384 (b)]. Now let p, q, r, s be the lengths of the tangents issued from the vertices A, B, C, D, respectively, to the sphere (U). It is readily seen that any edge of $ABCD$ is equal to the sum of two of these four segments, and that the edge opposite is equal to the sum of the remaining two segments, hence the proposition.

788. Theorem. *In a circumscriptible tetrahedron the four in-circles of the four faces lie on the same sphere, and each of these circles is tangent to the remaining three.*

Indeed, these circles are the sections, by the faces of the given tetrahedron $ABCD$, of the sphere (U) touching the edges of $ABCD$.

Furthermore, the point of contact of the edge BC with the sphere (U) is also the point of contact of BC with the incircle of the face ABC and with the incircle of the face DBC, hence the two circles are tangent to each other. Similarly for the other edges. Hence the proposition.

789. Converse Theorem. *If the incircles of two of the faces of a tetrahedron each touch the incircles of the remaining three faces, the tetrahedron is circumscriptible.*

Let the incircle of the face ABC (Fig. 73) of the tetrahedron $ABCD$ be tangent to the incircles of the other three faces, and let X be its point of contact with the edge BC. The point X is therefore also the point of contact of BC with the incircle of BCD, hence the perpendiculars erected at X to BC in the planes

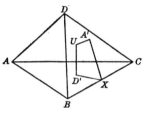

FIG. 73

ABC, DBC will pass through the incenters D', A' of the triangles ABC, DBC. The plane $A'D'X$ is thus perpendicular to BC, and therefore to the planes BCA, BCD. Consequently the perpendiculars d, a erected to ABC, DBC at D', A' lie in the same plane $A'D'X$. In a similar way we may show that d is coplanar with each of the perpendiculars b, c to the planes CAD, BAD erected at the incenters B', C' of the triangles CAD, BAD.

Now if we suppose again that the incircle of DBC is also tangent to the incircles of the remaining three faces, we may prove in the same way as above that the line a is coplanar with the lines b, c, d.

The perpendicular b is thus coplanar with a and d. But b cannot lie in the plane $ad \equiv A'D'X$, for the plane $A'D'X$ containing b would then be perpendicular to DAC, and since BC is also perpendicular to $A'D'X$, the line BC would then be parallel to DAC, which is absurd. Hence the line b passes through the point U common to a and d. The line c passes through U, for similar reasons. It is now readily seen that U is the center of a sphere touching the edges of $ABCD$.

790. Theorem. *If the three sums of the three pairs of opposite edges of a tetrahedron are equal, the tetrahedron is circumscriptible.*

Suppose that in the tetrahedron $ABCD$ we have (Fig. 73)

(1) $$AB + CD = AC + BD = AD + BC.$$

If X is the point of contact of the edge BC with the incircle of the triangle ABC, we have (C. G., p. 74)

(2) $$BX = \tfrac{1}{2}(BC + AB - AC).$$

Now from (1) we have

$$AB - AC = BD - CD,$$

hence (2) becomes
$$BX = \tfrac{1}{2}(BC + BD - CD),$$

which shows that X is also the point of contact of BC with the incircle of the triangle DBC.

In a similar way we may show that the two points of contact of any other edge of $ABCD$ with the two incircles which touch that edge coincide, hence the proposition (§ 789).

791. Theorem. (a) *If the six edges of a tetrahedron are tangent to the same sphere, the three lines joining the points of contact of the three pairs of opposite edges are concurrent.* (b) *The six points in which the edges of the tetrahedron are met by the tangent planes to this sphere passing through the respectively opposite edges are coplanar.*

The proofs of these propositions are the same as the proofs of the corresponding propositions concerning four mutually tangent spheres (§§ 630, 631).

792. If $ABCD$ is a circumscriptible tetrahedron, let p, q, r, s denote the lengths of the tangents from A, B, C, D to the sphere (U) touching the edges of $ABCD$. We have then

$$AB = p + q, \qquad BC = q + r, \qquad CA = r + p.$$

Using the known formula giving the area (D) of the triangle ABC in terms of its sides, we get

$$(D)^2 = (p + q + r)pqr.$$

On the other hand, denoting by d the inradius of ABC, we have

$$(D) = d(p + q + r),$$

hence
$$d^2 = pqr : (p + q + r),$$
or
$$\frac{1}{d^2} = \frac{1}{qr} + \frac{1}{rp} + \frac{1}{pq}.$$

Hence, denoting by a, b, c the inradii of the triangles $BCD, CDA,$ DAB, we get
$$\frac{1}{a^2} + \frac{1}{b^2} + \frac{1}{c^2} + \frac{1}{d^2} = 2 \left(\frac{1}{pq} + \frac{1}{pr} + \frac{1}{ps} + \frac{1}{qr} + \frac{1}{qs} + \frac{1}{rs} \right).$$

Thus: *If a sphere touches the edges of a tetrahedron internally, the sum of the reciprocals of the six products of the pairs of segments into which the six edges are divided by the respective points of contact is equal to one half of the sum of the reciprocals of the squares of the radii of the circles along which the sphere is cut by the faces of the tetrahedron.*

793. Let X, Y, Z (Fig. 74) be the points of contact of the sphere (U) (§ 792) with the edges AB, AC, AD of $ABCD$. We have

$$AX = AY = AZ = p.$$

The chord XY is twice the altitude of the right triangle AXI, where I is the incenter of ABC, and we have, using the lemma (§ 284) and the formula for the inradius from the preceding article (§ 792),

$$\frac{4}{XY^2} = \frac{1}{p^2} + \frac{1}{pq} + \frac{1}{pr} + \frac{1}{rq}$$
$$= \frac{(p + q)(p + r)}{p^2qr}$$

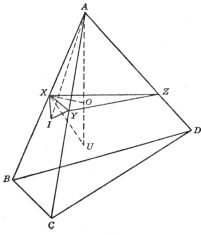

FIG. 74

and analogous formulas for YZ, ZX. Hence

$$XY \cdot YZ \cdot ZX = (2p)^3 qrs : (p + q)(p + r)(p + s).$$

If O is the circumcenter of the triangle XYZ, the area S of this triangle is (C. G., p. 107)

$$S = XY \cdot YZ \cdot ZX : 4XO,$$

therefore

$$\text{vol. } A\text{–}XYZ = \tfrac{1}{3}AO \cdot XY \cdot YZ \cdot ZX : 4XO.$$

The axis of the triangle XYZ passes through A and through the center U of (U). Thus from the right triangle AXU we have

$$AO : XO = AX : UX = p : u,$$

where u denotes the radius of (U), hence

$$\text{vol. } A\text{–}XYZ = (2p)^3 pqrs : 12u(p + q)(p + r)(p + s).$$

Now if V denotes the volume of $ABCD$, we have

$$\text{vol. } A\text{–}XYZ : V = AX \cdot AY \cdot AZ : AB \cdot AC \cdot AD$$
$$= p^3 : (p + q)(p + r)(p + s),$$

hence

$$V = 2pqrs : 3u.$$

794. If in a tetrahedron $ABCD$ the incircle of the face ABC and the excircles relative to the vertex D of the remaining three faces are tangent to each other, the edges of $ABCD$ are all tangent to the same sphere (W). This sphere touches AB, BC, CA internally, and the edges DA, DB, DC externally.

It is readily shown that in this case the three differences of the three pairs of opposite edges of the tetrahedron are equal.

If s' represents the length of the tangent from D to (W), and w the radius of this sphere, we have (§ 793)

$$V = 2pqrs' : 3w.$$

EXERCISES

1. In a circumscriptible tetrahedron the feet of the perpendiculars dropped from the center of the sphere touching the edges upon the faces of the tetrahedron coincide with the incenters of these faces. Conversely.

2. The radius of the sphere which is tangent to the edges of a regular tetrahedron is the mean proportional between the circumradius and the inradius of the tetrahedron.

3. Let X, Y, Z, U, V, W be the points of contact of the edges BC, CA, AB, DA, DB, DC of the tetrahedron $DABC$ with a sphere (R). Show that the lines UX, VY, WZ have a point M in common and that the polar planes of M with respect to $DABC$ and (R) coincide.

4. Given a circumscriptible tetrahedron, there are two real points M, M' such that the distances from M (or M') to the vertices of the tetrahedron are proportional to the segments into which the edges of the tetrahedron are divided by the points of contact of these edges with the sphere touching all the edges.

5. In the tetrahedron $OABC$ let $OA = a$, $OB = b$, $OC = c$, $BC = x$, $CA = y$, $AB = z$, and let A denote the dihedral angle having for edge the edge opposite a, etc. Show that if any one of the two equations

$$a \pm x = b \pm y = c \pm z$$

be true, then will also be the corresponding of the two equations

$$A \pm X = B \pm Y = C \pm Z.$$

6. In a circumscriptible tetrahedron the four radical axes of the circumcircles and the incircles of the four faces are coplanar.

7. If the radical axis of the circumcircle and the incircle of a face of a tetrahedron is coplanar with two of the remaining three analogous axes of the faces of the tetrahedron, the tetrahedron is circumscriptible.

8. (a) A necessary and sufficient condition for the vertices of a tetrahedron to be the centers of four spheres which touch each other externally is that the tetrahedron be circumscriptible. (b) The radius of each of the four spheres is equal to the sum of a pair of opposite edges diminished by one half of the perimeter of the triangle opposite the vertex considered. (c) Extend these propositions to the case when three of the edges touch the sphere externally.

9. The four internal isoclinal lines of the four trihedral angles of a circumscriptible tetrahedron are concurrent, and conversely.

10. The four lines joining the vertices of a circumscriptible tetrahedron to the Gergonne points of the respectively opposite faces are concurrent. Conversely.

11. The four lines joining the vertices of a circumscriptible tetrahedron to the Nagel points of the respectively opposite faces are concurrent. Conversely.

12. Construct a sphere tangent to the sides of a skew quadrilateral.

2. The Orthocentric Tetrahedron

795. Theorem. *An orthocentric tetrahedron (§ 208) is conjugate with respect to one sphere, real or imaginary, and only one.*

The center of the required sphere (H) necessarily coincides with the orthocenter H of the tetrahedron $ABCD$ (§ 456); the vertex A and the foot A_h of the altitude AA_h are inverse points with respect to (H), hence $HA \cdot HA_h = h$, where h is the square of the radius of (H) (§ 395). On the other hand the four products of the segments into which H divides the altitudes of $ABCD$ are equal (§ 217), hence (H) is uniquely determined.

796. Definition. The sphere (H) (§ 795) is called the *conjugate* or *polar* sphere of the orthocentric tetrahedron.

The sphere (H) is real, if H lies outside of $ABCD$, and imaginary, when H lies inside of $ABCD$.

797. Theorem. *In an orthocentric tetrahedron the mid-points of the edges and the feet of the bialtitudes are twelve points on the* *same sphere the center of which coincides with the centroid of the tetrahedron.*

The three bimedians of an orthocentric tetrahedron being equal (§ 210), the centroid G of the tetrahedron is the center of a sphere (G) which passes through the ends of these bimedians, i.e., through the mid-points of the edges.   The sphere (G), obviously, is cut by each face along the nine-point circle of this face, hence (G) passes through the feet of the altitudes of each face.   But these feet are also the end-points of the bialtitudes of the tetrahedron (§ 215), hence the proposition.

798. Definition.   The sphere (G) (§ 797) is called the *first twelve-point sphere* of the orthocentric tetrahedron.

799. Theorem.   *The first twelve-point sphere of an orthocentric tetrahedron is orthogonal to the polar sphere of the tetrahedron.*

The ends P, Q of a bialtitude of an orthocentric tetrahedron are conjugate points with respect to the polar sphere (H) of the tetrahedron, for they lie on two opposite edges of the tetrahedron, which lines are conjugate with respect to (H).   But the bialtitude passes through the center H of (H) (§ 215), therefore P, Q are inverse points with respect to (H) (§ 435), hence the proposition (§ 413).

800. Theorem.   *The centroids and the orthocenters of the faces of an orthocentric tetrahedron lie on the same sphere.   This sphere cuts the altitudes of the tetrahedron again in the points one third of the distance from the orthocenter to the vertices.*

The center of the sphere lies on the Euler line of the tetrahedron and divides the distance between the orthocenter and the circumcenter internally in the ratio 1 : 2.

This is the twelve-point sphere of the general tetrahedron (§ 764), since in the case of the orthocentric tetrahedron the Monge point coincides with the orthocenter (§ 231), and therefore the point A'' (§ 766) coincides with the foot of the altitude of the tetrahedron, which foot is the orthocenter of the face considered (§ 216).

The proposition may, however, be proved directly.   The medial tetrahedron $G_a G_b G_c G_d$ (Fig. 75) of the given tetrahedron $DABC$ is homothetic to $DABC$ with the centroid G of $DABC$ as homothetic center, the ratio being $-1 : 3$ (§ 176).   The circumcenter O_g and the orthocenter H_g of $G_aG_bG_cG_d$ lie on the Euler line of $DABC$, and we have

$$GO_g : GO = GH_g : GH = -1 : 3,$$

hence

$$HH_g : H_gO = 2 : 1, \qquad HO_g = O_gH_g = \tfrac{1}{3} \cdot HO.$$

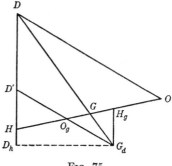

The lines O_gG_d, OD are homothetic, and therefore parallel, hence from the triangle HOD we have that O_gG_d meets HD in the point D' such that $HD' = \tfrac{1}{3} \cdot HD$, and from the congruent triangles $O_gG_dH_g$, $O_gD'H$ we have $O_gD' = O_gG_d$, hence D' is the diametric opposite of G_d on the circumsphere (O_g) of the medial tetrahedron.

Fig. 75

Finally, the diameter G_dD' of (O_g) subtends a right angle at the orthocenter D_h of ABC, hence D_h lies on (O_g). Similarly for the other faces of $DABC$. Hence the proposition.

801. Definitions. The sphere (O_g) (§ 800) is called the **second twelve-point sphere** of the orthocentric tetrahedron.

The tetrahedron formed by the feet of the altitudes of $DABC$ is called the *orthic tetrahedron* of the given tetrahedron.

802. Remark. The radius of the second twelve-point sphere of an orthocentric tetrahedron is equal to one third of the circumradius of the tetrahedron.

The orthocenter H and the centroid G are the centers of similitude of the circumsphere (O) and the second twelve-point sphere (O_g).

803. Theorem. *In an orthocentric tetrahedron the isogonal point of the orthocenter coincides with the orthocenter of the medial tetrahedron.*

Indeed, the projections of H upon the faces of $DABC$ lie on the second twelve-point sphere (O_g) (§ 800), and H_g is the symmetric of H with respect to O_g (§ 800), hence the proposition (§ 747).

804. Corollary. The lines joining the vertices of an orthocentric tetrahedron to the orthocenter of its medial tetrahedron are perpendicular to the faces of the orthic tetrahedron (§ 742).

805. Theorem. *The circumsphere, the first twelve-point sphere, the second twelve-point sphere, and the polar sphere of an orthocentric tetrahedron are coaxal.*

(a) The vertex A and the foot A_h of the altitude AA_h of the orthocentric tetrahedron $ABCD$ are inverse points with respect to the conjugate sphere (H) of $ABCD$. Hence the inverse of the circumsphere (O) of $ABCD$ with respect to (H) is the sphere determined by the feet of the altitudes of $ABCD$, and therefore coincides with the second twelve-point sphere (O_g). Thus (O), (H), (O_g) are coaxal (§ 672).

(b) The sphere (H) is thus a sphere of antisimilitude of (O) and (O_g) (§ 673). The second sphere of antisimilitude of (O) and (O_g) has for its center G (§ 802) and is orthogonal to (H) (§§ 588, 589), therefore this sphere coincides with the first twelve-point sphere (G) (§ 799). Hence the proposition.

806. Remark I. The radical plane of this coaxal pencil (§ 805) is the polar plane of H with respect to the sphere (G), and also the polar plane of G with respect to (H), since (H) and (G) are orthogonal.

807. Remark II. The sphere (GH) having the segment GH for diameter is the sphere of similitude of the spheres (O), (O_g) (§ 802), and therefore is coaxal with them (§ 589), i.e., (GH) belongs to the coaxal pencil (§ 805).

808. Theorem. *In a orthocentric tetrahedron the polar plane of the orthocenter with respect to the tetrahedron coincides with the polar plane of the same point with respect to the first twelve-point sphere.*

The polar plane of the orthocenter H of $DABC$ with respect to $DABC$ is determined by the harmonic conjugates H', H'', H''' of H with respect to the pairs of end-points of the bialtitudes of $DABC$ (§ 215). Now these three pairs of end-points lie on the first twelve-point sphere (G) (§ 798), hence the points H', H'', H''' also determine the polar plane of H with respect to (G) (§ 422).

809. Definition. The plane $H'H''H'''$ (§ 808) will be referred to as the *orthic plane* of the orthocentric tetrahedron.

The orthic plane of an orthocentric tetrahedron is perpendicular to the Euler line of the tetrahedron.

810. Theorem. *The orthic plane of an orthocentric tetrahedron cuts the faces of the tetrahedron along their orthic axes.*

Indeed, the orthic axis of the face ABC is the trilinear polar of D_h (§ 800) with respect to ABC (C. G., p. 222, ex. 1), hence this line lies in the polar plane of H with respect to $DABC$ (§ 717).

811. Theorem. (a) *The orthocenter and the orthic plane of an orthocentric tetrahedron are center and plane of homology of this tetrahedron and its orthic tetrahedron.*

(b) *The orthic plane of an orthocentric tetrahedron is the harmonic plane of the orthocenter with respect to the orthic tetrahedron of the given tetrahedron.*

Indeed, the orthic tetrahedron is the cevian tetrahedron of the orthocenter, hence the proposition (§ 721).

812. Theorem. *The segment of the altitude of an orthocentric tetrahedron between the orthocenter and the second point of intersection with the circumsphere is trisected by the corresponding face of the tetrahedron.*

The second twelve-point sphere (O_g) and the circumsphere (O) are homothetic with respect to the orthocenter H of the tetrahedron $DABC$ (§ 802), and the homothetic ratio is $1 : 3$. Now to the foot D_h of the altitude DD_h which lies on (O_g) (§ 800) corresponds on (O) the trace of HD_h on (O), hence the proposition.

813. Theorem. *In an orthocentric tetrahedron the square of the radius of the polar sphere is equal to one third of the power of its orthocenter with respect to the circumsphere of the tetrahedron.*

Indeed, if J_d is the second point of intersection of the altitude DD_h with the circumsphere (O), the power of H with respect to (O) is

$$HD \cdot HJ_d = HD \cdot 3HD_h \quad (\S\ 812).$$

Now $HD \cdot HD_h$ is the square of the radius of (H) (§ 795), hence the proposition.

EXERCISES

1. Construct an orthocentric tetrahedron given (a) its base; (b) one of its trihedral angles.

2. In an orthocentric tetrahedron (T) the symmetric of a vertex with respect to the orthocenter lies on the line joining the circumcenter of (T) to the centroid of the face opposite the vertex considered.

3. Let P be any point on the line joining the vertex D of the orthocentric tetrahedron $DABC$ to the orthocenter of the medial tetrahedron of $DABC$. The sphere determined by the projections of P upon the faces of $DABC$ passes through the foot D_h of the altitude DD_h of $DABC$.

4. The altitudes of an orthocentric tetrahedron determine on the circumsphere of the tetrahedron the vertices of a tetrahedron similar to the orthic tetrahedron of the given tetrahedron.

5. In an orthocentric tetrahedron the line joining the orthocenter to the centroid of a face passes through the diametric opposite, on the circumsphere, of the vertex opposite the face considered.

6. If AA', BB', CC', DD' are the altitudes of an orthocentric tetrahedron $ABCD$, and P, Q are any two points in space, the four spheres $(PQAA')$, $(PQBB')$, $(PQCC')$, $(PQDD')$ are coaxal.

7. If the six mid-points of the edges of a tetrahedron are cospherical, the tetrahedron is orthocentric.

8. In an orthocentric tetrahedron the distance of the circumcenter from a face is equal to half the difference of the segments into which the orthocenter of the tetrahedron divides the altitude relative to the face considered.

9. With the same vertex of an orthocentric tetrahedron as center two spheres are drawn respectively orthogonal to the first and the second twelve-point spheres of the tetrahedron. Show that the ratio of the squares of the radii of the two spheres is equal to $3 : 4$.

10. In an orthocentric tetrahedron the products of the pairs of opposite edges are inversely proportional to the respective bialtitudes.

11. The radical center of four spheres having for diameters four cevians (concurrent or not) of an orthocentric tetrahedron coincides with the orthocenter of the tetrahedron.

12. The sum of the powers of a given point with respect to two spheres having for diameters a pair of opposite edges of an orthocentric tetrahedron is the same for any pair of edges.

13. The four lines joining the mid-points of the altitudes of an orthocentric tetrahedron to the circumcenters of the corresponding faces are concurrent and bisect each other.

14. The perpendicular from the orthocenter H of the tetrahedron $DABC$ upon the circumradius DO meets the face ABC in U. Show that the tangent plane to the second twelve-point sphere (O_g) at the foot D_h of the altitude DD_h bisects the segment HU.

814. Theorem. *The polar plane, with respect to the conjugate sphere of an orthocentric tetrahedron, of a point on the circumsphere of the tetrahedron trisects the segment joining the orthocenter of the tetrahedron to the diametric opposite of the given point on the circumsphere.*

Let M (Fig. 76) be any point on the circumsphere (O) of the orthocentric tetrahedron $DABC$, and let P be the second point common to (O) and the line MH joining M to the orthocenter H of $DABC$. The trace Q on MHP of the polar plane of M with respect to the conjugate sphere (H) of $DABC$ is the inverse of M with respect to (H), hence $HM \cdot HQ$ is equal to the square of the radius of (H) and therefore equal to one third of the power $HM \cdot HP$ of H with respect to (O) (§ 813). Thus $3HQ = HP$.

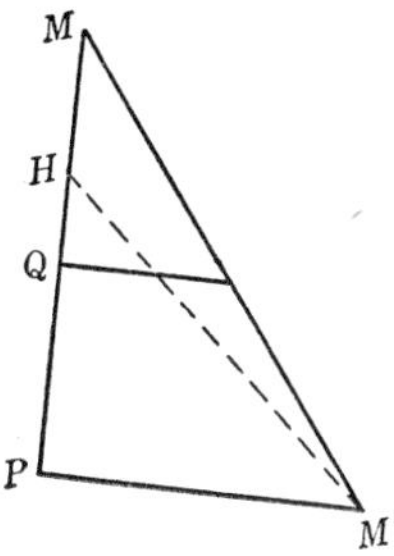

Fig. 76

Let M' be the diametric opposite of M on (O). The trace, in the plane MPM', of the polar plane of M with respect to (H) is perpendicular to HMP, and therefore parallel to PM', hence this trace trisects HM'.

815. Theorem. *The four parallels, through the orthocenter of an orthocentric tetrahedron, to the lines joining the vertices to a point on the circumsphere meet the corresponding faces in four coplanar points.*

Let P be the trace, in the face BCD of the orthocentric tetrahedron $ABCD$, of the parallel HP through the orthocenter H of $ABCD$ to the line AM joining A to the point M on the circumsphere (O) of $ABCD$. The polar plane of P with respect to the conjugate sphere (H) of $ABCD$ passes through A and is perpendicular to PH, hence also to AM, i.e., this plane passes through the diametric opposite M' of M on (O). Thus P and M' are conjugate with respect to (H), hence P and its analogous points Q, R, S lie in the polar plane of M' with respect to (H).

816. Problem. *Construct an orthocentric tetrahedron given its circumcenter, its centroid, and one vertex.*

The circumcenter O and the vertex D determine the circumsphere (O). The symmetric H of O with respect to the given centroid G is the orthocenter of the required tetrahedron (§ 214).

If D' is the second point of intersection of DH with (O), construct D_h so that $HD_h : HD' = 1 : 3$, and draw the plane through D_h perpendicular to DH (§ 812). In the circle of intersection of this plane with (O) an infinite number of triangles may be inscribed having D_h for their orthocenter (C. G., p. 96).

If *ABC* is one of these triangles, the tetrahedron *DABC* satisfies the conditions of the problem.

817. Problem.   *Construct an orthocentric tetrahedron inscribed in a given sphere and conjugate with respect to a second given sphere.*

The condition of possibility for the solution of the problem is that the square of the radius of the conjugate sphere (*H*) shall be equal to one third of the power of its center *H* with respect to the circumsphere (*O*) (§ 813).

If this condition is satisfied the problem has an infinite number of solutions (§ 816).   Thus the problem is, in general, impossible. But if it has one solution, it has an infinite number of them.

818. Theorem.   *The two spheres having for diameters a pair of opposite edges of an orthocentric tetrahedron are orthogonal.*

The vertices *D*, *A* of an orthocentric tetrahedron *DABC* are conjugate with respect to the polar sphere (*H*) of *DABC*, hence the sphere (*DA*) described on *DA* as diameter is orthogonal to the sphere (*H*) (§ 514), and the same is true for the sphere (*BC*), for analogous reasons.   Now the first twelve-point sphere (*G*) of *DABC* is also orthogonal to (*H*) and its center *G* is collinear with the centers of (*DA*) and (*BC*), hence the three spheres are coaxal (§ 568), and since (*G*) has for diameter the line of centers of (*DA*) and (*BC*) (§ 797), the proposition is proved (§ 571).

OTHERWISE.   The two opposite edges *DA*, *BC* of *DABC* are equal to the diagonals of a face of the rhomboid circumscribed about *DABC*, and the bimedian corresponding to these two edges is equal to an edge of this rhomboid (§ 209), hence the sum of the squares of the radii of the spheres (*DA*), (*BC*) is equal to the square of the line of centers, which proves the proposition (§ 402).

819. Remark I.   The circle common to the three spheres (*DA*), (*BC*), (*G*) (§ 818) contains the feet of the two bialtitudes relative to the other two pairs of opposite edges of the tetrahedron.

820. Remark II.   The first twelve-point sphere (*G*) is the radical sphere of (*DA*) and (*BC*) (§ 818), and therefore of each of the three pairs of spheres having for diameters the three pairs of opposite edges of the orthocentric tetrahedron.

821. Lemma.   *The two lines joining a point of intersection of two orthogonal circles to the ends of a diameter of one of these circles determine in the second circle the ends of the diameter which is* *perpendicular to the first diameter considered.* CONVERSELY. *Given two orthogonal diameters of two orthogonal circles, the lines joining an end of one of these diameters to the two ends of the other pass through the two points common to the two circles.*

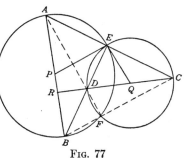

FIG. 77

Let the lines *EA*, *EB* (Fig. 77) joining the common point *E* of the two orthogonal circles (*P*), (*Q*) to the ends *A*, *B* of the diameter *AB* of (*P*) meet (*Q*) in the points *C*, *D*. Since *CED* is a right angle, *CD* is a diameter of (*Q*). In the two isosceles triangles *AEP*, *CEQ*, where *P* and *Q* are the centers of the given circles, we have

$$\angle EAP = \angle AEP, \qquad \angle ECQ = \angle CEQ,$$

hence

$$\angle EAP + \angle ECQ = \angle AEP + \angle CEQ = 90°,$$

for the angle *PEQ* is a right angle, by assumption. Thus the angle *ARC* of the triangle *ARC*, where $R \equiv (AB, CD)$, is a right angle, which proves the proposition.

It follows immediately that the lines *FA*, *FB*, where *F* is the second point common to the two circles, pass through the points *C*, *D*, for there is only one diameter of (*Q*) which is perpendicular to *AB*.

The converse proposition follows from the fact that each of the lines *AEC*, *BFC*, *ADF*, *EDB* is determined by two of its points.

822. Theorem. *The ends of two skew rectangular diameters of two orthogonal spheres are vertices of an orthocentric tetrahedron.*

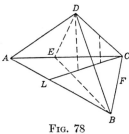

FIG. 78

Let *AB*, *CD* (Fig. 78) be two rectangular diameters of two given orthogonal spheres (*AB*), (*CD*). The plane through *DC* perpendicular to *AB* cuts the plane *ABC* along the orthogonal projection *CL* of *CD* upon *ABC*, and *CL* is perpendicular to *AB*. The plane *ABC* passes through the center of (*AB*), hence *ABC* cuts the two spheres (*AB*), (*CD*) along two orthogonal circles (p. 176, Ex. 19).

The center of the small circle is the projection of the mid-point of CD upon CL. Hence C is one end of the diameter of the small circle which is perpendicular to the diameter AB of the great circle. Therefore, according to the lemma (§ 821), the lines CA, CB pass through the points E, F common to the two circles.

The point E thus belongs to the sphere (CD), hence AB and CD subtend each a right angle at E, i.e., AEC is perpendicular both to ED and to EB, and therefore also to BD. Considering the point F we may show that AD, BC are also rectangular. Hence the proposition (§ 208).

EXERCISES

1. A variable orthocentric tetrahedron has a fixed vertex and a fixed second twelve-point sphere. Show that the locus of its orthocenter is a sphere.

2. If the rectangular diameters AB, CD (§ 822) vary, (a) the locus of the orthocenter of the tetrahedron $ABCD$ is a plane; (b) the locus of the circumcenter of $ABCD$ is a plane; (c) what is the locus of the orthocenters of the faces? (d) what is the locus of the centroids of the faces?

3. From the orthocenter H of a tetrahedron perpendiculars are dropped upon the four lines joining the vertices to a point M in space. The traces of these perpendiculars in the respective faces of the tetrahedron are coplanar, and their plane is perpendicular to the line MH. Consider the case when M coincides with the centroid G, with the circumcenter O, etc., and state the resulting special propositions.

4. (a) In an orthocentric tetrahedron the feet of the perpendiculars dropped from the orthocenter upon the four lines of intersection of a given plane with the faces of the tetrahedron are coplanar. (b) State the proposition when the given plane coincides with the orthic plane of the tetrahedron.

5. The traces, in the respective faces of an orthocentric tetrahedron, of the perpendiculars dropped from the orthocenter upon the planes determined by the four vertices and a fixed line in space, are collinear.

6. Two rectangular skew segments AB, CD are so situated that the sum of their squares is equal to four times the square of the distance between their mid-points. Show that the lines AC, BD are rectangular, and that the same is true about the lines AD, BC.

7. The lines AM, BM, CM, DM joining a point M to the vertices of the orthocentric tetrahedron $ABCD$ meet the respective opposite faces in P, Q, R, S. The planes through A, B, C, D perpendicular, respectively, to HP, HQ, HR, HS, where H is the orthocenter of $ABCD$, meet the respective faces of $ABCD$ in four coplanar lines.—State this proposition when M coincides with the centroid of $ABCD$.

8. If the lines of intersection of the faces of an orthocentric tetrahedron with a given plane are projected from the opposite vertices, and perpendiculars are dropped from the orthocenter upon the projecting planes, these perpendiculars will meet the respective faces in four points which are projected from the opposite vertices by four concurrent lines.

9. Let P, Q, R, S be the traces, in the faces of the orthocentric tetrahedron $ABCD$, of the lines joining a given point M to the respectively opposite vertices. The perpendiculars dropped from A, B, C, D upon the lines joining P, Q, R, S to the orthocenter H of $ABCD$ meet the respective faces of $ABCD$ in four coplanar points. The plane of these points is perpendicular to MH.

823. Let R be the circumradius of the orthocentric tetrahedron $DABC$, and h the square of the radius of the polar sphere (H) of $DABC$. Thus h is positive or negative according as the orthocenter H of $DABC$ lies inside or outside of the tetrahedron (§ 796).
We have (§ 813)

$$3h = HO^2 - R^2.$$

On the other hand the bimedians of $DABC$ being diameters of the first twelve-point sphere (G) of $DABC$, we have, denoting by m the length of a bimedian (§§ 799, 214),

$$h + \left(\frac{m}{2}\right)^2 = \frac{HO^2}{4},$$

hence, eliminating HO^2, we obtain

$$h = R^2 - m^2.$$

824. Let p, q, r, s be the powers of the vertices A, B, C, D with respect to (H) (§ 823). The two points A, B are conjugate with respect to (H), hence (§ 572)

$$AB^2 = p + q,$$

and similarly

$$CD^2 = r + s,$$

therefore

$$AB^2 + CD^2 = p + q + r + s.$$

Thus: *The sum of the squares of a pair of opposite edges of an orthocentric tetrahedron is equal to the sum of the powers of the vertices of the tetrahedron with respect to its conjugate sphere.*

825. We have (§ 211)

$$AB^2 + CD^2 = 4m^2,$$

hence (§ 823)

$$4R^2 = 4h + (p + q + r + s).$$

Now

$$p = AH^2 - h, \qquad q = BH^2 - h, \text{ etc.,}$$

hence

$$AH^2 + BH^2 + CH^2 + DH^2 = 4R^2.$$

Thus: *In an orthocentric tetrahedron the sum of the squares of the distances of the orthocenter from the vertices of the tetrahedron is equal to the square of the circumdiameter of the tetrahedron.*

826. Definitions. Let A_5 be the orthocenter of the tetrahedron $A_1A_2A_3A_4$. The five points considered are such that the line joining any two of them is perpendicular to the plane determined by the remaining three points. Five such points will be said to form an ***orthocentric group.***

Each point of an orthocentric group is the orthocenter of the tetrahedron determined by the remaining four points. Thus A_4 is the orthocenter of the tetrahedron $A_1A_2A_3A_5$, for the line A_4A_1 is perpendicular to the plane $A_5A_2A_3$, etc. Hence the five points determine an *orthocentric group of five tetrahedrons.*

827. Theorem. *The five Euler lines of an orthocentric group of tetrahedrons are concurrent.*

The centroid G_5 (Fig. 79) of the orthocentric tetrahedron

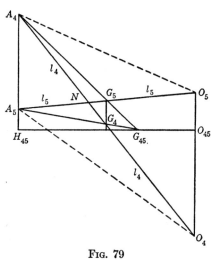

FIG. 79

$(A_5) \equiv A_1A_2A_3A_4$ is determined by the median A_4G_{45} joining the vertex A_4 to the centroid G_{45} of the face $A_1A_2A_3$ and the perpendicular erected to this face at the nine-point center of the triangle $A_1A_2A_3$ (§ 797). The Euler line l_5 of (A_5) is the line joining G_5 to the orthocenter A_5 of (A_5).

Again the centroid G_4 of the tetrahedron $(A_4) \equiv (A_1A_2A_3A_5)$ lies on the median A_5G_{45} and on the same perpendicular to $A_1A_2A_3$ as above. The Euler line l_4 of (A_4) joins the orthocenter A_4 of (A_4) to the centroid G_4 of (A_4).

The lines A_4A_5, G_4G_5 being perpendicular to $A_1A_2A_3$ are parallel, and we have

$$G_{45}G_5 : G_{45}A_4 = G_{45}G_4 : G_{45}A_5 = 1 : 4.$$

Applying Menelaus' theorem to the triangle $G_{45}G_5A_5$ and the transversal A_4G_4 we find that the Euler line A_4G_4 of (A_4) meets the Euler line A_5G_5 of (A_5) in a point N such that

$$G_5N : NA_5 = 1 : 4.$$

Thus the Euler line of (A_5) is met by the Euler line of another tetrahedron of the orthocentric group in a point which is independent of the choice of the latter tetrahedron, hence the proposition.

828. Definition. The point N (§ 827) will be referred to as the *orthic point* of the orthocentric group of points.

Readers familiar with the theory of the center of gravity will readily notice that the orthic point is the center of gravity of the given orthocentric group of points.

829. Theorem. (a) *The centroids of an orthocentric group of tetrahedrons form an orthocentric group of points.* (b) *The circumcenters of an orthocentric group of tetrahedrons form an orthocentric group of points.*

The five centroids form a figure homothetic to the points of the given orthocentric group, the homothetic center being the orthic point (§ 828), and the homothetic ratio being $-1:4$ (§ 827).

The circumcenter of an orthocentric tetrahedron being the symmetric of the orthocenter with respect to the centroid (§ 214), the circumcenters of an orthocentric group of tetrahedrons are homothetic to the five given points with respect to the orthic point as homothetic center, the homothetic ratio being $-3:2$.

830. The preceding propositions are analogous to the corresponding propositions dealing with the orthocentric group of four points in the plane (C. G., pp. 98–102). The orthic point (§ 828) corresponds to the nine-point center in the plane. But the analogy cannot be pursued much further, for, contrary to what happens in the plane, the five tetrahedrons of an orthocentric group do not have the same orthic tetrahedron.

Let A_5 be the orthocenter of the tetrahedron $(A_5) \equiv A_1A_2A_3A_4$, and let H_{45} denote the orthocenter of $A_1A_2A_3$, i.e., the trace of A_4A_5 in $A_1A_2A_3$ (§ 216), with analogous meanings for the points H_{15}, H_{25}, H_{35}, so that these four points are the vertices of the orthic tetrahedron of (A_5).

Let H_{14}, H_{23} be the feet, on the edges A_1A_4, A_2A_3, of the bialtitude of (A_5) corresponding to these two edges. These two points are collinear with A_5 (§ 215). Let H_{12}, H_{34}, H_{13}, H_{24} be the analogous points on the other edges of (A_5).

In the orthocentric tetrahedron $(A_4) \equiv A_1A_2A_3A_5$ having A_4 for its orthocenter the plane $A_2A_3A_5$ is perpendicular to A_1A_4 and meets this line in H_{14}, hence this point is the foot of the perpendicular from the vertex A_1 of (A_4) upon the face $A_2A_3A_5$, i.e., H_{14} is a vertex of the orthic tetrahedron of (A_4), and it is similarly seen that the other three vertices of this tetrahedron are H_{24}, H_{34}, H_{54}. The orthic tetrahedrons of (A_1), (A_2), (A_3) are obtained in a similar way. These orthic tetrahedrons are thus seen to be different. They are all determined by the ten H's.

831. Again, contrary to what happens in the plane, the circumspheres of the five tetrahedrons of an orthocentric group are not equal. This may be seen as follows. The perpendicular to the face $A_1A_2A_3$ (§ 827) at its circumcenter O_{45} (Fig. 79) meets the two Euler lines NA_4G_4, NA_5G_5 in the circumcenters O_4, O_5 of the tetrahedrons (A_4), (A_5). The lines A_4A_5, O_4O_5 are parallel, but the diagonals A_4O_4, A_5O_5 of the trapezoid $A_4A_5O_4O_5$ are not equal, for in constructing the orthocentric group A_1, A_2, A_3, A_4, A_5, we may take NA_4 not equal to NA_5. Hence the sides O_4A_5, O_5A_4 of the trapezoid are not equal, and these two lines are the circumradii of the tetrahedrons (A_4), (A_5).

832. In the orthocentric group of points A_1, A_2, A_3, A_4, A_5 one of these points, say A_5, lies within the tetrahedron determined by the remaining four points, while the contrary is true about any of the other points. Now each of the five tetrahedrons of the orthocentric group has a conjugate sphere, and these spheres have for their centers the five given points (§ 456). Hence one of these five polar spheres, namely the one having for center the point A_5, will be imaginary. The remaining four will be real.

833. Theorem. *The five polar spheres of an orthocentric group of tetrahedrons are mutually orthogonal.*

Let (P_4), (P_5) be the two polar spheres of the two tetrahedrons (A_4), (A_5) (§ 826), and let P_4, P_5 be the squares of the radii of these two spheres. We have

$$P_4 = A_4A_5 \cdot A_4H_{45}, \qquad P_5 = A_5A_4 \cdot A_5H_{45},$$

hence

$$P_5 + P_4 = A_4 A_5 (A_4 H_{45} - A_5 H_{45}) = A_4 A_5^2,$$

hence the two spheres are orthogonal. Now this proof is valid whether the two spheres are both real, or if one is real and the other imaginary. Hence the proposition.

834. Converse Theorem. *If five spheres are mutually orthogonal, their centers form an orthocentric group of points, and each sphere is the polar sphere of the tetrahedron determined by the centers of the remaining four spheres.*

If A_1, A_2, A_3, A_4, A_5 are the centers of five mutually orthogonal spheres, the points A_1, A_2 are conjugate with respect to the sphere (P_5) having A_5 for center (§ 576). Similarly for the pairs of points A_1, A_3; A_1, A_4, hence $A_2 A_3 A_4$ is the polar plane of A_1 with respect to (P_5). Similarly for the points A_2, A_3, A_4. Thus the tetrahedron $A_1 A_2 A_3 A_4$ is conjugate with respect to (P_5), and the center A_5 of this sphere is the orthocenter of the tetrahedron (§ 456), which proves the proposition.

EXERCISES

1. (a) The isogonal conjugate of each of the five points of an orthocentric group is constructed with respect to the tetrahedron determined by the four remaining given points. The five points so obtained form an orthocentric group. (b) The centers of the second twelve-point spheres of an orthocentric group of tetrahedrons form an orthocentric group.

2. Given five mutually orthogonal spheres, the sum of the squares of the distances from the center of one of these spheres to the centers of the remaining four is equal to the square of the diameter of the sphere determined by the centers of the last four spheres.

3. Restate the propositions involving the powers of the vertices of an orthocentric tetrahedron with respect to its polar spheres as theorems involving the radii of the five polar spheres of an orthocentric group of tetrahedrons, or as theorems relating to five mutually orthogonal spheres.

4. In an orthocentric tetrahedron the sum of the squares of the distances of the orthocenter from the mid-points of the edges is equal to three times the sum of the squares of the radii of the circumsphere and the polar sphere.

5. The sum of the squares of the radii of five mutually orthogonal spheres is equal to one half of the sum of the squares of the radii of the five spheres determined by their centers taken four at a time.

6. (a) The vertices of an orthocentric tetrahedron $ABCD$ are taken for centers of four equal spheres. The sphere (A) meets the edges BC, CD, DB of the opposite face BCD in the pairs of points A_1, A_1'; A_2, A_2'; A_3, A_3'; and similarly for the other faces. Show that the mid-points of the twenty-four segments AA_1, AA_1', AA_2', $\cdots$ lie on the same sphere (S_1). (b) With the centroids of the faces as centers the spheres are described orthogonal to (S_1). Show that the four circles determined by these spheres in the respective faces of $ABCD$ lie on the same sphere (S_2).   (c) Find the locus of the intersection of the spheres (S_1), (S_2) when the radius of the sphere (A) varies.

3. The Isodynamic Tetrahedron

a. The Lemoine Point and the Lemoine Plane

835. Definition. The tetrahedron in which the three products of the three pairs of opposite edges are equal will be referred to as an *isodynamic* tetrahedron.

836. Theorem. *In an isodynamic tetrahedron each edge is met in the same point by the two symmedians of the two face angles of the tetrahedron opposite the edge considered.*

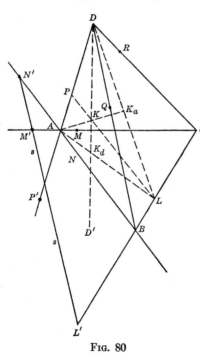

FIG. 80

In the tetrahedron $DABC$ (Fig. 80) let $BC = a$, $CA = b$, $AB = c$, $DA = a'$, $DB = b'$, $DC = c'$. In the triangle ABC the symmedian of the angle A meets BC internally in a point L such that (C. G., p. 225)

$$BL : CL = c^2 : b^2$$

and the symmedian of the angle D of the triangle DBC meets BC internally in a point K such that

$$BK : CK = b'^2 : c'^2.$$

Now $DABC$ being isodynamic we have

$$bb' = cc',$$

or

$$c : b = b' : c',$$

or

$$c^2 : b^2 = b'^2 : c'^2,$$

hence K coincides with L, which proves the proposition.

837. Converse Theorem. *If in a tetrahedron each of two non-opposite edges is met by the two symmedians of the corresponding faces in coincident points, the tetrahedron is isodynamic.*

If the symmedians of the angles CAB, CDB (Fig. 80) of the triangles ABC, DBC meet BC in the same point L, we have

$$BL : CL = c^2 : b^2 = b'^2 : c'^2, \quad \text{or} \quad bb' = cc'.$$

Again, if the symmedians of the angles ACB, ADB, in the triangles ABC, ADB, meet AB in the same point N, we have

$$AN : BN = b^2 : a^2 = a'^2 : b'^2, \quad \text{or} \quad aa' = bb'.$$

Thus

$$aa' = bb' = cc'$$

and the tetrahedron is isodynamic (§ 835).

838. Theorem. *The lines joining the vertices of an isodynamic tetrahedron to the Lemoine points of the respectively opposite faces have a point in common.*

The lines joining the vertices D, A (Fig. 80) to the Lemoine points K_d, K_a of the faces ABC, BCD (C. G., p. 228) of the tetrahedron $DABC$ lie in the plane DLA (§ 836), hence the two lines DK_d, AK_a have a point in common. In a similar way it may be shown that any two of the four lines DK_d, AK_a, BK_b, CK_c have a point in common. Now these four lines cannot be coplanar (for that would imply that the four points D, A, B, C are coplanar), they have therefore a point, say K, in common.

839. Definition. The four lines AK_a, $\cdots$ (§ 838) are called the **symmedians,** and the point K the **Lemoine point** of the isodynamic tetrahedron.

The point K_d always lies within the triangle ABC, hence the symmedian DK_d lies within the tetrahedron $DABC$, and the same is true for the other symmedians. The Lemoine point K thus lies within the tetrahedron.

840. Converse Theorem. *If in a tetrahedron one of the four lines joining the vertices to the Lemoine points of the respectively opposite faces meets two of the remaining three analogous lines, the tetrahedron is isodynamic.*

If the line DK_d joining the vertex D of the tetrahedron $DABC$ to the symmedian point K_d of the face ABC is met by the analogous line AK_a relative to the vertex A, the two symmedians AK_d, DK_a of the two triangles ABC, DBC meet the edge BC in the same point, namely the trace L of the plane (DK_d, AK_a) on the line BC.

Similarly, if DK_d is met by BK_b, the two symmedians BK_d, DK_b of the triangles ABC, ACD meet the edge AC in the same point, hence the proposition (§ 837).

841. Corollary. *If the four lines joining the vertices of a tetrahedron to the symmedian points of the respectively opposite faces are concurrent, the tetrahedron is isodynamic.*

842. Theorem. *The three lines joining the three pairs of points determined on the three pairs of opposite edges of an isodynamic tetrahedron by the twelve symmedians of the faces of the tetrahedron (§ 836) pass through the Lemoine point of the tetrahedron.*

The line LP (Fig. 80) joining the point L (§ 836) to the analogous point P on the edge DA lies in the plane DAL and therefore meets the two symmedians of the tetrahedron issued from the vertices D and A. But the line LP also lies in the plane BPC, hence LP meets the symmedians of $DABC$ issued from the vertices B and C, and therefore LP passes through the common point K of the four symmedians (§ 838). Similarly for the two lines MQ, NR analogous to LP and relative to the other two pairs of opposite vertices of the tetrahedron. Hence the proposition.

DEFINITION. The three lines LP, MQ, NR may be referred to as the **bisymmedians** of the isodynamic tetrahedron.

843. Theorem. *The four Lemoine axes of the four faces of an isodynamic tetrahedron are coplanar.*

The trace L', on the edge BC (Fig. 80) of the isodynamic tetrahedron $DABC$, of the tangent at D to the circumcircle of the triangle DBC is the harmonic conjugate, with respect to B, C, of the trace L on BC of the symmedian DL (C. G., p. 227) of the triangle DBC, and L' is a point of the Lemoine axis of DAB (C. G., p. 229). Now the line AL is a symmedian of the triangle ABC (§ 836), hence L' is also a point on the Lemoine axis of the triangle ABC.

It may thus be shown that any two of the four Lemoine axes of the four faces of an isodynamic tetrahedron have a point in common, hence the four axes are coplanar. (They cannot be concurrent, for their common point would then lie in all four faces of the tetrahedron.)

844. Remark. The tangent DL' (§ 843) lies in the tangent plane at D to the circumsphere (O) of $DABC$, hence L' is the trace of this tangent plane on BC, and similarly for the other points analogous to L'. Thus: *The faces of a given isodynamic tetrahedron are cut by the corresponding faces of its tangential tetrahedron along the Lemoine axes of the faces of the given tetrahedron.*

845. Converse Theorem. *If the Lemoine axis of one face of a tetrahedron is coplanar with the Lemoine axes of two other faces of this tetrahedron, the tetrahedron is isodynamic.*

If the Lemoine axes of the faces ABC, DBC of the tetrahedron $DABC$ have a point L' in common, this point necessarily lies on the edge BC, hence the two symmedians issued from the vertices A and D in the two triangles ABC, DBC, respectively, meet BC in the same point, namely in the harmonic conjugate L of L' with respect to B, C. Similarly for the other Lemoine axis which meets the Lemoine axis of ABC, hence the proposition (§ 837).

846. Corollary. *If the four Lemoine axes of the faces of a tetrahedron are coplanar, the tetrahedron is isodynamic.*

847. Theorem. *If the tangent plane to the circumsphere of a tetrahedron at a vertex cuts the opposite face along the Lemoine axis of the triangle of that face, the tetrahedron is isodynamic.*

Let the plane which touches the circumsphere (O) of the tetrahedron $DABC$ at the point D cut the plane ABC (Fig. 80) in the Lemoine axis s of the triangle ABC. The line DL' joining D to the point $L' \equiv (s, BC)$ is the tangent to the circle DBC at D, hence L' belongs to the Lemoine axis of the triangle DBC. Similarly for the points $M' \equiv (s, CA)$, $N' \equiv (s, AB)$. Hence the proposition (§ 845).

848. Definition. The plane containing the four Lemoine axes of an isodynamic tetrahedron (§ 843) will be called the **Lemoine plane** of the isodynamic tetrahedron.

849. Theorem. *The six mediators of the edges of an isodynamic tetrahedron meet the respectively opposite edges in six coplanar points.*

The lines $L'A$, $L'D$ (§ 844) are tangent to the circumsphere (O) (Fig. 80) of the tetrahedron at the points A and D, respectively, hence $L'A = L'D$ (§ 384), i.e., L' lies in the mediator of the edge DA. Thus the six points considered lie in the Lemoine plane of the tetrahedron (§ 843).

850. Theorem. *The Lemoine point and the Lemoine plane of an isodynamic tetrahedron are tetrahedral pole and polar plane with respect to the tetrahedron.*

The line joining the vertex D (Fig. 80) of the isodynamic tetrahedron $DABC$ to the Lemoine point K of $DABC$ meets the face ABC in the Lemoine point K_d of the triangle ABC (§ 838). Now the trilinear polar of K_d with respect to ABC is the Lemoine axis of the triangle ABC (C. G., p. 229), and this axis lies in the Lemoine plane of $DABC$. Likewise for the other vertices of $DABC$. Hence the proposition (§ 717).

OTHERWISE. Consider the bisymmedian LKP (Fig. 80) relative to the pair of opposite edges BC, DA (§ 842). The harmonic conjugates L', P' of L, P with respect to the pairs of vertices B, C; D, A lie in the Lemoine plane of $DABC$ (§ 843). Similarly for the other two bisymmedians. Hence the proposition (§§ 709, 713).

851. Theorem. *The symmedians of an isodynamic tetrahedron pass through the poles of the respective faces with respect to the circumsphere of the tetrahedron.*

The line DD' joining the vertex D (Fig. 80) of the isodynamic tetrahedron $DABC$ to the pole D' of the face ABC with respect to the circumsphere (O) of $DABC$ has for its conjugate with respect to (O) the line of intersection of the plane ABC with the tangent plane to (O) at D, i.e., the Lemoine axis s of the triangle ABC (§ 844). Now the plane ABC meets the conjugate DD' of s in the pole of s with respect to the circle ABC (§ 442). But this pole coincides with the Lemoine point K_d of the triangle ABC (C. G., p. 229), hence the line DD' is a symmedian of $DABC$. Similarly for the other symmedians of $DABC$. Hence the proposition.

852. Corollary I. *The Lemoine plane of an isodynamic tetrahedron is the polar plane of the Lemoine point with respect to the circumsphere of the tetrahedron.*

Indeed, the Lemoine point K lies on the symmedians of the tetrahedron, hence the polar plane of K with respect to the circumsphere (O) contains the conjugates of the symmedians with respect to (O), and these conjugates lie in the Lemoine plane of the tetrahedron, as was shown in the proof of the last proposition (§ 851).

It should be observed that since K lies inside the tetrahedron (§ 839), it necessarily lies inside of (O), hence the Lemoine plane does not cut the circumsphere (O).

853. Corollary II. *An isodynamic tetrahedron and its tangential tetrahedron are perspective, the Lemoine point and the Lemoine plane being the center and the plane of perspectivity.*

CONVERSELY. *If a tetrahedron is perspective to its tangential tetrahedron, it is isodynamic.*

Let L', M', N' be the points of intersection of the edges BC, CA, AB of the tetrahedron $DABC$ with the tangent plane at D to the circumsphere (O) of $DABC$. If $DABC$ is perspective to its tangential tetrahedron, the point L' is also the trace on BC of the tangent plane to (O) at A, i.e., L' is a point on the Lemoine axis of the triangle ABC. Similarly for the points M', N'. Hence $L'M'N'$ is the Lemoine axis of the triangle ABC, which proves the proposition (§ 847).

854. Definition. The line joining the circumcenter O of an isodynamic tetrahedron to the Lemoine point K of the tetrahedron will be referred to as the ***Brocard diameter*** of the tetrahedron.

The Brocard diameter is perpendicular to the Lemoine plane of the tetrahedron (§ 852).

855. Theorem. *The Brocard diameter of an isodynamic tetrahedron meets the four altitudes of the tetrahedron.*

The altitude DD_h of the isodynamic tetrahedron $DABC$ has the point D in common with the symmedian DD' (§ 851) and is parallel to the line OD', for OD' is perpendicular to the plane ABC, hence DD_h lies in the plane DOD'. Now the Brocard diameter OK meets the lines DD', OD' in the points K, O, respectively, hence OK lies in the plane DOD', i.e., DD_h and OK are coplanar. Similarly for the other altitudes of $DABC$.

EXERCISES

1. In an isodynamic tetrahedron each edge is met in the same point by the two internal (external) bisectors of the two face angles of the tetrahedron opposite the edge considered.

2. If in a tetrahedron each of two coplanar edges is met in the same point by the internal (external) bisectors of the two respective face angles of the tetrahedron, the tetrahedron is isodynamic.

3. (a) The lines joining the vertices of an isodynamic tetrahedron to the incenters of the opposite faces are concurrent. (b) State and prove analogous propositions involving excenters, or incenters and excenters.

4. (a) If one of the four lines joining the vertices of a tetrahedron to the incenters of the respectively opposite faces is met by two of the remaining three lines, the tetrahedron is isodynamic. (b) State and prove analogous propositions involving excenters, or incenters and excenters.

5. The three lines joining the three pairs of points determined on the three pairs of opposite edges of an isodynamic tetrahedron by the twelve internal bisectors of the face angles of the tetrahedron (see Ex. 1 above) are concurrent.

6. The six points determined on the edges of an isodynamic tetrahedron by the twelve external bisectors of the face angles of the tetrahedron (see Ex. 1 above) are coplanar.

7. If the points determined on the edges of a tetrahedron by the external bisectors of the face angles of the tetrahedron are coplanar, the tetrahedron is isodynamic.

8. The three edges of an isodynamic tetrahedron which pass through a given vertex are proportional to the altitudes of the face opposite this vertex.

9. The antiparallel sections of an isodynamic tetrahedron are equilateral triangles. The centroid of such a section lies on the respective symmedian of the tetrahedron.

10. The inverses of the vertices of an equilateral triangle, with respect to a center of inversion not in the plane of the triangle, and the center of inversion are the vertices of an isodynamic tetrahedron.

11. If k is the product of a pair of opposite edges of an isodynamic tetrahedron, and V, R its volume and its circumradius, we have $8VR\sqrt{3} = k^2$.

12. (a) If M is the point common to the four lines joining the vertices of an isodynamic tetrahedron $DABC$ to the incenters of the opposite faces (see Ex. 3 above) show that, with the usual notations for the edges of the tetrahedron, we have

$$DM : MI_d = k(a + b + c) : abc = k : 2R_d r_d$$

where I_d is the incenter of ABC, R_d the circumradius, and r_d the inradius of ABC, while k is the value of the product of a pair of opposite edges of the tetrahedron. (b) Derive an analogous formula for the Lemoine point of the tetrahedron.

13. In an isodynamic tetrahedron the product of the sines of a pair of opposite dihedral angles is constant.

b. *The Lemoine Tetrahedron*

856. Definition. Given the isodynamic tetrahedron $DABC$ and its Lemoine point K, the harmonic conjugates K', K'', K''' of K with respect to the three pairs of opposite edges DA, BC; DB, CA; DC, AB (§ 45) will be referred to as the *harmonic associates* of K with respect to the tetrahedron.

The points K', K'', K''' lie in the harmonic plane of K with respect to $DABC$ (§ 708), i.e., in the Lemoine plane of $DABC$ (§ 850).

The tetrahedron $KK'K''K'''$ will be referred to as the **Lemoine tetrahedron** of the isodynamic tetrahedron.

The isodynamic tetrahedron and its Lemoine tetrahedron are mutually self-polar (§§ 723, 725).

857. Theorem. *The four symmedians of an isodynamic tetra-hedron meet the circumsphere of the tetrahedron in the vertices of a tetrahedron self-polar to the given tetrahedron.*

The harmonic conjugates A'', B'', C'', D'' of the vertices A, B, C, D of the given isodynamic tetrahedron $ABCD$ with respect to the point K and the Lemoine plane $K'K''K'''$ (§ 856) determine the tetrahedron $A''B''C''D''$, and the three tetrahedrons $ABCD$, $KK'K''K'''$, $A''B''C''D''$, form a desmic system (§ 735). Now K and $K'K''K'''$ are pole and polar plane with respect to the circumsphere (O) of $ABCD$ (§ 852), hence $A''B''C''D''$ is inscribed in (O). The lines AK, BK, CK, DK being the symmedians of $ABCD$, the proposition is proved.

858. Theorem. *The tetrahedron $A''B''C''D''$ (§ 857) is iso-dynamic.*

In the harmonic homology having K for center and $K'K''K'''$ for plane of homology (§ 857) the tangent planes to (O) at the two corresponding points D and D'' correspond to each other, hence to the line of intersection s of the first of these planes with the plane ABC corresponds the line of intersection s' of the second tangent plane with the plane $A''B''C''$. But s lies in the plane of perspectivity $K'K''K'''$, hence s' coincides with s. Thus the faces of the tetrahedron $A''B''C''D''$ meet the corresponding faces of its tangential tetrahedron in four lines lying in the plane $K'K''K'''$, hence $A''B''C''D''$ is perspective to its tangential tetrahedron (§ 62), which proves the proposition (§ 853).

859. Remark. The two tetrahedrons $ABCD$, $A''B''C''D''$ (§ 858) have the same Lemoine tetrahedron $KK'K''K'''$.

860. Definition. The two tetrahedrons $ABCD$, $A''B''C''D''$ will be referred to as *associated* isodynamic tetrahedrons.

861. Theorem. *The Lemoine tetrahedron of an isodynamic tetrahedron is self-polar with respect to the circumsphere of the isodynamic tetrahedron.*

The three tetrahedrons $ABCD$, $A''B''C''D''$, $KK'K''K'''$ form a desmic system (§ 858), hence the two tetrahedrons $ABCD$, $A''B''C''D''$ correspond to each other in four harmonic perspectivities having for centers the vertices of $KK'K''K'''$ and for planes of perspectivity the respectively opposite faces of this tetrahedron (§ 738). Thus the lines $K'A$, $K'B$, $K'C$, $K'D$ joining K' to the vertices of $ABCD$ pass through the vertices of

$A''B''C''D''$, hence the harmonic conjugates of K' with respect to these pairs of vertices will be conjugate to K' with respect to (O). But on account of the harmonic perspectivity considered these harmonic conjugates must lie in the plane $KK''K'''$, hence this plane is the polar plane of K' with respect to (O). Similarly for K'' and K'''. Hence the proposition.

862. Corollary I. *The Lemoine tetrahedron (K) of an isodynamic tetrahedron (T) is orthocentric, and the circumsphere of (T) is the polar sphere of (K). The circumcenter of (T) is the orthocenter of (K).*

863. Corollary II. *Each harmonic associate of the Lemoine point of an isodynamic tetrahedron (T) has the property that its polar plane with respect to (T) coincides with the polar plane of this point with respect to the circumsphere of (T).*

864. Corollary III. *A symmedian of an isodynamic tetrahedron is divided harmonically by the Lemoine point of the tetrahedron and the second point of intersection of this symmedian with the circumsphere of the tetrahedron.*

Indeed, the two vertices K and D'' of the two tetrahedrons $KK'K''K'''$ and $A''B''C''D''$ (§ 861) are separated harmonically by the vertex D and the face ABC of the third tetrahedron $DABC$ of the desmic group of the three tetrahedrons.

865. Theorem. *The line joining the circumcenter of a face of an isodynamic tetrahedron to the Lemoine point of the tetrahedron meets the corresponding altitude of the tetrahedron and divides this altitude in the ratio 2 : 1, the shorter segment being adjacent to the face considered.*

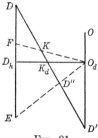

FIG. 81

The circumdiameter of the isodynamic tetrahedron $DABC$ perpendicular to the face ABC passes through the circumcenter O_d (Fig. 81) of the triangle ABC and through the pole D' of the plane ABC with respect to the circumsphere (O) of $DABC$. The symmedian DD' of $DABC$ (§ 851) meets ABC in the Lemoine point K_d of the triangle ABC and the sphere (O) in the point D''. If we cut the harmonic pencil $O_d(DD'', D'K_d)$ by the altitude DD_h we have, since OD' and DD_h are parallel,

$$DD_h = D_hE, \qquad \text{or} \qquad DE : D_hE = 2,$$

where $E \equiv (DD_h, O_dD'')$.

Again, the two pairs of points D, K_d; K, D'' are harmonic (§ 864), hence if we cut the harmonic pencil $O_d(DK_d, KD'')$ by the altitude DD_h, we have

$$DF : FD_h = DE : D_hE = 2 : 1,$$

where $F \equiv (O_dK, DD_h)$.

866. Problem. *Construct an isodynamic tetrahedron given one vertex, the circumcenter, and the Lemoine point.*

If D, O, K are the three given points, the point K is assumed to lie inside the sphere (O) having O for center and OD for radius.

Let D'' be the second point of intersection of DK with (O), and let K_d be the harmonic conjugate of D with respect to K, D''. Let s denote the line of intersection of the polar plane of K with respect to (O) with the tangent plane to (O) at D.

Let (O_d) denote the circle of intersection of (O) with the plane (s, K_d), and let ABC be any triangle inscribed in (O_d) and having K_d for its Lemoine point (C. G., p. 234, Ex. 9). The tetrahedron $DABC$ satisfies the conditions of the problem.

Indeed, it is obvious that D and O are respectively a vertex and the circumcenter of $DABC$. The intersection s of the polar planes of D and K with respect to (O) is the conjugate of the line DKK_d with respect to (O), hence s is the polar of K_d with respect to (O_d) (§ 442), and since K_d is, by construction, the Lemoine point of ABC, the line s is the Lemoine axis of ABC, hence $DABC$ is isodynamic (§ 847).

The line DK_d is a symmedian of $DABC$ (§ 838), and, by construction, the point K is harmonically separated from D'' by D and K_d, hence K is the Lemoine point of $DABC$ (§ 864).

The problem has an infinite number of solutions, for the triangle ABC may be chosen in an infinite number of ways.

EXERCISES

1. The Lemoine plane of an isodynamic tetrahedron is the harmonic plane of the Lemoine point of the tetrahedron with respect to the tetrahedron determined by the four Lemoine points of the faces of the given tetrahedron.

2. The six ends of the three bisymmedians of an isodynamic tetrahedron and the six traces of the Lemoine plane on the edges of the tetrahedron are the twelve vertices of a desmic system of three tetrahedrons.

3. The lines joining a vertex of an isodynamic tetrahedron to the harmonic associates of the Lemoine point of the tetrahedron meet the opposite face in the harmonic associates of the Lemoine point of this face.

4. Construct an isodynamic tetrahedron given a vertex, the Lemoine point, and the Lemoine plane.

c. *The Neuberg Spheres*

867. Theorem. *The twelve Apollonian circles of the four faces of an isodynamic tetrahedron are, in pairs, concentric and equal.*

The point L' (§ 849) is the trace on the edge BC of the tangents to the circles ABC and DBC at the points A and D respectively, hence L' is the center of an Apollonian circle of the triangle ABC and also of the triangle DBC (C. G., p. 235), the radii of these circles being the segments $L'A$ and $L'D$, respectively. Now these two segments are equal (§ 384), hence the two Apollonian circles considered are equal. Similarly for the other traces of the Lemoine plane on the edges of the tetrahedron. Hence the proposition.

868. Definition. The six spheres having for great circles the Apollonian circles of an isodynamic tetrahedron (§ 867) will be referred to as the **Neuberg spheres** of the isodynamic tetrahedron.

Consequences. (a) *The six centers of the Neuberg spheres lie in the Lemoine plane of the tetrahedron.* (b) *The Neuberg sphere having its center on a given edge of the tetrahedron passes through the two vertices of the tetrahedron lying on the opposite edge.* (c) *The Neuberg spheres are orthogonal to the circumsphere of the tetrahedron* (§ 413).

869. Theorem. *The Neuberg spheres of an isodynamic tetrahedron $ABCD$ are the spheres of similitude of the four spheres (A), (B), (C), (D) described with the vertices of $ABCD$ as centers and with radii p, q, r, s, whose squares are proportional to the products of the three edges passing through the respective vertices.*

The tetrahedron being isodynamic, we have (§ 836)

$$aa' = bb' = cc',$$

hence

$$a : b = b' : a'.$$

Now we have

$$p^2 : q^2 = a'bc : b'ca = a'b : b'a = b^2 : a^2,$$

hence

$$p : q = b : a.$$

Thus the centers of similitude of the two spheres (A), (B) divide the segment AB in the ratio $CA : CB$. But these points of division are also the ends of a diameter of the circle of Apollonius of the triangle ABC passing through the vertex C, hence this circle of Apollonius and the sphere of similitude of the two spheres (A), (B) have a diameter in common, i.e., this sphere of similitude is identical with a Neuberg sphere of the tetrahedron. Similarly for the other pairs of the four spheres considered. Hence the proposition.

870. Corollary I. *The six Neuberg spheres of an isodynamic tetrahedron form a coaxal net* (§§ 634, 602 ff.), *whose plane of centers is the Lemoine plane of the tetrahedron.*

The radical axis of this net is the Brocard diameter (§ 854) of the tetrahedron, for the circumsphere of the tetrahedron is orthogonal to the spheres of the net [§ 868 (c)].

871. Corollary II. *The six Neuberg spheres have two real points in common.*

Indeed, the circumsphere (O) of the tetrahedron belongs to the coaxal pencil conjugate to the net formed by the Neuberg spheres [§ 868 (c)], and (O) does not cut the Lemoine plane (§ 852).

872. Definition. The two points T, T' common to the six Neuberg spheres of an isodynamic tetrahedron (§ 871) will be referred to as the *"Neuberg points"* of the tetrahedron.

(a) The Neuberg points lie on the Brocard diameter of the tetrahedron [§ 604 (b)].

(b) They are the limiting points (§ 557) of the coaxal pencil of spheres determined by the circumsphere of the tetrahedron and the Lemoine plane as radical plane of the pencil. They are therefore inverse with respect to the circumsphere (§ 560) and symmetric with respect to the Lemoine plane of the tetrahedron (§ 610).

873. Theorem. *The squares of the distances of a Neuberg point of an isodynamic tetrahedron from the vertices of the tetrahedron are proportional to the products of the three edges passing through the respective vertices* (§ 640).

874. Theorem. *The distances of the vertices of an isodynamic tetrahedron from the Lemoine plane of the tetrahedron are propor-*

tional to the products of the three edges passing through the respective vertices (§§ 632, 633).

875. Theorem. *Two Neuberg spheres of an isodynamic tetrahedron which have their centers on two opposite edges of the tetrahedron are orthogonal.*

The point L' (§ 867) lies in the tangent planes at D and A to the circumsphere (O) of the tetrahedron, hence L' is conjugate, with respect to (O), to any point of the line DA, and in particular to the point P', the analogue of L' on DA. Now the two Neuberg spheres having L' and P' for centers are orthogonal to (O) [§ 868 (c)], hence they are orthogonal to each other (§ 573).

876. Theorem. *Two Neuberg spheres of an isodynamic tetrahedron which have their centers on two coplanar edges intersect at an angle of 120 degrees.*

The three Neuberg spheres (L'), (M'), (N') having their centers L', M', N' on the edges BC, CA, AB of the isodynamic tetrahedron $ABCD$ are cut by the plane ABC along the three Apollonian circles of the triangle ABC (§ 868), hence L' is a center of similitude of the two spheres (M'), (N') (C. G., § 475), and since the three spheres are coaxal [§ 602 (g)], (L') is a sphere of antisimilitude of (M'), (N') (§§ 588, 589). Thus in the inversion having (L') for sphere of inversion, the spheres (M'), (N') correspond to each other and the sphere (L') remains invariant (§ 673), hence the angle of intersection of the spheres (L'), (M') is equal to the angle of intersection of the spheres (L'), (N') (§ 670).

The argument about the sphere (L') may be repeated about the sphere (M') and again about the sphere (N'). Thus the three spheres considered are such that each bisects the angle between the remaining two. Hence the angle between any two of these spheres is equal to 120 degrees.

877. Problem. *Construct an isodynamic tetrahedron given three of its vertices.*

The three spheres (L'), (M'), (N') having for great circles the three Apollonian circles of the triangle ABC determined by the three given points will be three Neuberg spheres of the required tetrahedron and each sphere will contain the required fourth vertex D [§ 868 (b)]. Now the three Apollonian circles considered have in common the two isodynamic points W_d, W_d' of the triangle ABC (C. G., § 470), hence the three Neuberg spheres considered have in common the circle (d) having $W_d W_d'$ for diameter and situated in the plane perpendicular to the plane ABC. The circle (d) is the locus of the required vertex D.

878. Theorem. *The lines joining a vertex of an isodynamic tetrahedron to the ends of the circumdiameter perpendicular to the opposite face meet this face in its two isodynamic points.*

The plane of the circle (d) (§ 877) (Fig. 82) passes through the radical axis of the coaxal net formed by the Neuberg spheres of the isodynamic tetrahedron $DABC$ [§ 602 (b)], i.e., through the Brocard diameter of the tetrahedron (§ 870), and therefore contains the circumcenter O of $DABC$. Now the circumsphere (O) of $DABC$ is orthogonal to the Neuberg

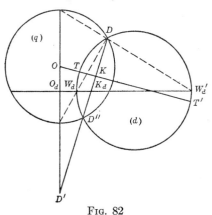

Fig. 82

spheres [§ 868 (c)], hence the plane of (d) cuts (O) along a great circle (q) orthogonal to (d) (p. 176, Ex. 19) and the two circles have the point D in common. Thus the lines joining D to the ends of the diameter $W_d W_d'$ of (d) will meet (q) in the ends of a diameter of (q) perpendicular to $W_d W_d'$ (§ 821). Now a diameter of (q) is a diameter of (O) and the plane of the two circles considered is perpendicular to the plane ABC, hence the proposition.

EXERCISES

1. The six radical planes of the circumsphere of an isodynamic tetrahedron with the six Neuberg spheres of this tetrahedron have a point in common.

2. The planes perpendicular to the faces of an isodynamic tetrahedron and passing through the Brocard diameters of the respective faces are coaxal.

3. The mid-points of the four segments determined by the isodynamic points of the four faces of an isodynamic tetrahedron are coplanar.

4. In an isodynamic tetrahedron the angle formed by the symmedian of the tetrahedron passing through a given vertex and the line joining this vertex to the circumcenter of the opposite face is bisected by the lines joining the vertex considered to the isodynamic points of the opposite face.

5. If the base of an isodynamic tetrahedron is fixed, while the opposite vertex varies, the four faces of its tangential tetrahedron pass each through a fixed line.

6. Construct an isodynamic tetrahedron given the circumcenter and three of its vertices.

7. Construct an isodynamic tetrahedron given the circumsphere, a vertex, the plane of the face opposite this vertex, and one of the vertices lying in this plane.

8. Two associated isodynamic tetrahedrons have the same Neuberg spheres.

9. (a) If the vertices of a given isodynamic tetrahedron are inverted with respect to a Neuberg point of this tetrahedron, the four points obtained are the vertices of a regular tetrahedron the circumcenter of which is the second Neuberg point of the given tetrahedron. (b) The inverse points, with respect to any center of inversion, of the vertices of a regular tetrahedron are the vertices of an isodynamic tetrahedron of which the center of inversion is an isodynamic point. (c) The vertices of a tetrahedron cannot be inverted into the vertices of a regular tetrahedron unless the given tetrahedron is isodynamic.

10. A Neuberg point of an isodynamic tetrahedron forms an isodynamic tetrahedron with any three of the vertices of the given tetrahedron.

11. The conjugate, with respect to the circumsphere of an isodynamic tetrahedron, of the bisymmedian of this tetrahedron relative to a given pair of opposite edges passes through the traces on these edges of the Lemoine plane of the tetrahedron.

12. The bisymmedian relative to a given pair of opposite edges of an isodynamic tetrahedron is coplanar with the conjugates of these edges with respect to the circumsphere of the tetrahedron.

4. The Isogonic Tetrahedron

879. Definitions. If the lines joining the vertices of a tetrahedron to the points of contact of the opposite faces with the inscribed sphere of the tetrahedron are concurrent, the tetrahedron is said to be *isogonal* or *isogonic.*

The common point, F, of the four concurrent lines will be referred to as the *Fermat point* of the isogonic tetrahedron.

The tetrahedron determined by the points of contact of the faces of an isogonic tetrahedron with the inscribed sphere will be referred to as the *Fermat tetrahedron* of the isogonic tetrahedron.

880. Theorem. *The Fermat tetrahedron of the isogonic tetrahedron is isodynamic.*

Let S, T, U, V (Fig. 83) be the points of contact of the faces BCD, CDA, DAB, ABC of a tetrahedron $ABCD$ with its inscribed sphere. The tetrahedron $ABCD$ is clearly the tangential tetrahedron of the tetrahedron $STUV$. Now if $ABCD$ is isogonic, the lines AS, BT, CU, DV have a point F in common (§ 879), hence $STUV$ is isodynamic (§ 853).

CONVERSELY. *The tangential tetrahedron of an isodynamic tetrahedron is isogonic.*

881. Corollary. *The Fermat point of an isogonic tetrahedron is the Lemoine point of its Fermat tetrahedron.*

882. Theorem. *An isogonic tetrahedron is self-polar with respect to the Lemoine tetrahedron of its Fermat tetrahedron.*

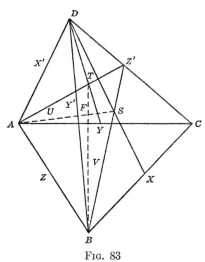

FIG. 83

The Fermat tetrahedron $STUV$ of the isogonic tetrahedron $ABCD$ (§ 880) is the cevian tetrahedron of the Fermat point F with respect to $ABCD$. Hence the harmonic conjugates of F with respect to the pairs of opposite edges of $ABCD$ coincide with the harmonic conjugates of F with respect to the pairs of opposite edges of $STUV$ (§ 719). Now the point F and its three harmonic conjugates with respect to the pairs of opposite edges of $STUV$ determine the Lemoine tetrahedron of $STUV$ (§§ 881, 856), hence the proposition.

883. Theorem. *The three edges of any face of an isogonic tetrahedron subtend angles of 120 degrees at the point of contact of the face considered with the inscribed sphere of the tetrahedron.*

Let $X, X'; Y, Y'; Z, Z'$ be the three pairs of points on the three pairs of opposite edges $BC, DA; CA, DB; AB, DC$ (Fig. 83) of the isogonic tetrahedron which are collinear with F (§ 882). Applying Menelaus' theorem to the triangles $Z'AC$, $Z'BC$ and the transversals DTY, DSX, and eliminating the ratio $CD : DZ'$, we obtain

$$Z'T \cdot AY : TA \cdot YC = Z'S \cdot BX : SB \cdot XC.$$

Multiplying this relation by the relation derived from the application of Ceva's theorem to the triangle ABC and the point

V, we have

$$Z'T \cdot AZ : TA \cdot ZB = Z'S : SB.$$

But [§ 384(b)]

$$Z'S = Z'T, \qquad TA = AV, \qquad BS = BV,$$

hence

$$AZ : ZB = AV : BV,$$

which shows that the line ZVC bisects the angle AVB.

Similarly, using in turn the points X' and Y' in the same way as we used the point Z', we may show that the line XVA bisects the angle BVC, and that the line YVB bisects the angle CVA.

Thus each of the three lines VA, VB, VC bisects the angle formed by the remaining two lines, hence each of the three angles AVB, BVC, CVA is equal to 120 degrees.

Similarly for the other faces of the tetrahedron.

EXERCISES

1. The tetrahedron self-polar with respect to an isogonic tetrahedron and having for one of its vertices the Fermat point of the given tetrahedron is orthocentric.

2. The four tangent planes to the inscribed sphere of an isogonic tetrahedron at the four points where this sphere is met again by the lines joining the vertices of the tetrahedron to the points of contact of the opposite faces with the inscribed sphere form an isogonic tetrahedron.

MISCELLANEOUS EXERCISES

1. In a hexahedron $ABCDA'B'C'D'$ the plane faces of which are $ABCD$, $A'B'C'D'$, $A'ADD'$, $D'DCC'$, $C'CBB'$, $B'BAA'$, the edges AA', BB', CC', DD' intersect in the points, say AA', DD' in P; BB', CC' in Q; CC', DD' in R; AA', BB' in S; that is, starting with the duad of lines PQ, RS, the four edges AA', BB', CC', DD' are the lines PS, QS, QR, PR which join the extremities of these duads. Similarly, the four edges AB, CD, $A'B'$, $C'D'$ are the lines joining the extremities of a duad, and the four edges AD, BC, $A'D'$, $B'C'$ are the lines joining the extremities of a duad. The question arises: "Given two duads, is it possible to place them in space so that the two tetrads of joining lines may be eight of the twelve edges of a hexahedron?" (The duad PQ, RS is considered to be given when there is given a tetrahedron $PQRS$ which determines the relative position of the two finite lines PQ and RS.)

2. Through a given point O an arbitrary plane $OABC$ is drawn meeting the edges of the given trihedron $S-ABC$ in the points A, B, C. The three parallels through O to the sides of ABC divide this triangle into three parallelograms and three triangles. Show that the sum of the reciprocals of the volumes of the three pyramids having for bases the three parallelograms and having the point S for their common vertex remains fixed when the plane $OABC$ revolves about the point O.

3. A variable line PAB through the fixed point P meets two given intersecting planes in the points A, B. Show that the locus of the symmetric of P with respect to the mid-point of AB is a cylinder of revolution.

4. A, B, C are three points on a horizontal plain at which the summits of three hills appear to be two by two in the same direction. If x, y, z are in heights of the hills, prove that

$$x(y - z) : BC = y(z - x) : CA = z(x - y) : AB.$$

5. Given the cyclic quadrilateral $ABCD$ and the point O not in its plane, show that

$$AB \cdot BD \cdot AD \cdot OC^2 + BC \cdot CD \cdot DB \cdot OA^2 = AB \cdot BC \cdot AC \cdot OD^2 + AC \cdot CD \cdot AD \cdot OB^2.$$

Show also that this relation may be put in the form

$$OA^2 \cdot BCD + OC^2 \cdot ABD = OB^2 \cdot ACD + OD^2 \cdot ABC,$$

where BCD, etc. represent the areas of the triangles.

6. If ABC and $A'B'C'$ are two positions of the same triangle in space, and P the point common to the mediators of the segments AA', BB', CC', show that the two tetrahedrons $PABC$, $PA'B'C'$ are not congruent, but symmetrical.

7. A, B, C, D are four fixed points on a sphere, P a variable one, (t) its tangent plane; if the angle formed by the intersections of PAC, PBC on (t) is p, and the other one formed in the same manner by PAD, PBD is q, then $p - q$ is (in regard to P) a constant magnitude.

8. Given the trihedral angle $O\text{-}ABC$, a point P is taken on the line common to the three bisecting planes of the dihedral angles of $O\text{-}ABC$ and through P a plane is drawn meeting the edges in A, B, C. Show that the value of the expression

$$(AOB + BOC + COA)^2 : AOB \cdot BOC \cdot COA$$

does not depend upon the orientation of the secant plane.

9. Three mutually rectangular lines have the point O in common. On one line we have the segments $OA = OA' = a$, on the second line $OB = OB' = b$, and on the third $OC = OC' = c$, so that we have the octahedron $CABA'B'C'$. Through any point I of CB' a plane (P) is drawn parallel to ABC cutting the faces of the octahedron along a hexagon (H). If $CI = x$ and $IB' = y$, find the area of the hexagon and the ratio of the volumes of the two solids into which the octahedron is divided by (P).

10. The square $EFGH$ inscribed in the base ABC of a given tetrahedron $SABC$ is the base of a cube $EFGHE'F'G'H'$ situated on the opposite side of ABC from the vertex S. Show that the lines joining S to the points E', F', G', H' meet ABC in the vertices of a square, and that the cube having this square for base is inscribed in $SABC$. If x denotes the edges of this cube and a the length of the side AC which 'contains two of the vertices of the square $EFGH$, h the corresponding altitude of ABC, and H the altitude of $SABC$, show that the reciprocal of x is equal to the sum of the reciprocals of a, h, and H.

11. If the angles of a skew hexagon are right angles, the lines of shortest distance of the three pairs of opposite sides have a director plane.

12. The points P, P'; Q, Q'; R, R'; S, S' are pairs of isogonal conjugate points in the faces BCD, CDA, DAB, ABC, respectively, of the tetrahedron $ABCD$. Show that if the lines AP, BQ, CR, DS form a hyperbolic group, the same is true of the lines AP', BQ', CR', DS'.

13. If a tetrahedron (T) inscribed in a sphere (O) is harmonic to the tetrahedron (P) conjugate to (O), then the tangential tetrahedron of (T) is also harmonic to (P).

14. If four lines taken in the four faces of a tetrahedron form a hyperbolic group, the four lines joining the trilinear poles, with respect to the corresponding faces, of these lines to the respectively opposite vertices of the tetrahedron also form a hyperbolic group. Conversely.

15. Construct four spheres so that the twelve centers of similitude of these spheres taken two by two shall coincide with the four vertices of a given tetrahedron and the eight centers of the spheres which touch the four faces of this tetrahedron.

16. The radical center of the four spheres each passing through a vertex of a given tetrahedron and through the circle of intersection of the opposite face with a fixed sphere is the tetrahedral pole, with respect to the tetrahedron, of the radical plane of this sphere and the circumsphere of the tetrahedron.

17. The sum of the squares of the areas of the three medial sections of a tetrahedron is equal to one fourth of the sum of the squares of the areas of the faces.

18. The sum of the squares of the reciprocals of the three bialtitudes of a tetrahedron is equal to the sum of the squares of the reciprocals of the four altitudes of the tetrahedrons.

19. Let X, U be the mid-points of the edges BC, DA of the regular tetrahedron $DABC$. If p, q are the two lines in the plane XDA making angles of 30 degrees with XU, (a) the sphere determined by the four projections, upon the faces of $DABC$, of any point on either of the lines p, q is tangent to the inscribed sphere of $DABC$; (b) the isogonal conjugate of a point on one of the lines p, q lies on the other.

20. A given trihedral angle, vertex S, and a plane through the given point B form a tetrahedron (T) of volume V. The product of the volumes of the four tetrahedrons obtained by joining the vertices of (T) to a given point A, collinear with S and B, is equal to P. Show that the ratio $P : V^3$ is independent of the orientation of the plane through the point B.

21. The dihedral angle of a regular tetrahedron is the supplement of that of a regular octahedron.

22. If on the altitudes of a tetrahedron produced through the vertices segments are laid off, starting from the vertices, inversely proportional to the respective altitudes, the tetrahedron determined by the ends of these segments has the same centroid as the given tetrahedron.

23. Any line through the centroid G of a tetrahedron cuts the faces in P, Q, R, S. Prove that $\Sigma(1/GP) = O$.

24. *A* is the apex of a tetrahedron *ABCD* (regular or otherwise) which stands on a horizontal plane, and *E* is a point on the edge *AB*. A fly descends from *E* by making a circuit of the tetrahedron and finally arriving at *B*. Find at which points it must cross *AC* and *AD* so as to maintain the same gradient to the horizon on the whole way down.

25. Three balloons move in straight lines with constant velocities. The positions of the balloons are given at two different instances. Construct a straight line on which a fourth balloon could move with constant velocity so that the first three balloons shall appear stationary to the balloonist in the fourth balloon.

BIBLIOGRAPHICAL NOTES

In the preparation of this book free use has been made of the following works:

E. CATALAN. *Théorèmes et problèmes de géométrie élémentaire*, seventh edition, Paris, 1873.

J. L. COOLIDGE. *A Treatise on the Circle and the Sphere*, Oxford, 1916.

N. F. DUPUIS. *Synthetic Solid Geometry*, Macmillan, 1893.

C. GUICHARD. *Traité de géométrie*, vol. 2, fifth edition, Paris, 1923.

J. HADAMARD. *Leçons de géométrie élémentaire*, vol. 2, Paris, 1901.

G. HOLZMÜLLER. *Elemente der Stereometrie*, vols. 1 and 2, Leipzig, 1900.

TH. REYE. *Synthetische Geometrie der Kugeln*, Leipzig, 1879.

ROUCHÉ et Comberousse. *Traité de géométrie*, vol. 2, seventh edition, Paris, 1900. The note at the end of this volume (pp. 643–664) "Sur la géométrie récente du tétraèdre" was contributed by J. Neuberg.

When quoted in the notes that follow these books will be referred to by the names of the authors printed in capitals and small capitals. In these notes frequent mention will be made of the following periodicals,—by the abbreviations listed printed in bold face italic type.

AM. *Annales de mathématiques*, 1810–1832. Founded by J. D. Gergonne. Nîmes.

Archiv. *Archiv der Mathematik und Physik*, 1841–1919. Founded by J. A. Grunert (1797–1872). Leipzig.

Crelle. *Journal für reine und angewandte Mathematik*, 1826—. Founded by A. L. Crelle (1780–1855). Berlin.

ET. Mathematical questions and solutions from the *Educational Times*, 1863–1918. Reprints. London.

JME. *Journal de mathématiques élémentaires*, 1877–1897. Founded by J. Bourget (1822–1887) and continued by G. de Longchamps (1842–1906). Paris.

Liouville. *Journal de mathématiques pures et appliquées*, 1836—. Founded by J. Liouville (1809–1882). Paris.

Mathesis. *Mathesis*, 1881—. Founded by Paul Mansion (1844–1919) and J. Neuberg. Ghent.

Monthly. *American Mathematical Monthly*, 1894—. Founded by B. F. Finkel (1865—).

NAM. *Nouvelles annales de mathématiques*, 1842–1927. Founded by O. Terquem (1782–1862) and C. Gerono (1799–1892). Paris.

NC. *Nouvelle correspondance mathématique*, 1874–1880. Founded by E. Catalan (1814–1894). Brussels.

The number in the front of each note refers to the corresponding article of the text.

1(e). The term " mediator " was introduced by J. Neuberg (1840–1926).

22. *Archiv,* vol. 37 (1861), p. 253.   *Mathesis,* 1901, p. 272.

23. J. Neuberg, *Mathesis,* 1913, p. 128.

24. J. Neuberg, *Mathesis,* 1898, p. 199.

26(a). This is a celebrated proposition in Projective geometry. It was first proposed as a problem by J. D. Gergonne, *AM.,* vol. 17 (1826–1827), p. 83, and solved by E. E. Bobillier (1797–1832) and by Garbinsky, *AM.,* vol. 18 (1827–1828), pp. 182–184. It was also solved by J. Steiner (1796–1863) in *Crelle,* 1827, p. 268. See also Garbinsky in *Crelle,* vol. 5 (1830), p. 174.—A proof may be found in most books on Projective geometry, as for instance in Th. F. Holgate's *Projective Geometry,* Macmillan, 1930, p. 247. Or see *Monthly,* 1924, p. 103.

27. The term was proposed by O. Hermes, *Crelle,* vol. 67 (1867), p. 171.

50. Homothetic figures were considered by L. Euler (1707–1783) in 1777.

56–57. HADAMARD, p. 108.

59. J. Neuberg, *Mathesis,* 1914, p. 110.

60. Homological figures in space were first considered by J. V. Poncelet (1788–1867), *Traité des propriétés projectives des figures,* 1822, pp. 369 ff.   The term " homology " is due to Poncelet.

66. The term was used by J. Neuberg.

67. CATALAN, p. 311.

79. *Monthly,* 1934, p. 55.

93–97. DUPUIS, p. 33.

100–102. HADAMARD, p. 56.

112–117. CATALAN, p. 309.

123–124. *Monthly,* 1933, p. 500.

126 and **128.** CATALAN, p. 310.

130–142. CATALAN, p. 316.

146. *Mathesis,* 1904, p. 124.

147. *NC.,* vol. 1 (1874), p. 63.

148–149. R. F. Muirhead, *Proceedings of the Edinburgh Mathematical Society,* vol. 15 (1897), p. 127.   *Mathesis,* 1898, p. 172.

151. The term " bimedian " was used by J. Neuberg, *Mathesis,* 1924, p. 446.

150. Numerous bibliographical references to the geometry of the tetrahedron may be found in (a) Max Simon, *Ueber die Entwicklung der Elementar-Geometrie im XIX. Jahrhundert,* Leipzig, 1906, pp. 202–208; (b) *Encyklopaedie der mathematischen Wissenschaften,* vol. III, 1, 2, pp. 1054–1067.

153. Gaspar Monge (1746–1818), *Correspondance sur l' Ecole Polytechnique,* 1809, p. 1.

166–167. G. Gallucci, *NAM.,* 1897, p. 16.

168. *Monthly,* 1934, p. 636.

170. Federigo Commandino (1509–1575), *De centro gravitatis solidorum,* 1565, p. 21, prop. 17.   Some historians surmise that the proposition was known to the Greeks.

178. *Mathesis,* 1885, p. 279.

179–181. *Monthly,* 1934, p. 338 and p. 334.

182–184. *Monthly,* 1933, p. 435.

185. Georges Dostor, *NAM.,* 1867, p. 453.

186. G. Dostor, *NAM.,* 1867, p. 453. *JME.,* 1878, p. 284. *Monthly,* 1918, p. 422. *Mathesis,* 1930, p. 255.

187–188. E. Brassine, *NAM.,* 1845, p. 141. Schnevikoff, *ET.,* vol. 53 (1890), p. 114. *JME.,* 1890, p. 262. *Mathesis,* 1930, p. 254.

189 ff. Monge, *Correspondance sur l'Ecole Polytechnique,* vol. 2 (1795), p. 266. A. Cayley (1821–1895), *Collected Works,* vol. 5, p. 550.

205. Given erroneously by J. Steiner, *Crelle,* 1827, p. 97, and correctly in his *Systematische Entwicklung* . . . , Berlin, 1832, Anhang No. 78. *NAM.,* 1859, p. 232.

208. For a bibliography on the orthocentric tetrahedron see *Monthly,* 1934, p. 499.

219. J. Steiner, *Crelle,* 1827, p. 97.

220–221. F. Joachimstahl (1818–1861), *Archiv,* vol. 32 (1859), p. 107.

223–224. *NAM.,* 1859, p. 357. H. Brocard (1845–1922), *NC.,* vol. 4 (1878), p. 108 and *NAM.,* 1884, p. 531. *Mathesis,* 1911, p. 143 and 1930, p. 255, note 28.

226–227. G. Fontené, *Bulletin des sciences mathématiques et physiques élémentaires,* vol. 6 (1900–1901), p. 22.

228–230. G. Monge. See reference to § 189. *NAM.,* 1869, p. 173. H. F. Thompson, *Proceedings of the Edinburgh Mathematical Society,* vol. 17 (1908–1909), pp. 51–53. H. G. Forder, *Mathematical Gazette,* vol. 15 (1930–1931), p. 470.

232–233. Amédée Mannheim (1831–1906). *JME.,* 1895, p. 225. H. F. Thompson, *Proceedings of the Edinburgh Mathematical Society,* vol. 17 (1908–1909), p. 51.

235. J. D. Gergonne (1771–1859), *AM.,* vol. 3 (1812–1813), p. 317.

237. Ernesto Cesaro (1859–1906), *NC.,* vol. 6 (1880), pp. 90–91. But also *AM.,* vol. 3 (1812–1813), p. 317.

242. Hermary, *Bulletin de la societé mathématique de France,* vol. 7 (1879), p. 138.

244–245. A. S. Bang, *Tidsskrift for Mathematik,* 1897, p. 48. See also Henry S. White (1861—), *Bulletin of the American Mathematical Society,* vol. 14 (1907–1908), p. 220.

247–253. The spheres inscribed in the truncs were considered by J. L. Lagrange (1736–1813) in 1773, *Nouveaux mémoires de l'Académie de Berlin* and *Collected Works,* vol. 3, Paris, 1869. The spheres inscribed in the roofs were considered by J. Steiner, *Crelle,* vol. 2 (1827–1828), pp. 97–98. J. Neuberg, *NC.,* vol. 6 (1880), p. 8. *ET.,* vol. 19 (1873), p. 20. *Monthly,* 1914, p. 231 and p. 273.

254–258. G. Fontené (1848–1923), *Bulletin des sciences mathématiques et physiques élémentaires,* vol. 7 (1901–1902), p. 225 and *NAM.,* 1909, p. 59. V. Thébault, *NAM.,* 1920, p. 55 and *Mathesis,* 1929, p. 81.

259–263. See reference to § 242 and Rouché, pp. 655–656.

264–273. These formulas are due to Lagrange, Steiner, and others. More formulas are given by HOLZMÜLLER, vol. 2, p. 221 ff.

274. G. Monge, *Correspondance sur l'Ecole Polytechnique*, vol. 1, p. 441.

275. The proposition is due to F. J. Servois (1767–1847).

277. E. Genty, *NAM.*, 1897, p. 381.

278–279. J. Mention, *NAM.*, 1859, p. 204.

280. A. Lévy, *Correspondance mathématique et physique*, vol. 4 (1828), p. 3. This journal was founded by A. Quetelet (1796–1874) and published from 1825 to 1839.

281. *AM.*, vol. 1 (1810–1811), p. 230 and p. 253. *Crelle*, vol. 6 (1831), p. 98. *NAM.*, 1863, p. 10. *ET.*, vol. 62 (1895), p. 114 and vol. 65 (1896), p. 82.

282. See note to § 286.

283. *AM.*, vol. 8 (1817–1818), p. 139. *Mathesis*, 1909, p. 25.

285. *Mathesis*, 1909, p. 26.

286. The proposition was presented to the Paris Academy of Sciences in 1783 by J. P. de Gua de Malves (1712–1785) and is often referred to as " de Gua's theorem." However, the theorem was known to Descartes (1596–1650), *Oeuvres inédites de Descartes*, Paris, 1859, and to his contemporary J. Faulhaber (1580–1635). The proposition is a special case of a more general theorem due to Tinseau, who presented it to the Paris Academy in 1774. See, for instance, Osgood and Graustein, *Analytic Geometry*, Macmillan, 1930, p. 517, theor. 2.

287. *Bulletin des sciences mathématiques et physiques élémentaires*, vol. 6 (1900–1901), p. 157. *Mathesis*, 1909, p. 25. *NAM.*, 1918, p. 115. *Monthly*, 1934, p. 527.

292–317. The isosceles tetrahedron was first considered by G. Monge, *Correspondance sur l'Ecole Polytechnique*, January 1809, pp. 1–6; *AM.*, vol. 1 (1810–1811), p. 355, arts. 7 and 8. C. F. A. Jacobi (1795–1855) in J. H. van Swinden's *Elemente* (1834), p. 457. E. Genty, *NAM.*, 1878, p. 223. E. Lemoine (1840–1912), *NAM.*, 1880, p. 133. *Zeitschrift für Mathematik und Physik*, vol. 29 (1884), p. 321. *Mathesis*, 1885, p. 117, and 1894, p. 69. Frank Morley (1860—), *ET.*, vol. 61 (1894), p. 26. D. Biddle, *ET.*, vol. 75 (1901), p. 133. *Mathesis*, 1931, p. 91.

318. E. Lemoine, *Mathesis*, 1889, p. 170. *ET.*, vol. 54 (1891), p. 50.

319–327. ROUCHÉ, pp. 652–653.

329. L. N. M. Carnot (1753–1823), *La théorie des transversales*, p. 71, Paris, 1806.

330–333. GUICHARD, p. 72.

334–337. J. Neuberg, *Mémoire sur le tétraèdre*, p. 14, Belgian Academy of Science, 1884, and *Mathesis*, 1885.

339–340. *AM.*, vol. 9 (1818–1819), p. 277 and vol. 12 (1821–1822), p. 178. *ET.*, vol. 45 (1886), p. 41, and vol. 4 (1918), p. 73.

342. G. Riboni, *Periodico di matematiche*, 1900, p. 3.

344. Frank Morley, *ET.*, vol. 36 (1886), p. 101.

345. Malet, *ET.*, vol. 44 (1886), p. 28. *Mathesis*, 1890, p. 253.

346–352. GUICHARD, pp. 80–82.

355–381. E. Rebuffel, *Bulletin des sciences mathématiques et physiques élémentaires*, vol. 3 (1897–1898), pp. 65–68. ROUCHÉ, pp. 221–223.

382. *Mathesis*, 1901, p. 172.

393. Inverse points were considered by J. V. Poncelet (1788–1867), *Traité des propriétés projectives des figures*, Paris, 1822.

419–421. REYE, pp. 24–25.

422. The theory of poles and polar planes with respect to a sphere developed as a part of the general theory of poles and polar planes with respect to a surface of the second degree. See the article on " Projective Geometry " in the *Encyklopaedie der mathematischen Wissenschaften*, vol. 3, 1, p. 398; or *Encyclopédie des sciences mathématiques*, vol. 3, 2, p. 11.

450–451. REYE, pp. 70–71.

460. J. Steiner, *Crelle*, vol. 2 (1827), p. 287. V. Thébault, *Mathesis*, 1923, p. 432.

462. Michel Chasles (1793–1880), *Aperçu historique* . . . , Paris, 1837, p. 368, note 26, and pp. 205–207. REYE, p. 35.

466. G. Monge, *Géométrie descriptive*, Paris, 1795. R. C. Archibald (1875—), *Monthly,* 1915, pp. 6–12 and 1916, pp. 159–161.

481. REYE, p. 53.

488. J. Neuberg, *Mathesis*, 1906, p. 77.

503. Louis Gaultier, " Sur les moyens généraux de construire graphiquement un cercle déterminé par trois conditions et une sphère déterminée par quatre conditions," *Journal de l' Ecole Polytechnique*, cahier 16 (1812), pp. 124–214. In this article the author considers and uses the power of a point with respect to a sphere. [The term " power " (Potenz) is due to Steiner *(Crelle,* vol. 1).] Gaultier considers and names the radical plane of two spheres, the radical axis of three spheres, the radical center of four spheres. He also considers pencils of spheres, under a different name.

513–514. J. B. Durrande (1797–1825), *AM.,* vol. 16 (1825–1826), p. 112.

517. See note to § 503.

536. Galucci, *NAM.,* 1897, p. 17.

538. R. W. Genese, *ET.,* vol. 6 (1918), p. 57.

539. *Monthly,* 1932, p. 193.

542–543. COOLIDGE, p. 233.

552. See note to § 503.

572–576. *Mathesis,* 1928, p. 337.

591. *Monthly,* 1931, p. 111.

594. COOLIDGE, p. 254. *Mathesis,* 1922, 181.

624. Gaston Darboux (1842–1917), *Mathesis,* 1885, p. 161.

625. *Mathesis,* 1931, p. 260.

626. See note to § 503.

628. J. B. Durrande, *AM.,* vol. 5 (1814–1815), p. 32 and p. 301. *Mathesis,* 1933, p. 227.

629–631. *Mathesis,* 1933, p. 227 and p. 350.

633. *Mathesis,* 1925, p. 37.

634. COOLIDGE, p. 244. *Mathesis,* 1926, p. 467.

638. *Monthly,* 1932, p. 194.

640. *Zeitschrift fuer mathematischen und naturwissenschaftlichen Unterricht,* vol. 27 (1896), p. 1455. *Monthly,* 1932, p. 195.

641. *Monthly,* 1933, 181.

646. C. Servais (1862—), *Mathesis,* 1924, p. 316.

648. The theory of inversion is a product of the second quarter of the last century. Among the prominent names connected with the early history of this theory may be mentioned: Poncelet, Steiner, Pluecker (1801–1868), Moebius (1790–1868), Liouville (1809–1882), William Thompson (Lord Kelvin, 1824–1907). For a detailed bibliography see Simon, p. 93 (see a note to § 150).

659. *AM.,* vol. 19 (1818–1819), p. 157. *Liouville,* 1842, p. 272.

694. The problem was first considered and solved, synthetically, by Pierre de Fermat (1601–1665). The first analytic solution was given by L. Euler (1707–1783). Bibliography in Simon, p. 97 (see note to § 150). R. Bouvais, *NAM.,* 1913, p. 446.

703. A. Miquel, *Liouville,* 1838, p. 485.

704. Samuel Roberts (1827–1914), *Proceedings of the London Mathematical Society,* vol. 12 (1880–1881), p. 117. Proved analytically by J. Neuberg, *Messenger of Mathematics,* vol. 13 (1884), p. 124. Proved both synthetically and analytically, *ET.,* vol. 4 (1903), p. 117. Other analytic proofs in *ET.,* vol. 5 (1904), p. 28 and p. 41. M. W. Haskell (1863—) rediscovered the proposition and extended it to n-dimensional space, *Monthly,* vol. 10 (1903), p. 30.

706–734. C. Stephanos, *Bulletin des sciences mathématiques et astronomiques,* 1879, p. 434. H. Schroeter (1829–1892), *Crelle,* vol. 109 (1892), p. 341. *Mathematics Student,* vol. 2 (1934), p. 107.

737–747. Neuberg, *Mémoire sur le tétraèdre,* pp. 10–12.

748. Rouché, p. 649. *ET.,* vol. 2 (1903), p. 120. For a bibliography on the cubic surface see *Monthly,* 1921, pp. 396–397. See also Clément Servais (1862—), " Sur la géométrie du tétraèdre," *Mathesis,* 1922, supplément.

749. *Archiv,* vol. 16 (1910), p. 19. *NAM.,* 1909, p. 59.

750. *Zeitschrift fuer mathematischen und naturwissenschaftlichen Unterricht,* vol. 33 (1902), p. 381.

752–754. Samuel Roberts, *ET.,* vol. 48 (1888), p. 37. J. Neuberg, *Mathesis,* 1915, p. 34.

755. *Mathesis,* 1915, p. 35. *NAM.,* 1925–1926, p. 37.

757. J. Neuberg, *Mémoire sur le tétraèdre,* p. 17.

758–761. Neuberg, *Mémoire sur le tétraèdre,* p. 22.

762. A. L. Crelle (1780–1855), *Sammlung mathematischer Aufsaetze,* 1821, p. 117. The proof is due to K. G. Chr. von Staudt (1798–1867), *Crelle,* vol. 57 (1860), p. 88. See also *NAM.,* 1847, p. 396.

763–767. Samuel Roberts (1827–1914), " On the Analogues of the Nine-Point Circle in Space of Three Dimensions," *Proceedings of the London Mathematical Society,* vol. 19 (1889), pp. 152–161. L. Ripert, " Sur la sphère et les quadriques de douze points du tétraèdre général," *Mathesis,* 1898, p. 218. See also *Mathesis,* 1899, p. 90, note 1.

768–785. *Tôhoku Mathematical Journal,* vol. 39, part 2 (1934), pp. 264–268.

786–794. J. B. Durrande, *AM.,* vol. 5 (1814–1815), p. 32 and p. 301. G. Dostor, *NAM.,* 1874, p. 564. *NC.,* vol. 2 (1875), p. 145. *Mathesis,* 1931, p. 295; 1933, p. 227 and p. 350. *Monthly,* 1915, p. 64.

795. See note to § 208.

800. E. Prouhet, *NAM.,* 1863, p. 138.

822. R. Goormaghtigh, *Mathesis,* 1935, p. 29.

835–878. J. Neuberg, *Mathesis,* 1884, p. 68; *Mémoire sur le tétraèdre* (1884); *Archiv,* vol. 16 (1909–1910), p. 54. *ET.,* vol. 13 (1908), p. 83. *Journal of the Indian Mathematical Society,* vol. 5 (1913), pp. 35, 115, 216–219. W. L. Marr, *Proceedings of the Edinburgh Mathematical Society,* vol. 37 (1919), pp. 59–63, and R. F. Davis, *ibid.,* pp. 63–64.

879–883. J. Neuberg, *Mémoire sur le tétraèdre.* B. H. Brown (1894—), *Monthly,* 1924, p. 371.

INDEX

References are to pages.

G

Gauche, 42.
Gergonne point, 100, 209, 261.
Gergonne's theorem, 71, 252.

H

Harmonic, associates, 246, 251, 282.
conjugate of line or point with respect to two skew lines, 15.
forms, 12–16.
homology, 22, 239, 283.
pencil of planes, 12, 13, 106, etc.
plane with respect to tetrahedron, 230, 231, 233, 235, 236, 240, 260, 264, 265, 279, 285.
pole, 231, 233, 255, 256, 264, 279, 280, 294.
tetrahedron, 235, 236, 240, 282, 283, 291, 292, 294.
Hexahedron, 212, 292.
Homological tetrahedrons, 21.
Homologous chords and points, 153, 169.
Homology, center of, 21, 239, 265, 281. *See also* Center of similitude.
plane of, 21, 22, 235, 265.
Homothetic, center, 16–21, 31, 53, 54, 79, 109, 151, 155, 244, 273, etc. *See also* Center of similitude.
figures, 16–21.
ratio, 16, 18–20, 53, 55, 109, 151, 154, 155, 244, 251, 273, etc.
spheres, 18, 80, 160, 251.
tetrahedrons, 19, 21, 109, 148, 151, 154, 209.
triangles, 19, 21, 31.
Hyperbolic group of lines, 9–11, 66, 68, 100–105, 110, 122, 149, 213, 250, 294.
harmonic, 15, 16, 106, 230, 233.
supplementary, *see* Supplementary.
Hyperbolic lines, *see* Hyperbolic group.

I

Icosahedron, 25.
Imaginary, circle, 150, 165, 174, 177, 179, 193, 196.
sphere, 149, 150, 160, 163–166, 168, 170, 178, 181, 186, 192, 201, 208, 211.

Incenter, 78, 79, 96, 97, 100, 122, 212, 239, 245, 250, 281, 282.
Incircles, 256, 257, 260.
Inradius, 96, 102, 212, 258, 259.
Inscribed, cone, 38, 39.
sphere, *see* Sphere.
tetrahedron in parallelepiped, 58.
Inverse points, 135, 136, 138, 139, 141–145, 149, 150, 163, 165, 172, 179, 187, 194, 201, 204, 214–216, 282, 290.
Inversion, 214–228.
center or pole of, 214–217, 219, 221–223, 282, 290.
power or constant of, 214–216, 219, 226, 227.
sphere of, 214, 215, 218, 219, 288.
Isoclinal lines and planes, 32–37, 39, 40, 65, 245, 261.
Isodynamic, point of four spheres, 204, 205, 208, 209, 289.
point of tetrahedron, 254, 255.
tetrahedron, 276–290.
Isogonal, lines, 240–247.
planes, 240–247, 256.
points, 81, 240–247, 250, 255, 263, 275, 294.
spheres, 222–224.
tetrahedron, 104.
Isogonic tetrahedron, 290–292.
Isosceles, skew trapezoid, 47.
tetrahedron, *see* Tetrahedron.

L

Lemoine, axis, 103, 278–280.
plane, 279–282, 285–287, 290.
point, 103, 104, 126, 248–250, 277–282, 284–286, 291.
tetrahedron, 282–286, 291.
Limiting, circle of coaxal net, 192–195, 197, 221.
points, 132, 178, 179, 186, 191, 204, 211, 222, 225, 228, 287.
Lines, *see* Cevian, Centroidal, Conjugate, Euler, Harmonic conjugate, Isogonal, Newtonian, Orthocentric, Orthocentric group, Polar, Reciprocal, Ruled system, Simson, Skew, Symmedian, etc.
conjugate, Polar or Polar reciprocal with respect to sphere, 144–150, 177, 190, 191, 201, 290.

harmonic conjugate, with respect to
tetrahedron, 230–232, 255.
supplementary ruled system of, 9.
Link, orthogonal, 139, 140, 211, 220.
Locus, 5, 18, 20, 23–25, 33, 37–39, 46,
47, 57, 75, 106, 107, 109, 123, 131,
134, 140, 148, 161, 164, 166–168,
171, 173, 176, 185, 188, 190, 191,
194, 196, 200, 210, 212, 220, 224,
247, 270, 276.

M

Mannheim's theorem, 69, 104, 252.
Medial tetrahedron, 53, 90, 260, 262–
264, 266.
Median, 51–59, 61, 65, 71, 90, 92, 94,
95, 109, 120, 129, 161, 167, 171,
208–210, 212, 250, 272.
Median or medial sections, 50, 91,
294.
Mediating plane, 1.
Mediator, 1, 6, 24, 50, 68, 71, 167, 168,
171–173, 204, 209, 217, 279, 293.
Mixed plane of similitude, 158.
Monge, plane, 68, 69, 171.
point, 68–70, 93, 96, 97, 110, 167,
176, 208–210, 251, 252, 262.
Monge's theorem, 68.

N

Nagel point, 100, 261.
Net, coaxal, *see* Coaxal.
Neuberg, points, 287, 290.
spheres, 286–290.
Neuberg's theorem, 203, 253.
Newtonian, line, 204.
plane, 203, 204, 206, 209, 210, 253.
Nine-point circle, 250, 251, 261, 272,
273.
Null sphere, 192, 193.

O

Oblique, circular cylinder, 131.
cone, *see* Cone.
projections, 3, 4.
Octahedron, 24, 25, 71, 90, 108, 293.
Orientation, 1, 32, 34, 44, 49, etc.
Orthic, axis and plane, 265–270.
point, 273.
tetrahedron, 263, 265, 266, 273.
triangle, 28, 64.
trihedron, 28–30, 35–37, 39, 65.

Orthocenter, 28, 29, 31, 41, 57, 62–66,
69–71, 91, 93, 98–101, 147, 252,
262–267, 273. *See also* Orthocentric tetrahedron and Tetrahedron, polar.
Orthocentric group, of lines, 28, 30,
35–37, 39, 65.
of points, 272–275.
of tetrahedrons, 272–275.
of trihedrons, 29.
Orthocentric line of trihedron, 27–31,
35, 65–67.
Orthocentric tetrahedron, 62–65, 69,
108, 147, 240, 261–276, 281, 292.
See also Orthocenter and Tetrahedron, polar.
Orthogonal, circle and sphere, 138,
139, 167, 175, 198.
circles, 139, 174–177, 187, 211, 268.
link, 139, 140, 211, 220.
projections, 3, 6, 32, 110, 179, 190.
sphere of four spheres, 202–208,
224, 225, 229, 247.
spheres, 136–140, 148, 151, 162–
166, 168, 172, 175, 177, 179–
181, 186, 187, 189, 191, 194,
195, 197, 198, 201, 209, 211,
215, 220, 221, 223–225, 229,
247, 264, 269, 275.
Orthological tetrahedrons, 148.

P

Parallelepiped, 23–25, 90.
circumscribed about tetrahedron,
58–63, 86, 87, 91, 93, 94, 95,
101.
Pencil, coaxal, *see* Coaxal.
of planes, *see* Coaxal.
Perspective, center and plane of, *see*
Homology.
Harmonic, 22, 239.
tetrahedron, 21, 22, 213, 239, 281.
See also Homological tetrahedrons.
Plane, of homology, *see* Homology.
of centers of coaxal net, 191.
isoclinal, 32–37.
Lemoine, 279–282, 285–287, 290.
mediating, 1.
Newtonian, 203, 204, 206, 209, 210,
253.
orthic, 265–270.
polar with respect to cone, 123–132.